Soil
and Civilization

EDWARD HYAMS

HARPER COLOPHON BOOKS
HARPER & ROW, PUBLISHERS
NEW YORK, HAGERSTOWN, SAN FRANCISCO, LONDON

*Dedicated to my wife
with love and in gratitude
for her patience*

This book was originally published in 1952 by Thames and Hudson, London and New York, and is fully protected under the terms of the Berne Copyright Convention.

SOIL AND CIVILIZATION. Preface to the Harper Colophon edition copyright © 1976 by Mary Hyams. All rights reserved. Printed in the United States of America. No part of this book may be used or reproduced in any manner without written permission except in the case of brief quotations embodied in critical articles and reviews. For information address Harper & Row, Publishers, Inc., 10 East 53d Street, New York, N.Y. 10022.

First HARPER COLOPHON edition published 1976.

LIBRARY OF CONGRESS CATALOG CARD NUMBER: 75-43490

STANDARD BOOK NUMBER: 06-090485-5

76 77 78 79 80 10 9 8 7 6 5 4 3 2 1

CONTENTS

PART ONE
Definitions

Preface to the Harper Colophon Edition		v
Preface		1
I	MAN IN HIS PLACE	3
II	MAN AND SOIL	9
III	THE SOIL COMMUNITY	17
IV	SOIL MEMBERSHIP AND SOIL PARASITISM	28

PART TWO
Man as a Parasite on Soil

V	MAN AS A PARASITE ON ALLUVIUM	43
VI	THE EUPHRATES—TIGRIS AND THE INDUS	55

PART THREE
Man as a Disease of Soils

VII	MAN AS A DISEASE ORGANISM	75
VIII	THE SOILS OF ATTICA AND THE RISE OF ATHENS	91
IX	SOIL AND THE HANNIBALIC WAR	115
X	OKLAHOMA: DEATH OF A SOIL	138

PART FOUR (I)
The Marginal Case

XI   - EURASIA AND CHINA   151

PART FOUR (II)
The Marginal Case

XII   INDIA: LAND-TENURE AS AN INSTRUMENT OF SOIL DESTRUCTION   183

PART FIVE
Man as a Soil Maker

XIII   THE SOILS OF THE WESTERN ANDES: THE INCA EMPIRE   201

XIV   ATLANTIC EUROPE: THE PERFECT ARTIFICIAL SOIL   230

XV   TOOLS, TECHNIQUES, AND STATES OF MIND AND SPIRIT   273

Notes   293
Index   305

Maps

1   THE BLUE NILE   45
2   THE NILE DELTA   49
3   THE EUPHRATES—TIGRIS   57
4   THE INDUS VALLEY   65
5   THE INCA EMPIRE   221

PREFACE TO THE HARPER COLOPHON EDITION

When this book was first published, conservationists were called cranks, ecology was a word you would have had to look up in the dictionary, and the word "environmentalism" had yet to be coined. My own inspirations were manifold: personal experience in reclaiming a few acres of degenerated wasteland, the terrible warning implicit in Professors G. V. Jack and R. O. Whyte's *The Rape of the Earth*, the Oklahoma disaster of the 1920's, the part entitled "Form and Reality" of Oswald Spengler's *The Decline of the West*, Arnold Toynbee's *Study of History*, and numerous lesser influences. My book, published in Britain, the United States, Germany and Italy made an impression; but perhaps as many reviews, articles and broadcasts based on it pooh-poohed the idea that scientific, mechanized farming could be a curse, as welcomed the implication that man is almost as much a creature of the soil he lives on as any other animal. In short, the book was, in one sense, premature as any cry of warning falling on ears reluctant to hear it is bound to be.

A quarter of a century having passed, an American and a British publisher find that the book has, as it were, come into its own and offer to republish it—and, gratifyingly, without revision. There are, however, one or two things to be said: hence this Preface.

In the first place there has been a change in attitude toward the matter of man's ecological place in the general creation: it would be fatuous to claim more than a small fraction of the credit for bringing that about, but disingenuous to pretend that my share is nil. In the United States, the Middle East, North Africa and elsewhere, the new science of creative ecology is being applied on a vast scale to the reclamation of old man-made deserts and the regeneration of new ones; increased understanding of the importance of soil texture has led to a more responsible use of chemical fertilizers in some parts of the world and increased respect for the arguments of what used to be called the "muck and magic" school of agriculturalists. The geneticists and plant-breeders are giving us the means, in such high-yielding crop-plant varieties as "miracle rice", to produce more nourishment from less soil. It is being slowly borne in on us that biological methods of plant-pest control are economically as well as ecologically sounder than chemical methods.

Yet the news is by no means all good: if miracle crop varieties yield more, they must also take more; the industrialization of farming continues, and although it is being done with more awareness, and where possible, avoidance, of its dangers, it is still doing damage. In the present state of our knowledge this damage need not and should not have been done, and will sooner or later have to be repaired at enormous cost to the world community. The pernicious vice of both industrial-capitalist and industrial-communist farming—calculations of success in terms of money return per man-hour-energy-acre instead of food-value return—is still with us; and the lamentable social consequences are still being ignored. It should never be forgotten that the road to hell is paved with good intentions: it would now appear that the completion at colossal expense of the Aswan Dam, destroying the millennia-old soil-regenerating operation of the Nile flooding, was a catastrophic blunder.

Advances in archaeology have made available information that, if I were revising the book, would entail minor changes, but for the most part so minor that they do not affect the argument (indeed there are one or two discoveries that strengthen it). For example, if radio carbon dating is to be relied on, Hassuna is a city more ancient than I said it was, which is of no importance in the context of *Soil and Civilization*; likewise, more of the traffic of the Indus Valley may have been waterborne than was thought in 1952.

In the chapter dealing with the effect of the Punic Wars on Italy's soil, and elsewhere in the book, I tried to give contemporary values to historical costs. The greed of bankers and the ineptitude of political economists have, since 1952, enormously debased every currency in the world, and have made nonsense of my figures. But there is no point in trying to correct them; they would be wrong again tomorrow. The same is true of the figures in Chapter XII, on India. That chapter deals with the subject of vicious systems of land-tenure destroying fertility and soil. All that has happened since 1952 strongly confirms me in my conclusion that both state ownership and capitalist ownership of farming land are economically and socially disastrous, and that the soundest system of tenure is working-farmer ownership without the right of alienation for gain. I have discovered that I share this view with the French anarchist and sociologist Pierre-Joseph Proudhon (1809–1865): he expounded it in his *Idée Générale de la Révolution au XIXème Siècle* and other books. If, in the capitalist and mixed economies, moneylenders' interest on loans made to farmers is paid for out of soil fertility (see Chapter X), equally in the state-capitalist or so-called communist economies, it is loss of soil fertility which pays for the primal idiocy of arrogant authority. This is demonstrated by the Oklahoma-like catastrophe to the Ukrainian soil that was the price paid by the Soviet people for tolerating Nikita Khrushchev, as the near ruin of all Soviet agriculture was a part of the price paid for tolerating the unspeakable Stalin.

The passage of time has, in short, left the argument of the book intact: clever animals though we be, we remain, our culture remains, our civilization remains, very much the creation of the soil we live on. No more than we ever could, can we afford exhaustive use—which is abuse—of fertility, or for that matter of any other natural resources.

The origins of evil lie far back in time and it is one of the functions of history to trace them out.

G. M. TREVELYAN, O.M.

PREFACE

THIS book is not a work of scholarship, for which I am not equipped. I have drawn upon a very large number of scholars and authorities in an attempt to express my own theme, and to some of them I owe thanks for actual help received.

I am grateful to the editor of the series in which this book appears for the chance to write it, and for the patient wisdom with which she has helped me on numerous occasions. When we have differed, and she has been unable to produce an absolutely downright authority, however, I have had my own way, and consequently the editor is not responsible for my mistakes or opinions. I should also like to acknowledge the help of Professor Christopher Hawkes, Professor R. E. Wheeler, and Dr. Henri Frankfort, who have read certain chapters and corrected mistakes which were due to my failure to use the latest authorities. The help they gave me was solely as to matters of fact, none of them having read the whole book, and they may quite likely disapprove of both theme and arguments.

I ought to thank numerous authors and their publishers for permission to quote from their works, but I do not want to make this preface long. However, I must mention the assistance which I received from Professor Roy Gittinger and the University of Oklahoma Press, and the kindness of the Society of Antiquaries in giving me access to their library.

On the subject of libraries, I am anxious to record my gratitude to the Librarian and staff of the Kent County Library for the sympathetic and imaginative way in which they interpreted my requests for a very large number of books which had to be sought all over Britain, and which were found and delivered to me with astonishing promptitude. Surely the County Library Service is the most efficient and valuable thing of its kind in the world.

A word about the book itself. I may have given the impression of believing the nature and state of soil to have been the only influence in shaping the character of the community living on it; and that character to have been the only influence on the health of the soil. This, of course, is not the case, but to have written otherwise would have entailed excursions into general social history, greatly lengthened the book, and taken me too far from my theme. At the cost of some distortion, therefore, I used the convention of ignoring all influences but those of men on soil and soil on men.

PART ONE: DEFINITIONS

CHAPTER I

MAN IN HIS PLACE

THE history of man is the history of his relations with the planet and what lives on it, and with the forces he has sensed or imagined as being responsible for the order which he perceives. These relationships have been recorded by historians, or reconstructed by reference to the material products of their active expression, dug up and interpreted by archaeologists. But only the poet has the power to go beyond the record of facts and reconstruction, and to make it apparent that only our want of understanding breaks the past from the present; makes the past seem to be separate from us in the present because we lack insight concerning what we are. Until the rise of the scientific man as the dominant type, the poet (the word is used in preference to the word artist which has been denatured) generally had some hand in the activities of man's relationships with the animals, plants and stones of his environment: consequently the things which men made with their tools and materials are able to speak, as it were. Not even those glossy guide-books of superb photographs, accompanied by an architectural analysis, can absolutely silence the cathedrals of Chartres or Canterbury; not even the interpretation offered by some scientific anthropologist can deprive the monoliths of Stonehenge of the power to convey something of the sense with which they were imbued by those who raised them.

When science enabled man to begin working across or against the grain of life as a whole, to ignore or destroy the balance between the manifold parts, which maintains the integrity of life on the planet, the poet became unable to take that part in all acts of creation which properly belongs to him. This is not for one moment a back-to-nature, anti-science plea: science in its proper place, as a servant only, ought to have placed material in ever more copious and diverse supply at the disposal of the poet, who would have made use of it in such a manner that man would have grown up without turning into a monster; but science, as a master, has turned man into a monster, upset the balance of the world, and enabled us to take our commodity from the planet, but to cease giving to it.

Scientific men and women have uncovered much of the past; but those workers who have interpreted what was uncovered have also, as a rule, been scientists. The result has been a kind of truth, no doubt, the kind which one gets in a court of Law; and one of the results has been to separate the present from the past by various artificial barriers, to make it extremely difficult to perceive that the past is permanent in our own minds and bodies, our own traditions, our errors and diseases; that it is not remote but immediate, and that the acts of men are eternal.

It is unfortunately much more difficult to overcome the illusion of separateness from our kind in time, than to overcome the same illusion in space. The city-dweller travels through the countryside in a train, and from the window of the train he sees a woman standing at a cottage gate, a man hoeing a patch of vegetables, a tractor drawing a trailer-load of straw, and cattle grazing in a meadow. He is suddenly aware not so much of curiosity concerning these manifestations of life to which he belongs, as of a poignant sense of wrongness in being outside, in being unfamiliar with what he now sees. But he has only to get out of the train, enter into the community which he has observed, and do some part of its work, to know intimately the corner of life which has thus attracted his attention.

But if the "train" happens to be Thucydides' account of the Peloponnesian War, and the "countryside" through which the man is being carried is remote from his own hearth not merely in space, but in time, the problem which confronts him is very much more difficult. It is then that the poet's technique becomes important, yet in interpreting man's past relations with the materials with which he performs his creative or destructive acts, the poet has been excluded by our dominant notion that the kind of truth called scientific is of a particularly sterling and pungent quality.

When the senses and intelligence of the poet place viable material at his disposal, the act, by means of which he illuminates the pattern of which this material is a part, and thereby shows it as beautiful with a life which only thus and then becomes apparent to those who hear or read him, he performs an act of revelation rather than one of creation. A man or woman is a poet by virtue of two faculties: the faculty of perceiving and experiencing phenomena with super-normal intensity; and the faculty of so describing what he has experienced that others are able to share and use the light by which he sees.

It is probable that the poet's high degree of sensibility to ideas and phenomena ought not to be beyond the capacity of any fully human being to attain for himself or herself. The poet must, of course, always be distinguished by mastery of a technique of expression, as the plumber is by his mastery of the technique of making a wiped joint; but the power of perceiving or feeling with the poet's penetration and intensity is perhaps not a special and singular divine gift, but rather, like 6/4 eyesight, an example of excellence, of perfection in a common faculty. If this be true it follows that the majority of us, who are unable to experience the world or any part of it as a poet does, are disabled persons, invalids. The poet is not an athlete among men of ordinary muscular development and control; but a fit man among the crippled and debilitated.

In that case it would be reasonable to expect that most men and women would, at some time in their life, enjoy spells of fitness: and, in fact, the majority of us do, sooner or later, have the experience of understanding an idea, perceiving a thing, a pattern or a person with such intensity and penetration that we seem to live, for minutes, hours or days, in a clearer light, among other and more excellent forms than those of the world which, as invalids, we know during the greater part of our life.

This poet's technique has rarely been applied to the study of the past and perhaps never to the study of the remote past. The scientific bias taken by our civilization has, especially of late, given to History and Archaeology a rôle, valuable and respectable of course, but not inspired. A few books suggest themselves as examples of the application of the poet's technique, the poet's seeing, mediumistic, revelatory powers, to the past: the Homeric poems, the novel *Salammbo* of Flaubert, Robert Graves' *Golden Fleece*, Hope Munz's *Golden Warrior*. There are others, of course. But all of them deal with past acts of love and war, religion, and that kind of creation distinguished as artistic; rarely with acts of husbandry.

Let any man whose mind is full of material gathered from works of archaeology and history, or pre-history, spend a summer night on some high point of the North Downs, below a hanging wood and with the country falling away to the sea before him. Let the sky be cloudless but with a haze between earth and heaven to dull the clamour of the stars. If it is August there might be part of a yellow moon, and enough light to keep a few sheep, on the small plateau at his feet, cropping the bitten turf far into the night. The sheep might be at first timid, then curious and at last so indifferent as to let the observer sink into the composition of the night and be still and receptive. The experience which he will then enjoy will not be supernatural: the moving beauty of the night and the place will briefly lend his spirit a tone, a sensibility superior to its norm and, with luck, the material about which he has been *thinking*, will become amenable to *feeling*, will transform itself into a direct, valid, no doubt personal, but none the less revealing experience of the past. It will not happen that the chalk-dwarfed sward will be peopled again with ghosts of ancient men, but only that the acts of those men will become his own acts. He will not again find their life in their artifacts, their knapped flints, bronze tools, their plough ridges or barrows, but in the needs and desires and aspirations which inspired the acts of creation which they performed. It will become apparent that there is no significance in the difference between breaking the sod with a stone hoe, or a Ferguson tractor-plough; but a world of significance in the similarities. The stone hoe, the bronze mattock, the wooden spade shod with precious iron, the plough without wheel or coulter, the Fordson drawing three shares, are all one, provided the act be the same, be familiar in spirit.

Acts of manipulation are the oldest human documents, but they have been neglected: it is to them that, like the poet, men should go for understanding of their place and meaning in the pattern of life. One such, not particularly ancient but which, because of its self-evidence makes a striking example, is that of reaping wheat. If I see a man reaping wheat with a scythe, in some Kentish field of an August evening, with the low sun casting a golden or a ruddy light, and throwing long, blue shadows under a high, pale sky, am I moved to pleasure solely by the beauty of objects and the rhythmic grace of the reaper's motions, the sweet curve of the scythe? Is what I enjoy no more, although that is much, than the pleasure of the eye? It is surely more, it is that the thing being done has been so often repeated as part of a life-giving order, that it is of the past, present and future, a proper motion for man, a sign that he is in his place.

The power of such a scene is the power of a work of art to move with the grain of life, to bring parts into balance and make of them a unity, an integrity. It does not matter whether the tool in the man's hand is a scythe and his motions smooth, periodic and curvilinear; or whether it is an immense and scarlet Massey-Harris combine-harvester (majestic engine, indeed, and formidable, yet absurd too, as a Heath Robinson drawing is absurd and madly logical), and the man's motions abrupt, aperiodic and angular. It is what he does that counts, not how he does it, provided that certain rules are observed, certain values held so respectable as to be sacred.

There are a few acts which have, indeed, been more often repeated than that of making a tilth: he who snares a rabbit or gathers blackberries has a more ancient occupational lineage than he who ploughs. But our subject is the relationship between man and the soil; our attempt, to arrive at an understanding of that relationship by perceiving what, in the present, is of the past, and to trace that back, by such means as we can, to its origins.

CHAPTER II

MAN AND SOIL

A STUDY of the relationships between men and the soil upon which, out of which, by the sole means of which they live, must begin by a definition of what the words "men" and "soil" mean in the particular context. This necessity may not at once appear; but a moment's thought will reveal that both concepts stand for complex and diverse groups of ideas, so that the author and reader could very easily be at cross purposes concerning them.

Man is flesh and mind and something which seems to be neither, which is the product of his awareness of the universe, and is called soul or spirit.

As flesh, man is part of the vast, complex and beautiful organism which is life on this planet. The well-being and continuance of that organism, or to be more exact, that association of organisms existing in an elaborate symbiotic partnership, depends upon the maintenance of a balance between the parts. It is possible to rearrange the parts within the whole without permanently impairing the balance; but only within certain limits.

Man resorts to such rearrangements in order less laboriously and more fully to serve the appetites of his flesh; in order to amuse, strengthen and satisfy his mind; in order to *liberate* his spirit. To liberate his spirit; that is to go beyond phenomena to an understanding of causes and ends, and to find his purpose. Because of his consciousness, of his subtle awareness, man is not content simply to function according to his kind.

All living creatures, animal and vegetable, live according to a rhythm: they disturb the order of things in the service of their existence, and then restore the order by terminating their life. They live by changing the form of matter, but only within such limits that the form can be restored again. In nature, living creatures are so organized that they are unable, however numerous the species within a community, so to damage their environment as to destroy themselves or it.

A blade of grass grows and by so doing consumes components of the earth in its neighbourhood, thus changing it. In the course of its life the blade of grass captures and transforms into matter a part of the energy of the sun, subsequently dies and rots back into the earth, restoring the components it has used, and perhaps something more. Nothing has been lost and something even gained, some fraction of the radiant energy of the sun.

Let the blade of grass be eaten by a caterpillar, which turns into a moth, which is eaten by a bird, which is eaten by a hawk, which is consumed by the bacteria of a disease and dies, falls to the ground and is eaten by a hyaena, which is hunted by a lion and eaten (though, perhaps, lions do not eat scavengers); the lion is trampled to death by a buffalo, which in turn dies of old age. The blade of grass has not been lost: the action of the buffalo has returned it to the earth, in the form of lion flesh.

Or suppose the blade of grass to be eaten by a deer, which is then shot by a hunter and eaten by his family. The blade of grass is now in the flesh of this human community. They die, and being sealed into a coffin, or perhaps burnt in a pyre, the best part of the substance of the blade of grass is lost, is shut off from return to earth, or has gone up in smoke. The fraction of fertility which the grass borrowed from the soil to combine with solar energy in the building of its substance, has been permanently withdrawn from the total stock.

Man as mere flesh has no more power seriously to disturb the balance of a soil than has any other creature. But man as spirit and flesh has very great powers of disturbing that balance, as is obvious and will appear hereafter. But while men retain close contact with the material of which they are made they seem to acquire a kind of knowledge, a feeling for the pattern of the whole organism which is life, a tact in manipulating the parts of the whole, in understanding the pattern. These powers enable them to work with the grain of life rather than across it. And this is true even of those activities which involve not the manipulation of matter, but of ideas and feelings, as in poetry: the artists and poets of the *balanced* phase of any civilization have a profound feeling for the grain of life. Poetry which runs against this grain, and is a product of the failure of the poet's community to retain their faculty of tact as members of life, may still be profoundly impressive: but so may any clever, bitter act of perversity and destruction.

The knowledge which is picked up by men who are feeling their way to such a control of their environment as will allow them to dominate without destroying it, is accumulated both as a body of consciously realized traditions, and, more subtly and more immediately available in action, as intuition in their dealings with their non-human fellow-creatures.

Consciousness, the attribute apparently peculiar to man among the animals, involves expression and religion: to understand what he experiences, man states it in such terms as he can devise, and then finds that there are forces to propitiate and to be grateful to. It is supposed that art begins as a means of religion; it is quite as likely that religion rises out of the products of art. The American philosopher Menken explained the invention of gods by reference to the fears of the people and the shrewdness of the priests.[1] Such an explanation entails a far too narrow view of human nature. The men who are gifted with that tact which enables them to live harmoniously with other natural objects, become conscious of forces which work with them, as well as with forces which work against them; and they ease their own path by seeking the help of forces which seem to be serving their ends. Therein these men resemble those primitive astronomers who believed the sun to move round the earth: they observed the phenomenon correctly, but they misunderstood the relation in which the parts stood to one another.

Man in nature prospers when he is working in such a way as to move with life's pattern, collaborating with the other members of the *Soil Community* to which he belongs. Far too much weight seems to have been given to fear of the environment as a formative influence in the story of mankind, far too little to the sense of belonging, of being in place. The men of science who have studied the origins of man's mind have been *only* men of science in most cases, specialists out of any living context. A sensitive and sincere critic of art could have corrected the grosser errors of these experts by reference to, for example, the Magdalenian drawings: only a satisfying sense of union with the other members of the soil community could have enabled the prehistoric painters to create those magnificently living beasts. Frightened men draw differently, a fact which appears most clearly in the work of a twentieth-century genius like Picasso.

Surely art and religion, as the products of men only recently become mind and spirit as well as flesh, would be, at least to some extent, an expression of the sense of being a working part of some balanced whole. Fear there would be, anxiety at man's own temerity in making changes in a pattern not of his creation. Some rites, some poetry, some painting would be designed to reassure the forces daily experienced as tending to maintain the balance of life, that any disturbance of that balance would subsequently be made good. Such disturbance, the felling of trees when that became technically possible, the ploughing of sod, would be undertaken with trepidation and perhaps, indeed probably, with a sense of sin.

These are speculations, but they are supported by reading in mythology of man's relations with soil (see Chapter XVI). And by an act of sympathy, possible to anyone whose imagination is not impaired, and who has had personal experience of working with living, non-human creatures, animal or vegetable.

In the attempt to understand the state of mind of the first men, in their relations with the other members of a soil community, anthropology is less useful than might be supposed, as, indeed, anthropologists are the first to admit. The material of the anthropologist is necessarily the living community of men, and there is no community in the world today which is not of very ancient origin in respect to its customs. The most "primitive" men of whom we have knowledge by direct study are not primitive at all: they are sophisticated, and perhaps even corrupt in their dealings, whether social, religious or scientific, with nature. However simple their economy, it does not have an air of freshness, but rather of decadence, as if these simple communities were the remnants of once much more elaborate cultures. An observer of the hill-peoples of the East Indian islands, if what is reported of them be true, might suppose that they had never evolved a complex social structure; but it seems quite as probable that they have lapsed from one. The same mistake might also be made by one observing the lapsed communities of Western civilized man, in the Appalachian country of North America.

That kind of knowledge which, at some risk of being dismissed as fanciful, I can only call intuitive, and of which I have been writing above, is not the kind to which much importance is now given. The antithetical kind is Intellectual knowledge. Intellectual knowledge of man's material environment rarely originates, like intuitive knowledge, in the practice of living in harmony with non-human life; nor indeed, until the seventeenth century of our era, did it even pretend to do so.

Ordered and deliberate thinking began in the Western Hemisphere with, apparently, the Greek philosophers, and extraordinarily little of significance seems thereafter to have been added to their results, although the practical application of methods devised by them was to have remarkable consequences. These methods were studied and perhaps refined, perhaps on the contrary falsified by their successors in our own different but (*vide* Arnold Toynbee's *Study of History*) affiliated civilization. Their application has led to the startling and largely catastrophic advances in analytical and mechanical sciences.

This ordered thinking of the Greeks, as, for example, in the work of Plato attributed by him to Socrates, is an attempt to arrive at something called Truth conceived of as both the explanation and purpose of man's being and that of the universe, by applying the intellect deliberately to all problems, moral, physical and even spiritual. Logic is the instrument devised for the use of the intellect in this exercise. The method fails, in fundamentals, because it can find no way round the ultimate reference back to basic knowledge, which is quite clearly not of intellectual origin. Unless enjoyed as exhibitions of mental athleticism, or as works of literature, the Platonic dialogues are dull because they are unreal. A conscientious application to the reading of philosophy will either convince the modest student that he is missing the philosopher's intention; or the arrogant one that this method of arriving at the truth concerning man and the macrocosm, although still earnestly persisted in, is singularly futile. The only valuable results of these works of pure intellect are to be found in the clarification of obscurities in man's psychological and spiritual functioning; and despite every attempt to look outwards it does not seem that any intellectual has yet succeeded in being anything but subjective.

How did this kind of thinking come into existence? I believe the answer to be very relevant to the theme of this book, because I believe that such thinking is one of the products of a destruction of soil community balance by the arrogant attribution by man, to himself, of a rôle outside that community.

When the mythology which gives expression to man's "intuitive" knowledge of his world and place in it is first evolved out of experience, it is fresh and lively, it is satisfactory and it works, and men can live by it. But when touch has been lost with these origins, and the mythology and associated religion and art are experienced isolated from their real-life context, then, after an interval during which the momentum of habit, the sacrosanctity of tradition can still be drawn on as if it were capital experience, the meaning of rituals and even of beliefs is lost sight of, and these rituals and beliefs are seen as senseless.

There grows up then a contempt for the ancestors who devised such nonsense; they are judged by their works and their works are so obviously absurd.

This major social disaster does not occur until there exist men isolated, by the advance of science or technics, and by the elaboration of social economy, from direct contact through hands and eyes and feet and noses, as well as minds, with the life of a soil community.

Socrates was a citizen of an advanced community of Imperialist soldiers, merchants and slave-owners.[2] In condemning him to death his fellow-citizens did an atrocious deed. But were they, perhaps (if not carrying out a judicial murder on political grounds), vaguely and inarticulately aware that he was, indeed, a terribly dangerous man? Did the court which tried him feel in its bones that the accused was flying in the face of the very Truth he sought, by trying to find it with a light which was not, and never would be, effective? There is a shocking arrogance in Socrates' humility.

Because, then, certain conditions which belong to the ageing of a dynamic (as opposed to a stable, that is a savage) culture, entail loss of touch with one, and perhaps the only valid source of real knowledge, there comes into fashion another kind of knowledge, that called Intellectual.

The material with which the intellect works at first is that which has been intuitively acquired. Nature is not applied to directly, with the result that an inverted and top-heavy pyramid of theory is built up, a collection of academic notions, degenerating rapidly into nonsense. A reaction from this imbecile misapplication of energy setting in, men realize that they have five senses which can be used for the collection of material from nature, upon which to work with the Intellect.

At first sight it appears that this phase in the work of thinking entails a most salutary simplification, a shedding of prejudices and preconceived ideas. Like his primitive ancestors, man is again applying to nature for his lessons. And so, in a sense, he is, but in a new sense. He is not learning as primitive men learnt, and as rabbits and cabbages and grape-vines learn, that is as parts of a working soil community. He is learning from outside, he is using not his instincts but his curiosity.

For some incomprehensible reason the rise of this kind of detached inquiry into phenomena is, like the rise of a western art and literature, called the Renaissance. But nothing was reborn: not even the most arrogant of the Greeks had quite attained to this notion of inquiring into nature as if man stood god-like outside it. Galileo, Leeuwenhoek, Newton, were, in their methods, expressing the peculiarly Judeo-Christian idea that men were God's principal tenants, the rest of creation the fittings and stock let with the property.

The method led, of course, to what are sometimes called the triumphs of science. Great discoveries were made, and it is not the business of this book to discuss whether the practical application of these discoveries has justified the faith of rational men in science. One of the last trades to which science, the method of inquiry into nature, but not of living as a part of nature, was applied, was that of the farmer.

It would be almost impossible to exaggerate the disasters which ensued.

CHAPTER III
THE SOIL COMMUNITY

THE word *Soil* is never used throughout this text to mean some inanimate collection of mineral and organic particles, but a biological, an organic, a living entity.

As commonly used the word soil means that granular matter which forms the skin of a great part of the planet, and in which vegetables grow. But for me the word means much more: that granular substance is only part of a process, rather than a thing; we are not here considering the physical and chemical properties of earths, but the significance of the <u>biological process which I call soil</u>. Blood is one thing to a chemist, quite another to a poet or an historian. Similarly, soil is one thing to a chemist, quite another to an ecologist. The ecologist's understanding of the term nevertheless includes the chemist's and the physicist's.

The mineral matrix of a soil consists of particles of rock, broken off from the substance of the Earth at or near the point where the soil occurs. Different kinds of rock break down, under the blows inflicted by weather, by acids, by animals, by heat and cold, by glaciation, by what the French call the insults of Time, into particles, the size of which depends upon the chemical and physical structure of the basic rock. When the particles are large, the earth is called sand, when small, clay.

This mineral matrix is not soil: it is at once the medium in which the living attributes of the soil are suspended, and one of the sources of supply of mineral salts which, by conversion into organic compounds of their kind, are later made over into the life of soil.

The organic, but not living, component of earths is the end

product of animal and vegetable carrion, and animal faeces. These substances are present in the crude form in most fertile earths, but they are also present in a reduced form, as a substance of which no chemist's description is yet available, and to which the word *humus* is properly applied. This word is commonly used to mean the raw material from which humus is made, that is decaying matter in which a cellular structure is still discernible. But in humus, strictly so called, no such structure is to be perceived: the stuff is chemically complex, physically so simple that it is a mere protoplasmic jelly.

The transformation from decaying matter into humus is wrought by ammonifying bacteria which are extremely numerous in any living soil. Or, in the absence of such bacteria, the work may be done by a fungus. Humus itself is worked upon by other bacteria, the nitrogen fixers, which in the course of finding their own provender therein, release nitrogen salts in a form suitable for plant food. These bacteria, and notably the *azobacters*, fix atmospheric nitrogen in combination with substance obtained from humus, to form nitrates. Both the ammonifying and the nitrogen-fixing micro-organisms are so essential to the validity of the idea *soil*, that they cannot be considered as merely creatures living in it, like wire-worms or moles, but are attributes of soil, without which the stuff is, in fact, not soil at all, but merely a dead mixture of mineral and organic particles. An earth without these bacteria is no more a soil than a corpse is a man. Their importance is such that should anything happen to inhibit the work and multiplication of the ammonifying bacteria, the soil fungi and the nitrogen-fixing bacteria, all life on the planet would come to an end in a matter of months.

Two more important elements of soil are atmosphere, of the same components as our own but in rather different proportions; and water, present as a film on each particle, and also as free water between the particles. This water is not pure, but is a solution of all the soluble mineral salts to be found in the soil. As plants take up their food in solution, and not otherwise, water is necessary to the life of a soil, but a mass of merely mineral particles has little or no power to hold water against its tendency both to seek its own level by sinking, or to be evaporated out. Organic particles, however, hold very large quantities readily: a soil high in humus and humus material is therefore moist, but a soil deficient in that substance tends to dry out.

Were we using the word "soil" in its accepted sense we should now have completed a description of it. But, as has already been suggested, the word is to have a wider meaning here, and therefore some further attributes of soil must be described.

The fungi which live in soil, and constitute an important member of soil considered as an organism, are numerous and diverse; some are micro-organisms, such as the moulds which form upon dead vegetable matter and begin the work of breaking it down into humus. But the most interesting of the fungi are those which live in such a manner that their life-function provides a physical demonstration of that symbiotic spirit in which soil, as the word is used here, exists: these are the fungi which form mycchorizal relationships, if the phrase is permissible, with many vascular plants.

Species of several genera are known to form these relationships; a number of the genus *Boletus* do so; the deadly Fly Agaric (*Amanita muscaria*) is another, and the brilliantly coloured *Lactarius deliciosus*. The familiar parts of these fungi are their *sporophores*, the spore-bearing structures, many of them edible, others poisonous, often called fruit-bodies. These super-terranean parts of the plants are thrown up from the frequently widespread and always greatly ramified phylae which correspond to the vegetative part of green plants, and are collectively known as mycelium.

Unlike green plants, fungi, having no chloroplast cells, are unable to make carbohydrates by photosynthesis. They are therefore somewhat in the case of animals, depending upon plants for their carbon components, which they consume in the form of dead vegetation, and are consequently called saprophytes. Dead vegetation occurs, in great quantity, in woodland soils, consequently the saprophytic fungi are numerous in such soils. Woodland top soils are, of course, composed of rotting vegetation—the annual leaf fall and the other dead parts of trees and undergrowth. Since the reaction of such soils is acid, and since such micro-organisms as the azobacters and nitrososomas, responsible for a stage in decay, function more vigorously in a neutral environment, the decay of forest vegetation is relatively slow. Consequently there is, in such soils, a relatively deep layer of top material, the elements of which have by no means reached that stage of decomposition when they would become available as food for living plants. But this material *is* available to saprophytic fungi.

The seeds which fall from trees in forests fall into material which is not yet quite soil from the plants' point of view. While the seedling is pushing roots into the soil proper, it would be very conducive to its well-being if it could, with special short and shallow roots, draw upon the top-layer of undecomposed vegetation. The seedlings, in suitable conditions, do, therefore, produce such short roots and these become infected with phylae of the mycelium of one or more species of fungus capable of forming such associations. The mycelium grows both into the substance of the root, forming a network between the cells, and all about the outside of the root until it is entirely encased in a felt of mycelium, giving the root and its branches a fat and coraline appearance. The root is, then, quite isolated from the surrounding soil, and cut off from any possibility of performing the nutrient and moisture collecting functions of a root. Nevertheless, seedling trees with such mycchoriza or fungus-roots, are very much more healthy and vigorous than seedlings not so provided; and the same is true of "adult" trees growing in similar associations with fungi. Many species of pine-trees, oaks, beeches, alders; all the orchidacæ; most of the ericas and many other plants form such association, and some orchids are entirely dependent upon them.

It would appear that the outer felting, the mantle of mycelium which is the exterior of such mycchoriza, collects the nutrients and passes them into the root. What does the fungus receive in return? Something, surely, for it must be in pursuit of its own interest that the mycelium penetrates the root in the first place. The whole subject of these associations is still obscure, but they do demonstrate, as no other relationship between members of a soil community do so clearly, the way in which the interests of species within such communities are fused in the interests of the commonwealth, and therefore of each other.

The soil is populated by a large and various range of animals, most of them insects, some of them mammals, such as the mole. Most of these can be dismissed as *in* soil but not *of* it: they contribute to its growth and well-being, by aerating it with their burrows and by dying and decaying in it; or they are pernicious in that they are inimical to the plant life which, as we shall see, is also *of* the soil.

One such living inhabitant must be considered separately, however: the earthworm. There are numerous species of earthworms, varying in size when mature from a fraction of an inch in length, to upwards of eleven feet, though these very long worms do not occur in European nor, I think, American soils. But they all have much the same habits: they burrow about in the soil, thus aerating and draining it; in that they could be bracketed, philosophically, with the moles. But, unlike the moles which, indeed, prey on them, they eat earth. Their object in doing so is to get nourishment from the decaying organic particles and reject the rest. As there is not very much nourishment in the débris of the food and bodies of vegetables and animals, they have to eat a great deal, and most of the bulk is passed out, being deposited as worm-casts. In passing through the gut of the earthworm, all parts of the soil are changed: mineral particles, used in the crop in place of teeth, are ground smaller: organic particles are digested and passed out reduced some further way towards their end as humus, if not, indeed, as humus itself. The earthworm's interior also has means for adding the universal sweetener, calcium, to what passes through it.

There is no doubt at all that humus can be and frequently is made without the aid of earthworms.[3] The author does not wish to pose as a scientist, or as a person capable of making a properly controlled scientific experiment; but he has demonstrated to his own satisfaction that a heap of organic matter, inoculated with ammonifying and nitrogen-fixing bacteria by the addition of animal urine and mature loam, will turn into a sweet, black soil even though earthworms be, as far as is possible, excluded. The exclusion must be imperfect, no doubt, for mature loam will probably contain some capsules of earthworm eggs, which will hatch out in the favourable conditions of such a compost heap. But they cannot have been numerous.

It is equally easy to prove that such a compost heap, into which some thousands of earthworms have been turned, will break down much more rapidly. And this is what one would expect, since, whereas the dung of higher animals and the decaying bodies of animals and plants still possess structure, the dung of earthworms, having carried the reduction of this material much further, is much nearer to being humus. There is far easier work for bacteria to do in a soil with a high population of earthworms, than in one without worms. And in any mature, fertile, living soil earthworms are numerous. Whether counts have been made in natural conditions, I do not know. But the average English acre of cultivated land (which, as we hope to make apparent is a genuine soil as the word is used in this book, although an artificial one) has (or had, when Darwin counted), about fifty thousand earthworms. Each worm deposits annually about seven ounces of dung, so that the total weight of worm-casts to an acre will be ten tons per annum. This is a very considerable figure, and in respect of it I propose that the earthworm be considered not merely an animal *in* the soil, but *of* it, like the bacteria. And if any reader doubts the justification of so doing, let him plant two identical plants in two identical pots to be identically treated, but one filled with any good loam and the other with worm-casts. The behaviour of the plants is all the evidence required to justify the inclusion of the earthworm as part of a soil.

But if a living and visible animal is to be so considered, what of the plants which are growing in the earth? ... we are considering here a natural earth which has never been cultivated. All the components of a soil which have been mentioned above are bound together in an association, a symbiotic relationship so close that none of them would have the significant attributes which belong to it as a part of a soil, were it not for the others. The significance of soil is not in its physical, chemical, biological attributes, but, like the significance of any other organism, a man or a mouse, in its function. But what I have hitherto described *will not function at all as it stands*. It will simply die, turn to dust, and wash or blow away, to expose the bare rock of the earth.

A soil is completed, given life and the power to endure alive almost indefinitely, by the plants which grow in it. They, as much as the mineral particles, the organic particles, the humus, the bacteria, the water, the gasses, the fungi, the earthworms, are components of the process, the life-system called soil. That this is the case is clear from what happens when these plants, be they trees or grasses, are removed and nothing done to compensate the other parts of soil for their removal. The soil ceases to be fertile, dies, soil erosion by wind and water follows, and where there was soil there is nothing . . . rock. On the other hand, any example of a true soil community, as it will henceforth be called, is stable, enduring, perhaps immortal.

Plants growing in earth take from it mineral salts and make from them, by the process known, but only imperfectly understood, as photosynthesis, compounds with atmospheric carbon (CO_2): the carbohydrates. Carbohydrates, such as starch and sugar for example, are the substance of all plants, and of all flesh whatsoever (unless certain micro-organisms making use of such substances as iron and sulphur be thought of as flesh). Nitrogen salts are of the first importance—though, as in any other organic process, no process or part can be considered as more important than another, since all are essential. Yet if the plants did nothing but consume minerals, there would be a constant loss of them, whether from humus or from the mineral matrix, a destruction of matter, in short. But the mere existence of organic matter in soil shows that the plants take nothing from the earth; they only borrow from it. Dying and falling where they grow, they decay, decaying provide fodder for earthworms and the soil bacteria, and so return all that they have borrowed for the maintenance of their life, whence it came.

In any soil community there is, as a condition of its stability, a balance between the parts. Even between plants of different genera growing in the same soil community, there is often something like a symbiotic partnership, for clearly the living processes of different kinds of plants growing in close association with each other must not be mutually hostile beyond the limit of one species to respond to the challenge of the others. Plants needing less than the average requirement of some mineral element must be of use to plants of some other kind which happen to require more of the same element. Gardeners notice that certain plants grow best in association together, for example tomatoes and maize; others are said to be mutually incompatible.

A soil, in our sense, can be regarded as complete at this stage; nevertheless, within most soil communities there will also be animal members, and if they do not also adjust themselves to their vegetable and mineral, cryptogamic, micro-organic, and chemical fellow-members, the balance vital to the stability of the whole will be upset, and the soil community will perish. If such animals eat the grass and leaves or roots of plants, they must also drop their dung and finally die and rot within the soil community, in order that the substance they have borrowed may be returned to stock, and used again and again.

It will occur to the reader who knows something of physics but little of biology, that the stability insisted upon as a distinction of a living soil, appears to be sustained in defiance of the First Law of Thermo-dynamics that matter can neither be created nor destroyed. From the description of a soil community it would appear that a number of animal and vegetable and bacterial lives are being sustained without any consumption of matter, although clearly these lives are continually consuming energy. There ought to be a permanently growing loss, from somewhere, to account for the consumption of energy used in merely living from day to day, and not simply in the creation of substance. If the tendril of a vine winds itself round a stick and draws the vine up to it; if an animal jumps ten feet to reach its prey; if a man lifts a stone and throws it at a coconut, energy is being consumed; where is it coming from? Not only is no loss apparent in the earth of the soil itself, but there is, in some conditions and soils, a steady gain. What the farmer calls virgin or maiden soil, that is a soil never yet planted with agricultural or horticultural subjects, never tilled, is always so rich that if the farmer is prepared to spend the capital locked up in it, rather than conserve it, he can crop it for years without the help of manure. There are examples, on the Eurasian and American steppes, of fertile top-soils nearly fifty inches deep, and yet the earth of these soils has supported a dense population of plants and animals for tens—perhaps hundreds—of thousands of years.

This gain, this better-than-balance, is due to several causes. In a healthy soil the activity of the soil-makers seems to be more than enough for the needs of the living members of the soil. Earthworms make frequent journeys into the dead matter of the subsoil, returning thence with a gutful of mineral particles to add to the top-soil. Deep-rooted plant-members of the community, such as trees, also have roots in the subsoil, and transform the nourishment they find there into leaves which fall, and die, decay on the surface, or just below it where they are drawn by worms and other creatures, and add to the organic material available some increment which was never organic before. Finally, there is the solar energy to account for. This energy is employed in working the transformation of carbon and other elements in the substance of the plant, but there may, perhaps, be a sort of surplus here too, which the plant may turn into matter. If this be so, then green plants are the means of adding to the earth's supply of fertility capital at the expense of the sun's energy; and something is lost to all the other components of the solar system whenever a blade of grass is exposed to sunlight in the presence of CO_2.

*

What happens when men are introduced into a soil community?

If the men are hunters and food collectors there is no reason why they should not fit into the community, be members whose activities are held in balance with those of all the others. Like all the other members, these men will be checked from growing so numerous or predatory as to upset the balance of the community, by the limitations of their own powers, and that measure of hostility between species and species which is an important factor in maintaining equilibrium. The men will be eaten by other beasts, preyed upon by micro-organic members of the soil community, poisoned by some of their fellow-members who are plants or reptiles, and will also, perhaps, check their own numbers and powers by internecine war. Life exists by virtue of cannibalism and of nothing else, so that there can be no practice so irrational as that of vegetarianism "on principle": who eats grass, eats flesh.

But when men pass the stage of food collecting and hunting; or when men who have passed this stage enter upon a hitherto undisturbed soil community, their powers are such that they are able to disturb the balance of the community to the detriment of other species and the advantage of themselves. If the men be few and the community large, this disturbance need not be disastrous. But if or when the men become numerous relative to the size of the community, the result may be very terrible: it may be the destruction first of the soil balance; then, as a consequence, of fundamental soil fertility; and this being the basis of life of the soil in question, all living members of it perish, including, in the end, the community of men which has brought this death about by turning from a contributing, co-operating member of a delicately adjusted organism, into a parasite upon it, and a parasite which it is not constructed to endure.

CHAPTER IV

SOIL MEMBERSHIP AND SOIL PARASITISM

A SPECIES living upon an alien organism as a parasite only develops into a disease organism of the host when its component individuals grow so numerous and active that the latter is debilitated. But there are, in nature, numerous examples of parasitism in which the vigour of the host is such that it is able to support the parasite without impairing its own health.

Perhaps such relationships may be unsound in the long run: the life of the host may be shortened or its vitality impaired. A dog with fleas, a rosebush with aphides, an apple-tree with mistletoe must always be losing energy to their parasites, for there is nothing in common between such relationships and those occurring between certain vascular plants and certain fungi, the distinctive phenomenon of which is the formation of mycorrhiza. Nor must such true parasitism, albeit relatively harmless, be confused with completely harmless epiphytism: the mistletoe feeds upon the substance of the tree, whereas the orchid epiphyte merely uses the tree as a mechanical support.

True parasites, however indifferent to the host, are always potential disease organisms, and their relative harmlessness, in certain conditions, is a function, not of their own nature, but of the surplus energy and power of resistance of the host.

There are certain soils, in a few favoured parts of the earth, which are to men what a healthy animal body is to fleas: they are capable of supporting a parasitic community for very long periods, and sometimes almost indefinitely. Such soils are resistant to the depredations of farmers, depredations which would rapidly debilitate and ultimately kill ordinary grass, park-land or forest soils. Moreover such resistant soils, when industrially exploited by "scientific" farmers, will tolerate the parasite even when, by density of population and intensity of cultivation, the latter becomes what would normally be a disease organism of the soil. Of the known primal civilizations, four out of six have been born on such resistant soils, soils of the river systems of the Nile, the Euphrates-Tigris, the Indus, and the Hwang-ho.

These exceedingly fertile alluvial soils do not owe their nearly inexhaustible resources only to stored capital accumulated during countless years of silting, but to annual renewal by present and continuing silting. These soils are themselves parasites, living upon the fertility of other, frequently very remote soils, which are continually losing substance, by wind and rain erosion, to the eponymous stream of the parasitic soil region. The river carries this valuable detritus down towards its delta, and deposits it by flooding upon the favoured deltaic soils. Such constantly renewed alluvial soils can be populated with a density, cultivated with an intensity which no other soil would support for more than a century or two.

And it is at least probable that alluvial soils were the natural habitats of the primaeval noble grasses, those cereal grains which were the ancestors of the staple food plants of all the high civilizations.

*

There is another and very different kind of soil which readily lends itself to exploitation by primitive human communities, provided that their members practise parasitism primarily by means of a pastoral, rather than an agricultural economy.

Loess is a fine, porous earth, uniform in structure, which leads to the conclusion that, like alluvium, it is deposited. But it is not deposited by water. The mineral matrix of *loess* consists of wind-borne particles of siliceous or calcareous dust. In both Europe and America *loess* soils occur beyond the terminal moraines of the last Ice Age, (*c.* 8000 B.C.?). As the ice melted back at its southern fringes it deposited mud which, drying into dust, was carried off by the wind, to be deposited and piled up against some natural obstacle, for example a range of foothills, or the vegetation of a *steppe* country. The word "loess" is also used to describe soils of aeolian, but not of glacial origin, composed of particles picked up by wind as it crosses a desert, and put down beyond the margin of that desert. Such *loess* soils of non-glacial origin occur in western China, where some are known to be as much as 2000 feet deep: however, this is not a typical figure, and in the case of glacial *loess* soils the depth is of the order of ten feet.

The conditions which, in certain regions, create *loess* soils, also tend to produce a semi-arid climate, and while they are very fertile indeed in the presence of ample water, in semi-arid conditions their fertility is not viable. Where annual rainfall is low, say below 20 inches, trees will not grow, at least not so as to become the dominant species and build up prosperous forest soil communities. Consequently, *loess* soils do not normally support forests, but become either grass *steppe*, or park-land.

The animal members of grass soil communities, or of park-land, are, of course, principally herbivores, although the carnivorous predators will also be present. Among these soil members are the ox, the horse and, in humid *steppe* verging on swamp, the buffalo. The domestication of these species was the device contrived by men of the *loess* soils, to enable them to exploit soil fertility capital, instead of living precariously off its increment. The horse was domesticated by Mongol or Turkish-speaking people on the Asian, and perhaps independently by Berber or Semitic people on the African *steppes*. Oxen must also have been domesticated by people living in the same soil community as such species as *Bos primogenius* and other wild cattle, that is, park-land.[4] And the first we hear of the buffalo, as a domestic animal, in Europe, is as a gift to the Langobard

Court, in Italy, about A.D. 600, sent from Asia by the Khan of the Avars, who were a typical *steppe* folk.[5]

*

As everybody knows, the earliest men of whom any record survives were hunters and food-gatherers. They were not, however, without creative powers; on the contrary, they included notable artists, and perhaps, by analogue with the recently extinct African bush-folk, whose painting is reminiscent of some prehistoric work, had a genuine literature of spoken tales and poems.

Men hunting and gathering food are full soil-community members and on a par, in relation to the soil, with all the other animal members. Most sophisticated literatures express traditions of a remote Golden Age, when men were simple and virtuous. This tradition must refer, as in the Jewish example of Adam and Eve in the Garden of Eden, to the primal hunting and food-gathering phase of our history as a species, when, speaking ecologically, men, although rather unenterprising, were virtuous indeed.

As soil-community members enjoying no special privileges, men would have been held in balance with soil fertility; they would have been subject to the checks which keep all soil members in equilibrium, the hazards which keep all member species from becoming excessive in relation to the other member species, and to soil-fertility increment.

In such conditions men, however talented, cannot make a civilization: competing, on more or less equal terms, with other and equally predatory genera; under the law of return, entailing specific sacrifice for communal advantage, men cannot become so numerous and so prosperous as to stockpile the surplus out of which civilization is made. *For the first step towards civilization is soil exploitation.*

Before a stable hunting and food-gathering community of men can begin to exploit soil as parasites, instead of living with it as members, a new economic tool is required. Such men may already possess language, aesthetic sensibility, artistic talent, weapons, tools, and the control of fire, yet still they are objects of natural history,[6] and cannot become makers of history.

Two economic instruments of emancipation were devised. Some men tamed and battened upon animals; they learnt to use the stomachs of fellow-species for the digestion of grass in their own interest, and became herdsmen, shepherds, and horsemen. Others tamed and battened upon esculent plants, particularly cereal grasses, and thus became farmers.[7] In both cases the men were parasitic upon soil fertility by means of animal and plant instruments, with which, in time, they learnt to live symbiotically. The ancient balance of natural soil communities had at last been upset by opportunist intelligence. Man stepped outside the scheme of nature, and started the process we call history.

Which of the devices for soil exploitation came first?

Scholars have a taste for systems and arbitrary patterns in their thought, which they tend to impose upon the processes and institutions that are the objects of their study. They like to arrange the events leading up to civilizations in an orderly series, and so they take the King of Hearts' advice in *Alice*: "Begin at the beginning, go on until you come to the end, and then stop." It was this almost mathematical bias which led to the confusion of Classical with Western Christian history, and the resultant invalid classification of historical epochs into Ancient, Mediaeval, and Modern. It is this same troublesome neo-scholasticism which has led to the illusion called Progress. And largely because of this passion for a serial order, it was once believed that the hunters and food-gatherers, our remote ancestors, first tamed animals, and only thereafter tamed plants; first became pastoralists, and subsequently settled down in one place and became farmers.

This was very neat but it did not conform with the observed facts of archaeology and history. The theory was discredited and an equally tidy one promptly put in its place. It was argued that plants must have been much easier to domesticate than animals, an argument which has a grave psychological weakness, and that therefore the farmer came before the herdsman. By means of his tamed grasses, it was suggested, the farmer would have been better able to attract, keep and maintain cattle. It has even been suggested that some established farming peoples took to the new craft of living off stock, and became pastoralists, in order to emancipate themselves from their bondage to plants, and take to a freer life. This latter argument is particularly weak, for the desire of most men is for secure bondage.

I have been able to find no evidence at all that either plant farming or animal farming came first, with the one dependent upon the other. It seems much more probable that in each case the principal instrument of soil exploitation, devised or borrowed by a particular people, must have been a product of the nature of the soil upon which they found themselves. This theory does not *necessarily* entail the corollary that each loess-dwelling people invented pastoralism for itself; or that each alluvial soil people invented tillage. It may have been so. But, in any case, a primitive community of hunters and food-gatherers would have tended to adopt, from some more advanced people, that form of soil exploitation most suited to its native soil environment.

When the loess-dwelling, Aryan-speaking branch of the Wiros people who were the authors of the body of hymns called the *Rigveda,* went over the Hindu Kush and down into the Indus Valley they found, by their own account, a people of farmers whom they called Dasas or Dasyu.

In the *Rigveda* these Indus valley farmers are described, rather offensively, as a black-skinned, flat-nosed or noseless, unclean people, accused of performing no sacrifices, and of inheriting through the maternal line. By Aryan standards all this was very contemptible, and the hymn expresses the opposition between two fundamentally different cultures. On the one hand we have, in the Aryans, a pastoral, patriarchal, God-worshipping, loess-soil people. On the other, an agricultural, matriarchal, goddess-worshipping,[8] alluvial-soil people. And we might suggest the theory that primal high civilizations were born of such fecund encounters, by the bringing together of two mutually complementary economic devices, and the resultant creation of surplus wealth.[9]

It would be a typical systematizer's mistake to maintain that, in the beginnings of soil exploitation, *steppe* soils on *loess* produced pure pastoralism, alluvial soils pure tillage. It is far more likely that both stock-raising and tillage were practised together, but that the type of soil assured, in each case, a preponderance of one practice over the other, in a measure determined principally by the extent to which the soil conformed to the "ideal" of its kind, as well as to other factors. For example, in what archaeologists call Phase I of the Danube Culture, mixed farming was already being practised before the people were quite emancipated from a hunting economy. But their soil was a "mixed" one. The *steppe* peoples of North America, primarily hunters and gatherers, practised tillage. But the North American *steppe* had only one ruminant, the bison, which was by no means a placable animal. If we bear this in mind we can safely pursue this line of thought concerning the influence of soil itself on the beginnings of soil exploitation and soil parasitism, without obstructing the argument with tedious reservations.

It is now generally accepted that the inventors of plant farming were women. It is at least probable that the inventors of stock farming were men. Some speculation concerning the origins of these two economic devices, origins not in the nature of man, but in the nature of soil, should not be out of place.

Among hunting species of animals both sexes hunt, and the muscular inferiority of females, if they are inferior, is not such as to make them incapable of the hardest work or the most dangerous hazards. The domestic tom-cat is not superior, as a mouser, to his mate, nor is the tigress less terrible than the tiger. But among humans, except in the fox-hunting English shires, it has always been the male who does the hunting. The work of the female has been, if not less arduous, certainly less dangerous.

There are several reasons for this: the human female is handicapped by a sexual rhythm entailing a periodical debility of rather high frequency. The period of gestation is also exceptionally long. The helpless infancy and childhood of the human young is enormously prolonged in comparison with those of other hunting carnivores. By these handicaps women are unfitted for hunting.

But they are not unfitted for seeking and collecting wild fruits, edible grubs, eggs, esculent roots and seeds; in short, they are perfectly capable of food-gathering, while their men are out hunting.

We do not know where the arts of farming first arose, nor even whether they were discovered once only, or several times in different places. The opinion of Breasted, that both tillage and stock-raising began somewhere in the east Mediterranean region, between the Nile delta and Persia, has much to recommend it, because in that region occurred not only wild grasses ancestral to our cereals, but wild cattle ancestral to our herds. Wild barley was probably to be found in Asia Minor, Transcaucasia, Persia, Anatolia, Arabia and Abyssinia. A wild wheat, *Triticum diococcum* (Emmer) occurred in Syria, Palestine and Mesopotamia, and another, *Triticum monococcum* in the Balkans, Asia Minor, North Syria, Kurdistan and Persia. But it is possible that other regions, which have received less attention, may have offered opportunities quite as good to the Neolithic peoples who were ready to pass from soil membership to soil parasitism.

The earliest sites of Neolithic agricultural communities which have been excavated reveal that these communities practised mixed farming. There is one exception, in which no animal remains not attributable to hunting have been found, but from the evidence revealed by the archaeologists the remains which *seem* to point to tillage, *may* point to the very successful harvesting of wild grain.

The nature of the soil community upon which a human tribe finds itself at the moment of passing from membership to parasitism, must put emphasis *either* on food-gathering, *or* upon hunting as the principal source of food. And in the same way, after the farming techniques had been discovered, the most powerful influence in giving first importance either to tillage, or to stock-raising, would have been the nature of the soil.

As for the discovery of stock-raising, there is no difficulty in imagining what took place: the hunter, sooner or later, would have a chance, as hunters still do, to take alive a calf, a foal or a fawn. The suckling foal stays by the body of its slain dam, for this is the only source of life and security which it knows. The wild cow hides her calf in a brake or in long grass while she goes abroad to graze. Found and taken by the hunter, the cries of the tethered calf might well call the cow, to be taken in her turn. Any one or several of a score of typical hunting accidents can be seen as the origin of pastoralism, so that it is not necessary to postulate an inventor, a genius or a folk-hero as the discoverer of stock-farming.

It is, however, almost certain that the discovery took place in exclusively masculine company, and probable that the development of the new device would have been a male speciality. In communities where the women's food-gathering was relatively unsuccessful, as it might well have been on *loess* park-land soils, and where, in the following stage, stock-raising turned out to be more profitable than tillage, the former would have tended to prosper at the expense of the latter. In the beginnings of agriculture and stock-raising on *loess* soils it was soon found necessary to keep on the move, and although, for example, the Danubian Neolithic farmers were both tillers and stock-raisers, they were semi-nomadic. The reason for this is obvious. Before the discovery of manuring techniques, eight or ten crops of grain exhaust the soil, and the community must move on and break maiden soil. Like certain Africans of our own time, these Neolithic farmers on the *loess* were forced to practise shifting tillage. In the course of these periodical removals, the communities would have found themselves dependent upon the cattle they took with them, and for this reason, as also because the clearance of forest is laborious, their movements would have followed the *loess*, the grass soils. And where they emerged on to the great grassy ocean of the Eurasian *steppe*, with its inexhaustible supply of cattle fodder, they would have tended more and more to develop the techniques of pastoral nomads, and to neglect those of tillage. And, in fact, the cataclysmic eruptions of pastoral nomad peoples from the *steppe* into "the sewn" have all come from the Eurasian or the Arabian *steppes*.

In a pastoral community, living first parasitically off half-wild herbs, later symbiotically upon tame cattle, the emphasis would have been on male principles and values. And, in fact, we find that pastoral communities were and are invariably patriarchal. And that this arises from the influence of their way of life, and therefore from the soil which made that way of life; that it has nothing to do with race, is clear from the fact that the institutions of such racially different peoples as the Aryans of the *Rigveda,* the Biblical and the Arabian Semites, the Turkish peoples of the Asian *steppe,* in short all pastoralists, are broadly similar in their early stages. Such pastoralists are always objects of fear and contempt to the farming communities with which they come into touch. They always have been, as we can see from the attitude of the Egyptians to the pastoralist Hebrews, or from that of the peasant state of eighteenth-century Russia to such pastoral folk as the Tartars, and even to such lapsed farmers as the Cossacks.[10]

*

On alluvial soils in the great river valleys, the story of man's emancipation from soil-community membership was very different. On such soils, woman's discovery of tillage would have become increasingly important, as we shall see. It is at least possible that this discovery was actually made on alluvium.

As to the nature of that discovery itself, let us suppose that some matron of a food-gathering tribe had gathered wild barley, either to grind it, or to make a simple frumentum—for the use of cereal grain does not at once imply the invention of either bread or porridge.[11] She has kept her gatherings in a bag or basket. Here, then, taken from Defoe's *Robinson Crusoe*, is what might easily be her account of the discovery of cericulture:

> What little remainder of corn had been in the bag had been all devoured by rats, and I saw nothing in the bag but husks and dust, . . . I shook the husks of corn out of it, on one side of my fortification, under the rock.
>
> It was a little time before the great rain just now mentioned, that I threw this stuff away; taking no notice of anything and not so much as remembering that I had thrown anything there: when, about a month later, I saw some stalks of something green shooting out of the ground, which I fancied might be some plant I had not seen; but I was surprised, and perfectly astonished, when after a little longer time, I saw about ten or twelve ears come out, which were perfect green barley, . . . It is impossible to express the confusion of my thoughts on this occasion. I had hitherto acted upon no religious foundation at all; indeed, I had very few notions of religion in my head, nor had entertained any sense of anything that had befallen me, otherwise than as chance. . . . But after I saw barley grow there . . . I began to suggest that God had miraculously caused this grain to grow. . . .

I have quoted the latter, as well as the former part of this passage, because it seems relevant to the theme. It is surely probable that with the accidental invention of agriculture must have occurred the invention of the Fertility Cult which is the primal, and most enduring, religion. The apparently spontaneous generation of barley turns Crusoe's mind to the idea of a Divine benefactor. A similar miracle might well, albeit in other terms, have had an identical effect on the mind of the fortunate matron of a primitive riparian community. It is true that Crusoe soon thought of the rational explanation of the phenomenon, whereupon his reverent awe departed. But no such explanation would have occurred to the primitive discoverer of agriculture, and between *her* reaction and that of Crusoe would be the difference between the soil-man relationships of a people native to a soil community from its cultural infancy, and those of a people at a highly sophisticated phase of civilization, invading an alien soil.

Moreover, the elaborate developments of the Fertility Cult would naturally have arisen from this beginning. A distinguished pomologist once told me that as a child he used to plant the feathers of birds, picked up in the garden, and was disappointed when they did not grow. It is not a long step from this state of mind to that of the Grimes Graves flint-miners expecting the Earth Mother to produce them a crop of flints, which were, for them, a food-substitute, viable as food by means of exchange.[12] The act of planting seed in earth would have its obvious analogue for most, although apparently not all, peoples, in the sexual act. Phallus worship, such as that of the Indus Valley *Dasas,* and, again, of the Norfolk flint-miners, occurs as a corollary to the worship of the Earth Mother, the Great Goddess, Demeter, Ceres, Mary.

Where the earliest mixed farming was practised on alluvial soils, such as those of the Tigris and the Nile Valleys, the case of the Neolithic farmers would have been very different from that of their contemporaries on *loess* soils. As we shall see in the next chapter, such fortunate primaeval farmers were *not* obliged to make the very difficult discovery of manuring, in order to be able to form permanent settlements. The rivers annually renewed their soils for them.

It is very difficult to arrive at a date for the earliest agriculture. It lies somewhere between 6000 B.C. and 4000 B.C. Probably the earliest settlement where grains were regularly reaped yet excavated is that of the so-called Natufians on the slopes of Mount Carmel in Palestine. A type of reaping tool, made by setting flint teeth in a wooden or bone shaft, has been found there. Similar tools are associated with early Neolithic peasant communities over a wide area. For our present argument, the excavated sites at *Merimde*, in the Nile delta, and *Tepe Gawra* on the Tigris alluvium, are significant. These sites were permanently occupied by farmers and stock-raisers over an enormous period of time: their inhabitants were not driven to shift their cultivation every decade or so.

The river valley soils would not only have enabled their early exploiters to make permanent settlements, and so found cities, and thus make civilization, while the *steppe*-dwelling pastoralists were forced to move with their herds and could not found cities; they would, while encouraging the rapid spread of tillage, have discouraged stock-raising. I do not mean that stock-raising would have been neglected to the extent that tillage was neglected by the pastoralists. We know that this was not the case. But there could be no question of developing vast, moving herds of cattle, horses or sheep, and stock-raising would have occupied much the same place as on a small English mixed farm of today. The emphasis would all have been on cultivation, which not only was a feminine discovery, but which was developed under female aegis, acquired a Goddess (with many names) and was encouraged to prosper by female fertility magic, rites and religions.[13]

In a social organization based upon a female economy, the emphasis would have been upon feminine values.[14] Nor, on an alluvial soil, would there have been much to upset female predominance until, perhaps, a pastoral and patriarchal people came into contact with the farming community, and encouraged its men to assert themselves. Women long remained in charge of their discovery of agriculture, perhaps until the plough and such-like heavy implements became more important than the digging-stick and the primal hoe.

We have arrived, although speculatively, at the conclusion that the earliest agricultural communities were matriarchal and feminine in their social values. And there are grounds, not speculative but archaeological, mythological, sociological and philological, for believing that this was, indeed, the case.[15]

Scholars have gone to remarkable lengths in their speculations and deductions, to show how, by what routes, under what social or climatic pressures, the great fundamental inventions of mankind, both in tools and in techniques, were carried to relatively backward communities from some centre of origin. The savants of the nineteenth century were dominated by this idea, as ordinary people were and are dominated by the notion of single inventors, of Prometheus, Tubal Cain, George Stevenson, Marconi, folk-heroes who by their genius bring enlightenment. Victor Heyn, for example, derives almost every economic plant and animal from South-west Asia, so that one receives from his works the impression of an almost empty outer world being filled with plants, animals and techniques from this gushing widow's cruze of a place! More recently scholars of the school of Perry and Elliot-Smith make every high culture, even the geographically remote ones of South and Central America, derive from a unique source, Egypt. Perhaps it was so: indeed, there can be no doubt that many inventions, whether of things or of techniques, were carried outwards from a centre of origin by war, trade or migration.

But it does seem to me that the great fundamental inventions of mankind, and especially the pastoral and agricultural devices for exploiting soil, may possibly have been made more than once, in several places independently. There would be nothing extraordinary in the same accidents, exploited by an identical opportunism, occurring at widely separated points in similar conditions of soil and climate. Any grass soil, populated by a hunting people at a certain stage of mental growth and under certain economic compulsions, might give rise to pastoralism. And the similar condition[16] obtaining in the valleys of the Nile, the Hwang-ho, the Indus, the Euphrates-Tigris, populated by equally intelligent peoples, might all tend to produce the beginnings of agriculture.

I do not assert or claim that this *did* happen, of course: for one thing, the time discrepancies in the beginnings, so far as they can be estimated, of the primal civilizations, argue in favour of the theory of a single original discovery. But this can be otherwise accounted for, and it is at least *possible* that whenever men and soils came together in certain conditions, the rural crafts were generated.

Pastoralism and agriculture are, as I have suggested, encouraged by different kinds of soil, by *loess* and by alluvial soil respectively. But it is, perhaps, when a pastoral and an agricultural people clash upon terms which can result in the total eclipse of neither, but rather in a fecund union, that the highest civilizations are produced.

Later, of course, when nomadic people, pastoralists in an advanced phase, descended upon the cities of sedentary folk, they did so to enslave or destroy them. But even that may be only partially true: how much does Arab culture owe to the sedentary people conquered by these pastoralists of the Arabian *steppe*? And what does our own Western culture owe to Arab stimuli?[17] In any case, we are dealing with primaeval, not historical events. And was not historical Athens the product of a fruitful encounter between the matriarchal Pelasgoi in possession of Attica, and the invading, patriarchal Lapithai?[18]

In the following chapters I have attempted to describe the soils which gave rise to several of the primal civilizations of history, and as a consequence of intelligent soil parasitism.

PART TWO:
MAN AS A PARASITE ON SOIL

*

CHAPTER V

MAN AS A PARASITE ON ALLUVIUM

THE NILE

THE source of the Victoria Nile is the Ripon Falls out of Lake Victoria, less than half a degree north of the equator. In its early reaches the river is turbulent, running through tropical forest and park-land. Collecting the surplus waters of Lake Albert, and thereafter, as the White Nile, it flows north through $13\frac{1}{2}$ degrees of latitude, receiving tributaries from its watershed on the east and west until it reaches lat. N. 10°. Between this point, and Khartoum, where it is joined by the Blue Nile, it receives no other streams.

The Blue Nile rises in Lake Tana, in Abyssinia, and is, with its tributaries, the principal carrier of the silt of which the soils of Egypt were, and continue to be, made. From Lake Tana the Blue Nile flows south through $1\frac{1}{2}$ degrees, west through three degrees of longitude and then roughly NNW. to Wadi Medani in the Sudan, where it is joined by two large tributaries from the south-west, the Rahad and the Dinder. As a single stream, the Blue Nile then flows north-west to join the White Nile at Khartoum.

From Khartoum and Omdurman, the United Niles flow north and west to approximately lat. 17° N. long. E. 34° where they are joined by the Atbara, a river which rises in the same Abyssinian highlands as the Rahad and the Dinder, its actual source being north-west of Lake Tana.

The Nile continues north as far as Abu Hamed, turns south-west to Ambukal, takes a westerly, north-westerly and then northerly bend to Dongola, whence it flows north to the Delta.

The total northerly displacement of water is through nearly thirty degrees of latitude, about 1600 miles, the total length of the Nile system being upwards of 3000 miles.

The Victoria–Albert–White Nile part of the system brings down little soil to contribute to Egypt, since its course is through intact soil communities not suffering from erosion. These rivers provide the steady flow of Nile water into which, at a certain season, the Blue Nile system and the Atbara pour their soil-laden torrents. These torrents, and the Nile floods which they cause, are produced by the south-west monsoon, a fact which, as we shall see, also accounts for the enormous quantity of soil material which they carry with them. The steadiness of the main-stream of the Nile is accounted for by the very slight landfall from source to mouth, a matter of five inches to the mile. On the other hand the Blue Nile, and the Atbara, coming from a high mountain country, are fast-flowing streams.

The mountains of Abyssinia are, for the most part, extinct volcanoes. As we have already seen in the case of the *Ager Romanus*, soils made up with volcanic detritus are very fertile, and the silt carried down by the Blue Nile system, and by the Atbara, is largely of volcanic material.

The volcanic Abyssinian highlands are subject to wind erosion throughout the year; but, in the spring, the south-west monsoon, laden with Atlantic water and the moisture of the equatorial African forests over which it has passed, strikes the Abyssinian mountains and there, in a Wagnerian uproar of continuous thunderstorms, cloudbursts, hail and rain, discharges itself. The quantity of rainfall varies widely from year to year so that:

> So many peoples and generations of Egypt have studied this vital question through and through, and yet the height of the flood, resulting from the rain, has never once been forecast for the following year.[19]

During the dry, winter season, the rivers of Abyssinian mountain provenance, the Dinder, the Rahad and the Atbara,

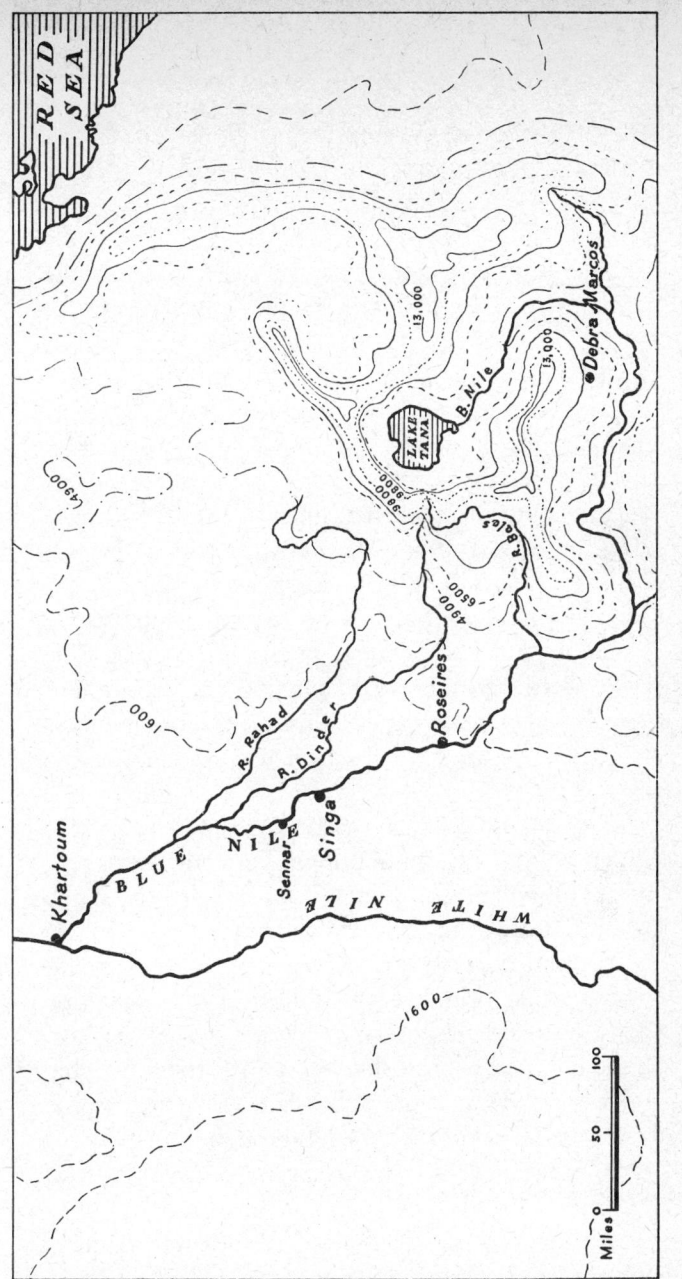

1. THE BLUE NILE

Source not only of Egypt's water, but of Egypt's top soil

run nearly dry, but the coming of the monsoon fills their beds with catastrophic violence, the rainfall pouring in torrents down the eroded volcanic slopes, carrying with it millions of tons of the material which is to re-create the Egyptian soils. This run-off has dug deep gulleys in the substance of the hills; every year they are deepened and widened, and the product of the torrent's work, particles of hornblende, mica, feldspar, of calcareous and ferruginous compounds, are the constituents of the Nile silt.

This mineral fertility is not all that the river brings down into Egypt. There is also mature soil and organic material, and these, as it happens, are the unintended gifts of the Abyssinian pastoralists to the Egyptian peasantry. Since prehistoric times, and the practice still continues, these herdsmen and shepherds have been burning off the scrub and the forest, so that fresh grass can grow and provide wider grazing for their beasts. Formerly, much of the Abyssinian highland was forest soil and, as we know, this means a natural control of the water cycle. The destruction of forest had the usual consequences; run-off and erosion. The Abyssinian highlanders, instead of providing new grazing for their animals, provide Egypt with the most fertile soil in the world.[20]

The quantity of silt annually carried down by the Nile varies between 70 and 150 million tons. Formerly, before the deforestation of highland Abyssinia, it must have been much less. But even if, during the 7000 odd years of Egypt's occupation by agricultural men, the annual mean has been only 50 million tons, the total weight of new soil carried into Egypt by the Nile floods and either deposited on the flooded valley lands, or used in the building of the delta, is 3.5×10^6 tons. A cubic yard of soil weighs about a ton, and a fair average top-soil is nine inches deep. Therefore the Nile has brought into Egypt in the last seven millenia more than three hunded times the total area of the whole European top-soil.[21]

The monsoon is at its height by mid-June: the flood reaches Egypt (north of Khartoum), in September. The river rises above its banks and floods the whole valley of Upper Egypt. This valley and the kingdom itself are co-extensive; there is no more Upper Egypt than the fertile strip created by the Nile. It consists of a cleft in the earth between two great deserts of arid *steppe*, the cleft being about 300 feet deep and bounded by limestone cliffs which are nowhere more than twelve miles apart, and in places only a few hundred yards. The length of the cleft from Khartoum to Cairo, the southerly and northerly limits of Upper Egypt, is 547 miles. This is the region which is flooded every September and October, and upon which, when the flood water recedes, the Egyptians have planted their crops during the past six or seven thousand years. And this silt *is* the soil of Upper Egypt.

In the months of low water the *fellahin* irrigate their crops, raising Nile water up to the level of the soil by means of a machine, the *shadouf*, which has been in use for at least 3000 years, and probably for 5000 years. It consists of a rod pivoted on a tripod; on the landward end of the rod is a counterweight, a lump of dried Nile mud; and on the river end, a bucket. The *fellah* stands in the water, pulls down the bucket until it fills, then lets it go, whereupon the counterweight swings it up so that it can be poured out into small irrigation ditches. In places as many as four *shadoufs*, one above the other, are required to get the water high enough. About 200 generations of *fellahin* have been doing this, without altering the *shadouf*.

Nowhere in the world is there a soil community comparable with this of the Upper Egyptian cleft. Its winter climate is warm, there is no measurable rainfall, and until recently the country people were exceptionally healthy. However, the stable health of the *fellahin*, like the stable economy of Egypt, both of which, since Herodotus first noticed them, have been the subject of remark by travellers, have been gravely impaired by a serious disturbance of the ancient soil balance, and will have to find a new equilibrium. The control of flood water, with the object of making water available during a longer period of months, and for irrigation on a large scale, has raised soil humidity, and therefore atmospheric humidity. The purpose of control, achieved by the building of dams and barrages, was to transform the economy of all Egypt from one of national subsistence to one of national cash-cropping. As a result, the great granary of the Roman Empire became a wheat-importing country, but a considerable exporter of long-staple cotton. The change was extremely profitable to European money-lenders, the Egyptian Khedive, and the Lancashire cotton spinners. It left the *fellahin* where they had always been, standing in the Nile working the *shadouf*. Potentially, no doubt, it left him better off. Meanwhile, the humidity, and the disappearance of clover, enabled the anopheles mosquito, the hook-worm, and the bilharzia fluke (*B. haematobius*) to rise out of their proper place in the soil community, and batten, like seven millenia of overlords, conquerors and usurers, upon the patient *fellahin*.

*

The second soil community created by the Nile is Lower Egypt, that is the Delta. It is made entirely of Nile silt, and first appeared above sea-level about 14,000 years ago. Since then, the delta has grown upwards and outwards thrusting into the sea, and as a growing land its appearance, and accounts of it, have changed from age to age; the number of the Nile mouths, for example, has varied between two and six.

In our own time the delta is an isosceles triangle, the base being a stretch of Mediterranean shore from the Rosetta (Canopic) mouth in the west, 85 miles as the crow flies to the Damietta (Pelusiac) mouth in the east. The apex of the triangle is at Cairo, 110 miles in a straight line from a point midway between the mouths. The whole area is about 4000 square miles of fertile soil 55 feet deep.

*

The earliest occupants of the two Nile soils progressed so rapidly in the arts of civilization, and the artifacts of one age were so quickly and deeply pressed into Nile mud by those of

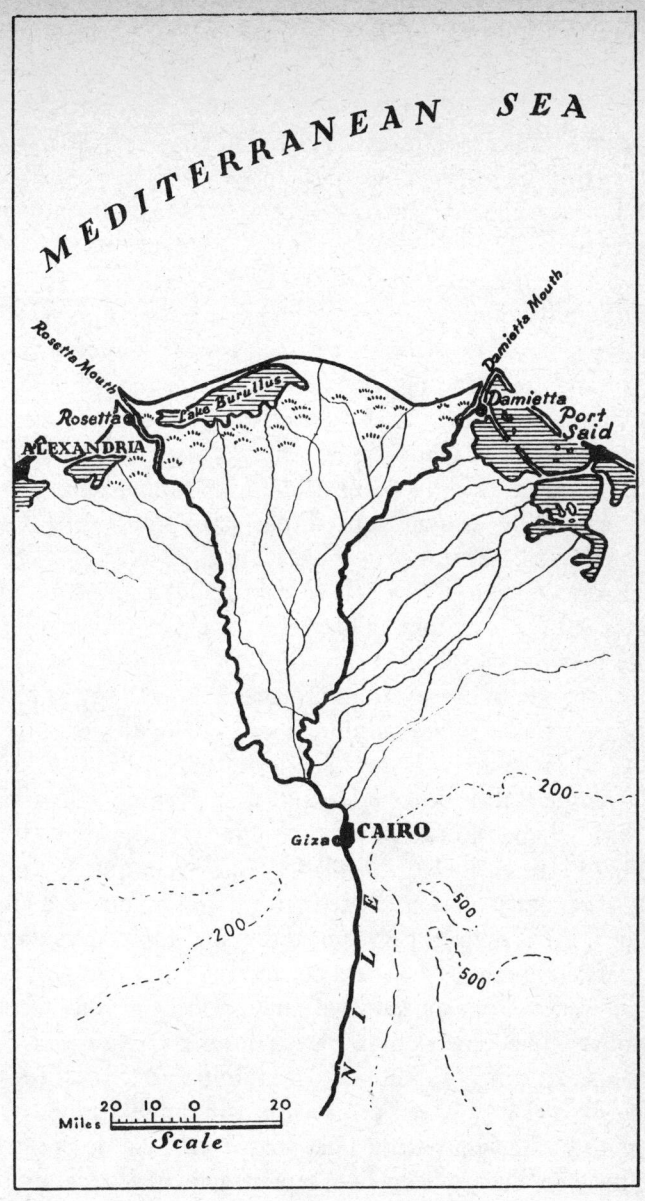

2. THE NILE DELTA

This shows 14,000 years of alluvial deposit. The soil of the Delta is carried by the Nile from Ethiopia

the next, that archaeology has revealed little of the early Neolithic peasantry in whom we are interested.

This precocity was related to the nature of the Nile soils.

Whether Egyptian women invented agriculture for themselves, or acquired the art by contact with inventors from elsewhere, we have no means of knowing. That they subsequently drew ahead in the race does not mean that they must have had a start to begin with. Very early pre-dynastic Egyptians of whom we have knowledge were already well advanced in both tillage and stock-raising.[22] At Merimde, near Cairo, in the Delta, was a settlement of Neolithic mixed farmers using flint reaping tools of the Natufian type, grain-storage jars and basket-lined pits of a kind also found in Mesopotamia. This settlement cannot be accurately dated, nor can a similar one in the Fayum. But it has this to distinguish it from Neolithic settlements on *loess* soil, that it was in continuous occupation over a long term of centuries. This permanence of settlement was made possible by the Nile silt.

This is one of the few glimpses we have, in Egypt, of the primaeval phase in soil exploitation, and for the manner in which the Neolithic villagers developed their culture we must look to the rather better "documented" Mesopotamian soils (see next chapter), or rely upon reasoning backwards from the earliest remains which are available in sufficient quantity.

We must make use of comparative anthropology and archaeology: in Chapter I it was noted that anthropologists do not believe that much can be learnt concerning long dead primitive communities, from the study of arrested *living* primitive communities. The objection is based upon the argument that although existing "primitive" communities are "arrested" in the sense that they have not developed into civilizations, they are not absolutely arrested. They may even have degenerated, and therefore their state does not represent an ancient condition. They *have* developed since Neolithic times, but developed very differently.

The opponents of this theory, however, while they agree that existing savage institutions cannot be taken as exactly what they were in Neolithic times, having stood still for fifty centuries, argue that the changes in the institutions of these existing tribes are such as can be allowed for. They believe, unlike their opponents, that Neolithic organization, deriving from Palaeolithic, was certainly tribal. They point out that when a tribe with a certain kind of totemistic, exogamous social system, believed by Morganists to be a universal Late Palaeolithic-Early Neolithic world-wide institution, fails to scrap this system when it has ceased to reflect economic (and therefore *soil*), conditions, and fails to allow a more suitable system to develop in its place, then social growth does not cease, indeed, but becomes morbid. It takes the form of increasing the complexity of the old system, until we arrive at the state of affairs obtaining in certain Australian tribes, where the totem and tabu system is so fantastically complex that Europeans can only understand it with great difficulty.

This being so, say the Morganists, we can cut away the morbid growth of the centuries during which other peoples have been developing capitalism and the political state, and so arrive at a tribal pattern which represents the state of social development reached in that late Neolithic time when economic conditions were beginning to call for a revolution, the revolution which gave rise to the political, instead of the social society. The tribes which did make this revolution did so in two senses; social *decentralization*, involving the emergence of the small, patriarchal, family unit, out of the communist group-families of the Palaeolithic and Early Neolithic system; and political *centralization*, involving the emergence of the State out of a congeries of tribes.

To return to the Egyptians: all but the earliest of whom we have knowledge were, as we have seen, already practising tillage and stock-raising. They worshipped numerous gods, most of whom were in animal form: Horus is a Falcon, Thoth an Ibis, Sebek a Crocodile. What is the origin of these gods? Applying the comparative method, we conclude that they were originally tribal totems;[23] and, in fact, excavation has unearthed certain objects, uncovered certain paintings, revealing that the Egyptians were formerly organized in totemistic tribes. From what we know of totemistic tribal society, the Neolithic Egyptians, graduating to soil-parasitism by way of tillage, rather than stock-raising, which their soil must have made necessary, *should* have been organized in a matrilinear and matriarchal society. There is evidence that this was the case, in the vestigial remains of such a system in later Egyptian society.

According to J. H. Breasted[24] no Egyptian male owned property in the Old Kingdom. The property belonged to his wife, and he had the use and control of it only by virtue of his marriage. Upon his death it passed to his eldest daughter. In the same spirit, royalty in Egypt was transmitted in the female line, and the only way by which the Pharaoh could make sure of his son succeeding him as High Priest and War Lord of the people, was by wedding the youth to the real heiress: thus, the sons of the Pharaohs married their sisters. Petrie says that "Sister marriage reconciled matriarchal property with paternal inheritance.[25] It did the same for royalty as for property, and the custom long outlasted the native dynasties, so that we find the Greek Ptolemys religiously marrying their sisters, and one of Julius Caesar's first tasks in Egypt was to settle the row between the Queen, Cleopatra, and her brother-bridegroom.

According to George Thomson[26] this matrilinear system endured in Egypt for most, and perhaps all, classes of society until as late as the Twelfth Dynasty, when it began to be replaced by a patrilinear system more in keeping with a society increasingly dominated by male values. This revolution was, it seems, greatly accelerated by the Hyksos conquest of Egypt. And this is what, reasoning from the soil upwards, we should expect. For the Hyksos (Shepherd) conquerors were *steppe* people, pastoralists, and therefore patriarchal in their society.

The soil of Egypt, then, called for and received a matriarchal, primarily agricultural society with the emphasis on tillage, as its first exploiter. But this phenomenon is commonplace all over the Eurasian and North African world at that time. Why, in Egypt, did it develop so rapidly into urbanization and high civilization?

*

It has already been said that on all soils but those which are annually renewed by silt, Neolithic farmers were forced to keep shifting, and could not settle in one place for long enough to found cities, states, in short, civilization. Before they could do this they had to discover the craft of manuring. But there was no reason why they should realize this. The accidental discovery of agriculture, or rather, in the first instance, a kind of horticulture, probably led the women of Early Neolithic tribes to plant in imitation of nature, the only difference being that they grew one kind of plant on their plot of land, which had formerly supported numerous kinds that were not carried and eaten, but died and rotted where they grew. But the Neolithic peasant women had no reason to suppose that their primitive monoculture would exhaust the soil; *they* were not exhausted by bringing forth young of the same kind every year, why therefore should Mother Earth be so exhausted? Probably the failure of crops would be explained by some failure in the efficacy of the ritual accompanying planting and cultivation, ritual expressive of the large corpus of magico-religious doctrine of the Fertility Cults. The move to new land would be made not for scientific, but for theological reasons. Neolithic settlements on *loess* soils, for example in Central Europe, show that the kind of tillage practised was, in fact, of the same order as that of the native African farmers of our own time, and of the Amerindians of the nineteenth century.

The discovery and application of manuring, when this is sufficiently effective to enable the farmers to live off an annual soil-fertility increment, entails an advance from soil parasitism, to soil creation, a subject to be dealt with in Part IV. But until this discovery is made, *soil-parasitism on loess does not lead to civilization.*

But, and it is to this that Egyptian civilization surely owes its precocity, the Egyptians were not obliged to discover manuring before settling, not obliged to advance from soil-parasitism to soil-making in order to found cities. Their soil was, as it were, auto-manuring, and the flood-waters of the Nile replaced every year what the Egyptian women, and later the men, took out of it.

Many of the supposititious advantages of the Egyptian and of Mesopotamian environment have been put forward to explain the precocious rise of their urban civilizations, while the peoples of other regions were still held back in the simpler ways of Neolithic culture. But the attribute of the Nile valley, which it shared with the Euphrates–Tigris delta, and which assured to the Egyptian and Mesopotamian peoples their long lead in the progress towards civilization, was surely the one which enabled them to settle down and exploit the soils of their countries as soon as they had learnt to till them, and without having to find a way of re-making the soil every year.

CHAPTER VI

THE EUPHRATES–TIGRIS AND THE INDUS

THE EUPHRATES–TIGRIS

THE three annually renewed alluvial soils to give rise to civilizations, which are described in Chapters V and VI, are by no means the only ones. They have been chosen because their human communities were the most precocious in growing towards civilization, and because the principal cause of their precocity was the nature of the soil itself. The civilization of China rose in the valleys of the Yangtse and the Hwang-ho, but its beginning was more than a thousand years later than that of Egypt and Mesopotamia, and at least half as much later than that of the Indus Valley. Our argument in these two chapters is that the exceptionally rapid rise of man from his beginnings as a primitive soil-exploiter to a high civic culture, in certain regions, must be related to the advantages offered by the soils of those regions.

The case of the Nile soil as a medium for the forcing of civilization has been dealt with at length in Chapter V because it is the extreme case. Not only did its people not have to discover deep ploughing and regular manuring before they could go on to found cities, but the Nile Valley soil has proved resistant to seventy centuries of what can only be called abuse. Egypt is as fertile today as she was before Pharaoh Menes was thought of, before the political state had emerged out of the social tribe. The same cannot be said of Mesopotamia or of the Indus Valley, the principal reason being that the soil of the Nile Valley is probably the only soil in the world which, by virtue of annual renewal combined with the unique topography of the country, has turned out to be nearly man-proof.

The case of the Euphrates–Tigris soil is in many ways not comparable with that of the Nile, but it *is* so comparable in the interesting particular of annual renewal by flood silting, and likewise in possessing a climate, flora and fauna offering opportunity for exploitation by relatively ill-equipped Neolithic people.

The country called Mesopotamia is an alluvial plateau enclosed between the Euphrates and the Tigris rivers, from the point of their nearest approach to each other in the latitude and neighbourhood of Baghdad, to their junction at Kurna in Lake Hammar, out of which their waters are drained by a single stream, the *Shat el Arab,* into the Persian Gulf.

Both rivers rise in the Armenian highland plateau to the east of Anatolia, the Tigris in two sources near Lakes Van and Geuljik, the Euphrates also in two sources, the *Murad Su* and the *Kara Su,* flowing as independent rivers for over 200 and 400 miles respectively to their junction at Arapkir. The watershed of the four sources lies between latitudes 38° and 40° N. and longitudes 38° and 40° E. Formerly this Armenian soil must have been forest, and even now rainfall is ample for the cultivation of such water-loving species as cotton, tobacco and the vine. The first two have been introduced in historical times, the one from India and the other from America, but the antiquity of viticulture in this region is incalculably great: indeed, the first domestication of the vine may even have been due to primaeval Armenians.[27] The clearing operations of the early vineroons, wheat growers and barley growers, as well as shepherds and cattle ranchers, would certainly have disturbed the water-cycle of the country, and given rise to floods of the Euphrates and the Tigris far more torrential than would have been their case before forest-clearance began.

From Arapkir the Euphrates flows south and west through the gorges of the Taurus to Samsat (Samosata) being thereafter joined by tributaries. The river flows south through Carchemish

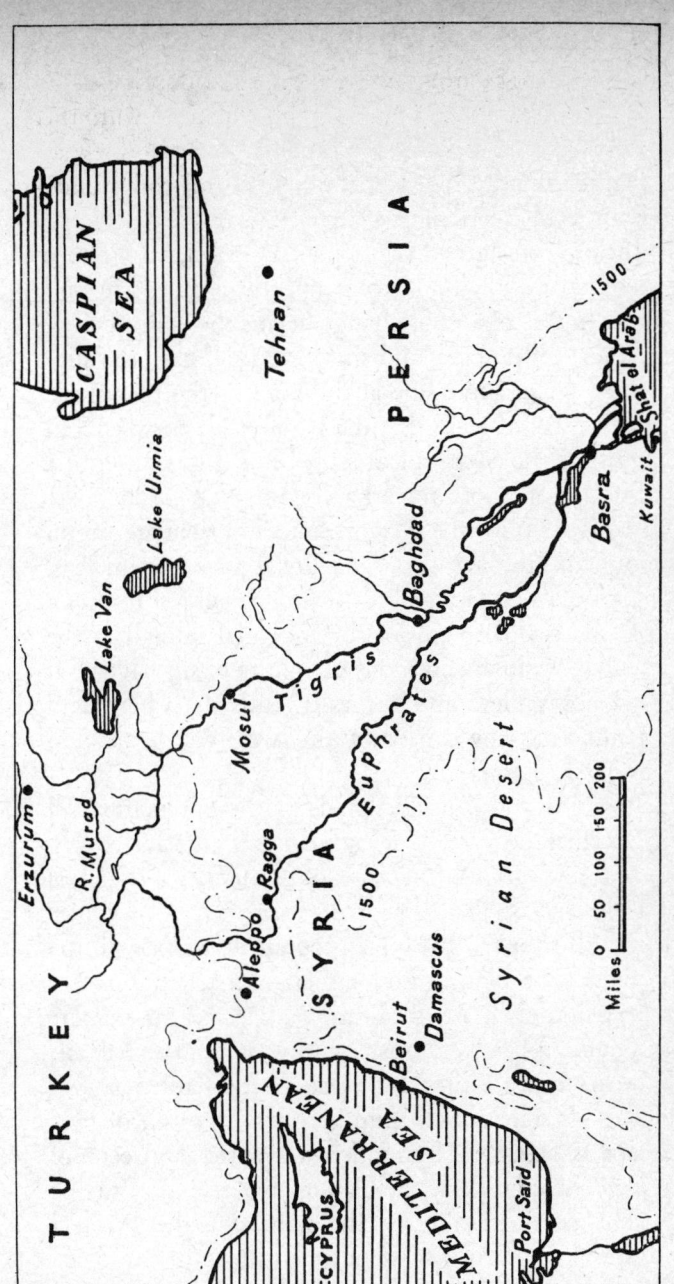

3. EUPHRATES—THE TIGRIS

The *Two Rivers* alluvial system, soil of the earliest civilization

to Mekene, thence to Raqqua where it is joined by the *Belikh*, south-west to Meyadin, standing at the junction with the *Khabur*, which is the Araxes of Xenophon. Beyond Ana, between that town and Hit, the nature of the soil community changes from a Mediterranean character to tropical Asiatic: typically, the olive tree gives way to the date-palm, both plants having been, and still being instruments of very successful soil exploitation. In this region of change begins the valley bed of alluvium, a few miles wide, and since Hit itself has been suggested as the ancient shore line at the head of the prehistoric Persian gulf, it would seem that the whole land between Hit and the mouth of the *Shat el Arab* must be of alluvial origin, a deposit of soil even more remarkable than that of the Nile delta, but which, unlike the delta, is not all of riparian origin. For the mountains to the east of the alluvial plateau, which is, significantly, slightly tilted towards them, are subject to much the same kind of violent erosion by torrential rainfall as the highlands of Abyssinia; enormous quantities of silt have been carried down by gulleys and gorges towards the valley, and this silt, as much as any carried by the two rivers, is the soil material of Mesopotamia.

But the region south of Hit,[28] made by the mountains and the river, has since been unmade by man; it is a treeless, open, badly eroded soil, or rather corpse of a soil dead of *Homo militaris,* a variant of the disease organism *Homo sapiens*.[29] It was forced to support, between 1500 and 600 B.C., in the Assyrian State, one of the most atrocious manifestations of militarist expansionism in all history. A career of warfare means, of course, a career of waste; and waste of materials, in whatever form, means ultimately, waste of soil fertility, a war debt which is too rarely taken into account. If, south of Hit, the landscape is described by modern travellers as a scene of appalling and heartbreaking desolation, we owe that to the ambitious and cruel brutality of Shalmaneser I, the Tiglath-pilesers, Asurbanipal and a score of other war-lords.

From Hit the Euphrates flows south and west, by Hilleh and

ancient Babylon, still through a man-made desolation where once was a man-made paradise. This soil supported the great ventures of the Hittites and those who came before and after them. The price has been paid. Even when Xenophon passed this way, at the head of his Ten Thousand on their march to the sea, it was fertile and teeming with game.[30] But the neglect of the ancient canals has created marshes, the water seeps away into them, and the river begins to shrink.

The region of prehistoric and early historic intensive tillage by irrigation, and of laying the river under contribution by means of the ancient device of the water-lifting wheel (Euphrates' equivalent of the Nile *shadouf*), begins at Feluja, west of Baghdad, and is co-extensive with the alluvial plateau upon which rose the civilizations of Sumer and Akkad, out of which came letters, and mathematics and astronomy. The irrigation canals divided this irregular oval into sections, each therefore an island between two canals, the Euphrates, and the Tigris, the flow of water being towards the latter river. At Gharab the water divides into two channels, to join again at Samawa, and flows thence to Nastiya, formerly its point of junction with the Tigris. But here again the failure of men to hold their ancient advance from soil parasitism to soil-creation, by maintaining the canals, has made marshes, so that the modern junction of the two rivers is at Kurna on Lake Hammar.

The courses of both Tigris and Euphrates have shifted during historical times: Mesopotamia is wider than it was in Sumerian times, and in Neolithic times it must have been a good deal narrower still.

The Tigris has three considerable tributaries, the Great and the Little Zab, and the Diala, and from its junction with the latter flows through arid *steppe* to Tekrit. The Euphrates too makes part of its way through a desert, the Syrian desert. Yet formerly this region cannot have been arid, for the tools of Upper Palaeolithic settlements are found there; food-gatherers and hunters flourished in a country which could not now feed a mouse. It was these food-gathering people who were replaced, in early Neolithic times, by others whose women first began to exploit the alluvium of the Two Rivers.

The annual silt-bearing floods of the Euphrates–Tigris, being the consequence of the melting snows of Armenia, and not, as in the Nile case, of the south-west monsoon, occur in the spring, so that the convenient autumn sowing practised in Egypt can never have been possible; yet a forcing-house climate must make the loss of a season of inconsiderable consequence. But still, whereas the Egyptians had nothing to do but clear papyrus reed and then throw and tread seed into the soil the Nile brought them (the treading in was done by their sheep), the Neolithic Mesopotamians had not only to clear reed and other wild plants, but, before they could reach the city-founding stage, to drain water-logged soils by means of ditches and canals, which later, with increasing aridity, might become irrigation canals. For it is at least possible that it was in getting rid of *surplus* water, that the techniques of making use of scarce water were evolved.

The digging of drainage and irrigation canals is an act of soil-creation which would entitle the Mesopotamians to be considered as soil-makers rather than as soil-parasites. And so, in their later history, they were. But we are here concerned with their beginnings as tillers, and in those beginnings they lived as parasites on the soil, like the Egyptians on Nile mud.

Perhaps the earliest tillers yet revealed to us by archaeology were the Natufian cave-dwellers of Mount Carmel in Palestine. Of these people Professor Gordon Childe says that they "hunted with an equipment of flints very similar to those current among Neolithic peoples in Europe. But they used some flints, mounted in rib-bones, as *sickles* for cutting grass stems or straw; a peculiar lustre on the flints proves this, but unfortunately does not disclose what sort of grass was cut, still less whether it was cultivated or wild".

If it was wild (and the fact that they seem to have had no hoes suggests it may well have been), then the Natufians were, of course, still food-gatherers, still in a Palaeolithic stage of economy. If cultivated, then the nature of the soil would have compelled the Natufians to adopt semi-nomadic tillage which would prevent them from settling and founding cities. But for communities at a similar stage of development—that of passing from soil-membership to soil-exploitation—on the alluvium of the Euphrates–Tigris, the case was different.

Not far from Mosul on the Tigris, opposite the site of Nineveh, is a *tell* called *Hassuna*. A *tell* is a mound created in the course of many centuries by the constant rebuilding of the huts and houses of a village on the same site. Most Europeans and Asiatics of our time have watched the rubble of a bombed building being levelled off and a new building raised on the site. Bombing is not necessary, however; the house has only to decay, to be knocked down, stamped into the soil, and a new one built over this foundation. The first dwellings of the *Hassuna* villagers were of reed, the later ones of mud, and *Tell Hassuna* is a township of the oldest farming community of settled agrarians yet unearthed. Its lowest levels reveal a partially settled people of gardeners and stock-raisers using stone hoes fastened to their handles with bitumen, doubtless from the bitumen lakes near Hit, and a corn grinding gear of stone pestles and mortars.

As the archaeologist works through the levels of the *tell*, he is able to show that the *Hassuna* people became more and more settled. Their tent-like huts of reed give way to houses of dried mud, bread ovens become identifiable in a room which is clearly a kitchen or house-place, there are sunk grain-storage bins in the courtyard. Proto-sickles are found, resembling those of the Natufians, but set in wood instead of bone. No exact dating can be given to define the limits of the *Hassuna* settlement, but its beginning probably antedates 5000 B.C. and it lasted for many centuries. Tigris mud had enabled its people to settle, perhaps to build up a surplus of wealth, to send out colonists to found other villages, ultimately to support great parasitic cities, temples, palaces, and armies.

Tell Hassuna is more or less representative of a number of other settlements in the same soil, for example, those of *Tell Halaf, Arpachiya* and *Tepe Gawra*. In the case of most of them it is possible to arrive at an approximate date for the first settlement, that is to gain some idea of the time that has elapsed since the revolution which advanced man from soil-membership to soil-parasitism. Huts of dried mud which were the houses of the Neolithic farmers of Mesopotamia, are still built and used by the present inhabitants, and they are known to last over a century before their dilapidation necessitates demolition and rebuilding. And as rebuilding is done upon the stamped-down débris of the old hut, at each such renewal a distinct layer is formed, in the manner explained above. Each layer therefore represents about a century, or rather more. The topmost layer at *Tepe Gawra* yielded pottery and other artifacts which could be dated by reference to archaeological finds in the great cities of the plateau, and beneath that layer Speiser counted twenty-six other layers: on this evidence, the layer level with the original soil was tentatively dated *c.* 5000 B.C. From this calculation, similar ones for the other Euphrates–Tigris *tells,* from the Natufian and the Egyptian evidence, it seems that men, or rather women, first became farmers about 7000 years ago.

It should be said that not by any means all the sites revealing early agrarian settlements are to be found within the influence of the Two Rivers soil-renewal system. In fact, what may be called the type site of the Neolithic farmers of the Near East, that called *Tepe Sialk,* is near Kashan in Northern Persia, and there are other settlements far from the rivers. Perhaps there are none, however, beyond the soil-renewal system of the Persian mountains which, by the erosion of their substance, annually poured new soil down into the country on their west. And the condition for permanent agrarian settlements—soil renewal—might be produced locally even beyond the limits of a great flood system. *Tepe Sialk* is in an oasis, with a good spring of water; moreover it is very difficult to judge what changes in the topography of the region may have occurred in 7000 years.

We are not concerned here with the actual rise of civilization in Mesopotamia, which entailed a soil-making act of drainage and irrigation. Our point is that settled soil-parasitism of very long duration—long enough for the techniques of drainage and irrigation to be developed—was possible on the Euphrates–Tigris soil, and that therefore the soil conditions for the rise of such relatively precocious civilizations as those of Kish and Ur did exist, and are probably the explanation of the precocity of these primaeval city states.

It should be said also, although this takes us beyond the immediate subject, that because in Egypt farming entailed, and entails, hardly more than the planting of seed in Nile mud, and subsequent irrigation by means of the *shadouf*, whereas in Mesopotamia, to maintain great cities, it was necessary to go a stage further and *make* a soil by means of elaborate irrigation works, the later histories of the two countries are very different. The unity of Upper Egypt as a soil community imposed upon the Egyptians the creation of a single political unit from the apex of the delta to Khartoum, and a similar condition had the same effect in Lower Egypt. Thus, there could be at most two political nations in that region (and there was usually only one). Moreover the viability of Egyptian soil for farming, for exploitation, owes almost nothing to man but a few simple muscular actions, so that, from the point of view of fundamental stores of soil fertility, Egypt is still potentially a great nation. Because, until our own time, the Egyptians remained parasitic on their inexhaustible soil, and made no great works of agricultural engineering, there was nothing to be neglected and to decay. But Mesopotamia is an artifact: before that soil could produce more than the grass upon which Nebuchadnezzar browsed, could support the cities of Lagash and Niniveh, Ur and Babylon, could feed the armies of Tiglathpileser and of Asurbanipal, it had to be made. And what is made, if it be thereafter neglected, decays. No unique annual event in the life of the river made all the people of the region dependent on a single natural phenomenon, as in the case of the

Nile flood. The soil of Mesopotamia did not demand a single economic unit in its extent, and therefore a single nation. Each Mesopotamian community could either use or neglect the conditions which the Two Rivers offered them. And *therefore* there arose in Mesopotamia and on its periphery not one great power, but a whole congeries of independent city states, which could only be united into a single nation by the rise of one among them to military pre-eminence, and the imposition of unity by force. But this necessity entailed another, the failure of the very soil upon which empire in Mesopotamia rested. The rise of great military powers meant the waste of soil fertility in war, that waste meant gradual impoverishment of the whole region, especially in man-power: that improverishment entailed neglect of the irrigation works, and such neglect the ruin of the soil itself. The agricultural machine which the men of Ur and Lagash and Nineveh made of Mesopotamian soil is still functioning, but because of the wars of the Assyrians, and of the failure of their successors to eschew a similar militarism and concentrate upon restoring the land, it is functioning at a level of productiveness and efficiency probably inferior to that of the predynastic era in the history of the Mesopotamian peoples.

THE INDUS VALLEY

In the Kailas range of the Himalaya mountains in Tibet rise the great rivers of Northern India, the Sutlej, the Bramahputra, the Ganges and the Indus. The sources of the Indus are in the glaciers of the Kailas, at an altitude of 20,000 feet. Flowing through Tibet and Kashmir, it turns south between Gilgit and Hunza, and across the Punjab frontier, at which point it is 800 miles long. Fifty miles further on its course, it is joined by the Kabul, coming from the mountains of Afghanistan, but its most considerable increment of waters is contributed by the Five Rivers, the Jhelum, Chenab, Ravi, Beas and Sutlej, which, as a single stream, join the Indus about 500 miles below Attock.

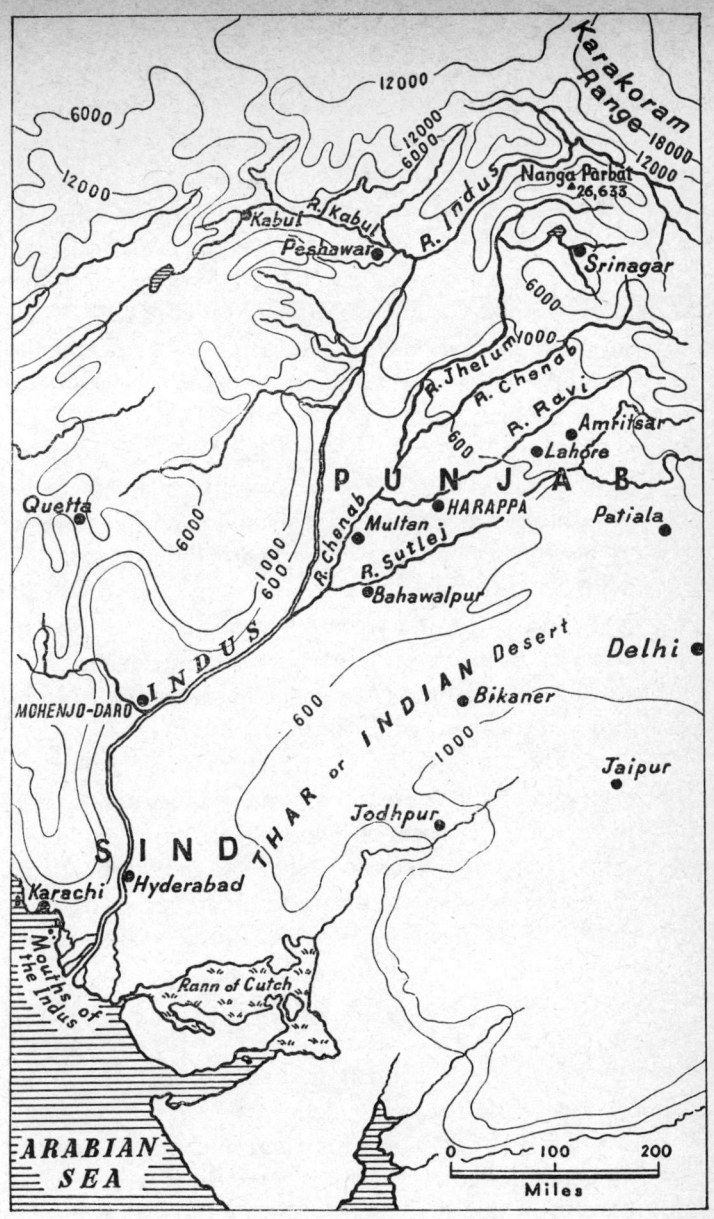

4. THE INDUS VALLEY
Sites of prehistoric Indian agrarian culture

The delta is in Sind and comprises 300 square miles of continually shifting silt, the mouths of the river being quite inconstant, but extending along the coast of the Arabian Sea from Karachi in the north, to a point about fifty miles south-east.

Between 2500 B.C. and 1500 B.C. there grew up in what are now Sind and the Punjab a high urban civilization based on the Indus and extending over a vast body of territory, the spine of which was defined by the course of the river from well above its junction with the Five Rivers, to the delta. The present delta is not navigable and has no useful port. The ancient delta was, however, by no means the same, and it is Professor R. M. Wheeler's opinion that the people of the Indus civilization may well have had a port in the delta. But there is very little evidence for the existence of any considerable shipping and the whole civilization seems to have been partially isolated from contact with other high civilizations of the time, in Mesopotamia, Egypt and Crete, and perhaps to have traded with them only through the intervention of middle men, merchants from small seafaring states on the coast to the north-west.

The Indus empire had twin metropolitan capitals, Harappa on the Ravi, about a hundred miles from modern Lahore in the Punjab; and Mohenjo-daro on the mainstream of the Indus, about 300 miles north of modern Karachi. In addition to these two great cities, there were at least seventeen urban centres of importance in the Mohenjo-daro part of the country, and at least fourteen in the Harappa "province". There were probably more such towns, but they are yet to be found and excavated.

The emergence of this Indus empire[31] with a strongly governed, highly ordered domain extending over perhaps one hundred thousand square miles, followed the establishment, over the same and a much wider area including modern Baluchistan, of Bronze Age peasant settlements which were probably well past the tribal stage in 2500 B.C., and might be linked together in political groups, each comprising a small agrarian republic or kingdom. A full and interesting account of all that is known of these people, their culture, their provenance and the cities which some of them subsequently founded, will be found in Professor Wheeler's *Five Thousand Years of Pakistan*,[32] and in Professor Stuart Piggott's *Prehistoric India*.[33] Here, we are concerned solely with two questions: the soil relationships of the North-west Indian Bronze Age states in general; and the reason for the growth of an urban empire out of the congenerous communities living on the Indus river system.

The Bronze Age Baluchi states were settled communities practising plantation (as opposed to shifting) agriculture and stock-raising, which implies either a rather advanced farming technique, or a frequently renewed soil. The discoveries of Sir Aurel Stein in this territory, and particularly in the Mashkai Valley and the Lakorian Pass, of massive dams and barrages of masonry designed to contain flood waters and use them for irrigation, bear out this conclusion. These flood waters would have come from the hills to the west of the country, and no doubt they carried the fertile silt of mountain erosion. But even with the assistance of a soil carried by flood from elsewhere, the Bronze Age Baluchis must have enjoyed a reasonably equable climate and a reasonably fertile soil, in order to maintain their stable tillage, for Baluchistan is not, like Egypt, a cleft in the earth almost designed to retain whatever soil the river deposits in it. Yet we know, from historical records, that before 300 B.C., Baluchistan was already, what it is today, a region of desolation, of icy winter winds, and burning summer heats, and of sporadic, unreliable rainfalls incapable of supporting more than a nomadic agriculture practised by a meagre population of migratory peasants.

It seems probable that the primaeval peasant states of Baluchistan were dependent upon a combination of flood-water and silt, controlled by irrigation, and moderate rainfall, for their soil fertility. In the absence of either flood-water, or of rain, they must fail, and a reduction in the annual mean of rainfall might well have made their position as settled farmers untenable. We do not know what, in fact, did happen, but it seems likely by reference to the state of affairs further south, in the Indus valley, and to events during our own times in Australia and South Africa, that we can find a clue to the failure of the Baluchi states to develop an urban culture, and, on the other hand, to the rise of just such a culture among the states in the Indus valley.

The modern climate and soil of the Punjab, in the neighbourhood of ancient Harappa, are still *relatively* equable and fertile, and the region is, in fact, one of the great granaries of Asia (and this is only partly due to irrigation works carried out in the nineteenth century). Sind, on the other hand, if we ignore the great irrigation works carried out by the British to make the country fertile by using Indus flood waters, is an arid and semi-desert province, and without irrigation could support no more than a thin population at a very low standard of living. Such a soil as that of modern Sind could not possibly have supported a large, settled population wringing from its fertility the surplus of wealth necessary for the building and maintenance of the great city of Mohenjo-daro, with all that civic culture implies of secondary industry, not to mention the numerous other urban centres. The mere existence of the towns, and of the high civilization which archaeology has revealed, implies either that the climate was much more equable 4000 years ago than is now the case, or that the Indus people installed a system of irrigation works equal to those of our own time, from the very beginning of their settlement. The latter implication is an absurdity, for no Bronze Age people in the first stages of real settlement could have carried out such work, nor, indeed, would they have ever settled in a country which clearly could not support them. True, in the later phases of the Indus empire, Sind was a made soil, and great irrigation works were built to control the flood waters of the river. But in the beginning conditions must have been very different from those of today, with a mean annual rainfall of 6 inches, and temperature extremes of 25° and 120°F.

What can we learn about the soil as it was when Mohenjo-daro was yet to be founded? Excavation in the Indus valley, in the neighbourhood of Mohenjo-daro, has revealed that the following animals were native species of the soil community: elephant, rhinoceros, water-buffalo, tiger, crocodile, bear, monkey, squirrel, parrot, deer, sambhur, jackal, wolf, mongoose, lizard and tortoise. Of the trees and other plants, which leave no bones for the taxonomist to identify, and which artists and craftsmen do not delineate so clearly as animals, we know next to nothing. But the animals are enough: what kind of soil community do they suggest? Surely, tropical Africa—say, for example, the valleys of the Dinder or the Rahad. Such a country is either humid park-land, or rain forest, with a climate held in control within equable limits by the trees, and an annual rainfall of *at least* 50 inches.

The present vegetation of Sind is tamarisk and scrub. In not dissimilar climatic conditions in Australia in our own times, such a vegetation has sprung up upon soils rendered semi-arid by forest clearance, by overstocking with cattle, or by soil-fertility "mining" with wheat.[34]

Faced with the need to explain the climatic change in Sind, a change which, if rather slight documentary evidence be reliable, may be relatively recent, authorities have suggested a shift in the south-west monsoon track sufficient to leave Sind outside its area.[35] Sind is, in fact, just beyond the limits of that track, but it is perhaps possible to find an explanation other than one for which there appears to be little other evidence than the case of Sind, and against which many arguments could be advanced.

Although we know nothing of the tree species of the primaeval Indian soil community, excepting that the deodar and the sissoo[36] may have flourished, we are forced, by the evidence of animal remains and the representations of animals by the craftsmen of Mohenjo-daro, to conclude that ancient Sind was a forest country; and for this there is evidence of another kind: all the very extensive building throughout the empire was done with baked bricks, and baking bricks calls for large quantities of fuel, which can only have been wood. As Sir John Myres long ago pointed out, far more devastation of forests has been due to the need for fuel, than to clearance for cultivation; this was particularly the case in the Mediterranean and in parts of China, but in England we have the cases of Cornwall, and the Weald of Kent, the latter deforested by the iron smelters. During what period of time were bricks being baked by the Indus people?

The beginnings of their civilization are dated *c.* 2500 B.C., and it was "destroyed" by the Aryan pastoralists about 1500 B.C. This gives us about a thousand years. In short, the Indus peoples had been cutting down trees during about thirty generations, cutting them down in immense numbers to feed the brick kilns, the forges of their metallurgists and smiths, the kitchen fires, the pottery kilns, the builders' and carpenters' and joiners' shops. The consumption of wood for brick-making in the Indus civilization might almost be compared with our own destruction of forests, and of soil balance, for the making of wood-pulp for newspapers and rayon, and within the limits of their territory these prehistoric Indians were as steadily destroying the one sure stabilizer of their precariously equable climate as were the Chinese a thousand years later, the Americans three thousand five hundred years later, and twenty other rising peoples at various times.

Could this deforestation *alone* account for the differences between the climates of modern and ancient Sind? I think it could. First, there is the question of temperature extremes: in high tropical regions, the difference between maximum shade temperatures over forest, and over *steppe*, is striking; the atmosphere over a forest soil is as much as 20°F. cooler than that over a *steppe* soil, the reason being the constant transpiration of moisture by the leaves of the trees.

The cutting down of the trees of Sind would, in all probability, account for the change in temperature conditions reflected in the disappearance of the animal species excepting the crocodile, which, by living in the river, is more or less independent of terrestrial and atmospheric conditions. It will also account, it would seem, for the change in the rainfall, as we shall see.

Water coming down as rain must first go up as evaporated moisture from soil, seas, lakes, oceans and rivers, and as transpired moisture from the leaves of green plants, especially trees. A single willow tree will transpire as much as 5000 gallons on a single summer's day. Of the total rainfall over even coastal areas of land, seven-ninths is due not to ocean evaporation, but to land evaporation and tree transpiration.[37] What part of this is due to transpiration, we do not know, but it is obvious that there cannot be much moisture to be had from arid *steppe*, for the water of any shower of rain is immediately lost again to the sun, whereas, in the presence of trees, it is filtered slowly into the soil, drawn up by the trees, transpired by their leaves, and, the transpiration cooling the atmosphere, conditions are created for the formation of clouds, and further precipitation. In short, over forest soils, water is used over and over again, and trees tend to hold water in their neighbourhood. Moreover, at tropical temperatures, rain-laden winds will pass over barren soils without precipitation, whereas if the same soils bear trees their cooling influence will create the conditions which bring about rainfall.

But if the deforestation of Sind is allowed to account for the change in the climate from equable to arid, what of the Harappa province which must have suffered similar deforestation, but which, although considerable climatic change may have occurred, has not undergone an identical desiccation? This difference may probably be accounted for by the difference in altitude, for higher land, like forests, induces water-laden winds to unload. It has been observed that the influence of complete forestation of a tract of country upon rainfall is equivalent to raising its altitude by 650 feet.[38] Mohenjo-daro stood nearly at 150 feet. Harappa at an altitude of 530 feet. In the matter of rainfall, that difference alone, given the other conditions, and notably its relative nearness to high mountain country, would have made the Harappa province more fortunate in the matter of rainfall, and would have helped to preserve the Punjab from the aridity which has come upon Sind.

While the agriculture which has replaced the forest continues to flourish, the progress of desiccation will be controlled. But since 1500 B.C. race after race has overrun India, empires have been founded upon her soil fertility; founded and destroyed. The desiccation of Sind has been man-made, but over a vast lapse of time.

To return, briefly, to Bronze Age Baluchistan, if the precariously-balanced climate of that province was upset by consistent deforestation, as in Sind, then the Baluchis must be considered as a disease of their soil: they killed it because its resistance was insufficient to keep it alive under intensive agriculture. Even today, any attempt to resume settled tillage, as Sir Aurel Stein has pointed out, results in the relapse of whole areas of cultivation into the appearance of bare, clay desert: in short, in one of the worst kinds of soil erosion. Kolwa, in Makran was, in the Bronze Age of North-west India, a thriving centre of farming settlements. Today, Sir Aurel Stein says that it is, "By far the greatest dry crop area of Makran, and its export of barley to other parts, in years of good rainfall, is considerable. Yet how rare such rainfall is, and how precarious this cultivation in Kolwa, is shown by the very scanty population of the tract being practically all nomadic."

That the soils farther south, in the Mohenjo-daro country, did not suffer the fate of those of Baluchistan until a thousand years later, but were able to give rise to and support a great urban civilization, can have been due to only one thing, large-scale irrigation. But irrigation with plain water would not have answered, in the absence of manurial techniques which we have no right to assume that these people possessed. True, they had the wood ashes of their kilns, which they may have had the sense to use: true, also, that they kept much cattle, but it is not very likely that they had devised the high-farming technique of stall-feeding their beasts to preserve the manure. It should be remembered too that the Indus people grew and exported cotton, a plant which, as the Americans of the southern United States have learnt, makes the most extravagant, and indeed spendthrift drafts on soil fertility.

The answer seems to be irrigation with muddy water of widespread spring floods, which provided not only moisture, but Indus silt, of which the river brings down millions of tons annually. The civilization of North-western India, like those of Egypt and Mesopotamia, grew in an annually renewed soil, the only kind of alluvium which would have enabled its creators to find the surplus wealth during a sufficient period of time, with which to build their cities, maintain their priesthoods, their elaborate government services, their municipal public utilities and their widespread trading relations. In short, the only type of soil which will tolerate man as a parasite almost indefinitely.

PART THREE:
MAN AS A DISEASE OF SOIL

*

CHAPTER VII

MAN AS A DISEASE ORGANISM

WHEN a micro-organism preys upon a macro-organism in such a way as to cause the latter no inconvenience, it is not noticed: when, however, its activity becomes excessively vigorous, perhaps due to some temporary weakness of the host organism, then we say that the latter is diseased, and that its condition is due to the micro-organism.

Philosophically, there seems to be no reason why we should distinguish, as disease, a condition brought about by one kind of organism, while withholding the distinction from conditions created by another and, from the point of view of the sufferer, a comparable one. For example, a community of men being consumed by the cholera bacillus is said to be suffering from the disease cholera. But the same community being consumed by a plague of tigers, is not said to be suffering from tiger disease. Yet there is, in the relations between the afflicting and afflicted species, in the functions, rather than in the forms involved, no significant difference. An excess of rabbits is never considered to be a disease of fruit-trees, although they may prey upon and kill an orchard quite as effectively as an excess of the microscopic botrytis fungus, which is recognized as a disease.

Disease is a failure of the balance by means of which species live together in community, whether in a relationship of mutual aid, or one of parasite and host. For, even in the latter case, there must be equilibrium; given an adjusted balance between parasite and host, the former is fed, the latter not debilitated. But should the parasite become too numerous or active, that is should the balance be destroyed, the host will collapse, and therefore the parasite also.

In a perfectly constituted and balanced soil community of plants, animals and men, while every species present would be living, to some extent, off all the others, none would be doing so to the serious detriment of any other. It is not pretended that no individuals of any species would suffer fatally as a victim of another, neighbour species: obviously, some men would be eaten by tigers, some tigers die of bacterial disease, some plants be eaten by herbivores, some herbivores by carnivores. But all member-species, in such a soil community, would be in such equilibrium with each other, that, in the long run, the strength of all would be stable. The soil community here envisaged is an ideal one: natural soil communities approximate to it, but do not exactly resemble it. I have read that such natural communities do exist, indeed that they are the rule in nature, but this seems rather doubtful: the rule seems to be for some species, from time to time, to upset the balance by becoming dominant, and thereby, in the long run, destroying itself. The balance is then restored until some other species becomes tyrannous.

The balance of any natural soil community, so nicely adjusted that it almost seems to be a single organism, can be disturbed in more than one way: the excessive, and necessarily temporary, prosperity of one species will upset the balance, and so will the introduction of a new species into the soil community. Men are frequently the culprits, either rising, within a native soil community, to dominate over their fellow-species until they are able to think of themselves as outside nature; or by invading a maiden soil community from outside. As a rule the latter occurrence leads to a very rapid destruction of equilibrium and the death of the soil, whereas the former occurrence leads to the slow debility of the soil. In India, the rise of native peoples to the dominance of Indian soil communities has taken thousands of years to reduce soil fertility within sight of the point at which soil dies and erosion occurs. But the invasion of the middle west of north America by man, as an intruding species, has led to the death of vast areas of soil within a hundred years: in the first case we have man as a wasting disease of soils;

in the second man as a galloping consumption. Man is not, of course, the only species which behaves in this manner: any species would do so if it could, for each struggles for its own ends and is only held in check, for the good of the whole community and therefore, in the long run, for its own good, by the equal and neutralizing effort of other species: it is a system of mutally cancelling tensions, like that of a weight hanging to a cord: the weight pulls down, the cord pulls up, and the result is stability. From time to time the artificial soil communities, normally well balanced, of England, are disturbed by the efforts of a species to dominate: in Essex, some years ago, the mite known as Red Spider made a partially successful attempt to step out of line; in parts of East Kent at this moment a weed known locally as Fat Hen (*Chenopodium album*) has shown remarkable and pernicious vitality.

But it is man with whom we are concerned.

Here, before coming to a practical case in point, is a simplified demonstration of the dominance of a soil community by a single species, which thus becomes distinguishable as a disease organism.

Imagine a natural soil community consisting of a wood of elm trees, grasses, rabbits and stoats. The community is well balanced: the grasses keep the soil in place and supply it with material in the organic substance of their dead. By their work they provide a satisfactory root environment for the elms, which contribute towards the commonwealth by tapping the mineral fertility in the subsoil and adding it to the top-soil in the form of the autumn leaf-fall. The elms also shade the lesser plants from too much sun, and break the possibly damaging force of torrential rains or strong gales. Moreover, as alembics, they evaporate from their leaves two-thirds of the rainfall, thus maintaining a circulation of water, and cooling the atmosphere. The rabbits eat the grass, preventing it from growing too rankly, and they might even overeat it were it not for the stoats which, at first sight mildly parasitic on the community, turn out, upon examination, to contribute to its essential stability by keeping the number of rabbits in check. They themselves might become too numerous, were it not for the ability of the rabbits to avoid them, and their own internecine warfare. The dung, and later the bodies of both these species, in which are locked up some part of the community's total soil-fertility capital, return in due course to the earth.

Such a community is, of course, far simpler than any which would occur in nature, but this simplicity in no way affects the argument.

Into the community we introduce a new species, the fungus known as Dutch Elm Disease, which causes a fatal debility in elm trees. In the course of a few years the rising prosperity of the fungus causes the death of all the elms. The parasite, which has been able to contribute nothing, destroys the host and therefore itself. The top-soil, deprived of its annual mulch of dead leaves, carrying their increment of plant nutrient substance from the subsoil, begins to decline. Torrential rains, pouring upon the now unprotected grasses, cause gullies and small morasses; they leach out soluble plant nutrients, while the sun, now able to bake the rain-beaten earth, produces a sealed surface depriving the soil bacteria of air, and causing subsequent rainfall to run off, instead of soaking in. The grasses, in these conditions, begin to deteriorate, provide inadequate fodder for the rabbits, which emigrate or grow ill-conditioned. The stoats, with fewer rabbits to feed upon, fight all the more fiercely over the remainder, until war and starvation reduce their numbers rapidly. The rabbits do not leave or die while there is any food to be had, so that they overtax the strength of the debilitated grasses, which die. The death of the grasses leaves the already damaged soil bare, and without renewal of its organic material. No more humus can be made, the soil dies, becomes dust, is blown away; or it is washed away as mud into some stream. Of a once flourishing community of living creatures nothing remains. The microscopic fungus has turned a sylvan landscape of apparently massive stability, into a barren moon-crater.

Consider a second demonstration, a semi-artificial soil

community involving men as one of the member species: again, let it be, for the sake of readier understanding of the principle involved, improbably simple.

There is a wood of sweet-chestnut trees in which also grow honeysuckles. No satisfactory balance could have been produced between these two species, since the honeysuckles are so vigorous that, growing unchecked, they would choke the sweet-chestnuts, enjoy a brief dominance, and perish for want of support and leaf-mould and shade. However, in the wood lives a family, a man and his wife and six children. Their only food is chestnuts, but they are not so primitive as to be mere food-gatherers; for recognizing that unless they take action the honeysuckles will choke their food-trees to death, they undertake the labour of keeping the honeysuckles in check.

It does not, however, occur to them to destroy the honeysuckles entirely. Perhaps the plant is a sacred one in the man's religion; and indeed he only prunes it with fear and propitiatory rites. As for his wife, she is not a religious woman, but she likes to have a few flowers in the house, and to do what pleases her husband.

The balance once established is stable while the children grow up, and even when they are adult it is not, at first, disturbed. The daughters, in this austere but not unpleasing soil community, like the flowers of honeysuckle with which to decorate their persons; one of the sons, a practical man, finds the bines useful as rope; another, the youngest, has an attitude towards the honeysuckles resembling that of his father, and yet not quite the same: his pleasure comes from beholding the way the plants grow, the colour of the flowers, the shape of the leaves, and he likes to make drawings of them on bits of chestnut wood.

The third son, however, is different. He is not conservative, and he does not hesitate to call his father's religion superstitious, his brother's art a waste of time, his sisters' vanity disgraceful. He proposes that instead of spending months every year in pruning the honeysuckles, they would do well to grub them all up and be done with it; that, he says, is the scientific, the rational way. And since everyone is rather ashamed of being irrational, and because the third brother is a forceful and determined man, his opinion prevails, and out come the honeysuckles. And in no time at all the bees, which lived in the wood for the honeysuckle, and incidentally fertilized the flowers of the chestnuts, abandon the wood and leave the human members of the community without food.

By what means do species rise to dominate, unbalance and destroy a soil community? In natural conditions this almost certainly happens much more rarely than in artificial soil communities. Just as savage cultures are ponderously stable, whereas civilized cultures are precarious, so natural soil communities are difficult, artificial ones easy to upset.

Consider, for a minute, a market garden as an artificial soil community in isolation. One of its common members is the cabbage white butterfly. The cabbage white butterfly in a natural soil community has to seek wild cabbages on which to lay its eggs, and wild cabbages are not particularly common—indeed I have only seen them growing once and in one place, in anything like profusion. But the market gardener having planted perhaps an acre of cabbages, the cabbage white suddenly finds its commodity with unnatural ease, and in unnatural quantity. These temporarily favourable conditions might enable it to rise to unexampled heights of prosperity as a race, to multiply very rapidly in conditions where the predators which keep it in check are not, until attracted later, present in their ordinary numbers. As a result, and supposing the market gardener to abandon brassica culture for some other crop, an exceptionally large number of cabbage whites would be forced to seek their living in natural conditions, and the wild cabbages would succumb to a plague of caterpillars, with a whole chain of related consequences which we need not follow here.

In the first half of the nineteenth century the rising class of machine-owning capitalists in Britain required hands to man their rapidly growing factories. Men and women were attracted away from work on the land, or in cottage industries, where the food they ate was only what they could produce by their own actions applied immediately, or at only one remove, to the soil. They were brought together in great and crowded numbers and food was brought to them in exchange for machine minding. Conditions were, in fact, created, in which they could propagate their kind, for a time and very uncomfortably, *without reference to "natural" supplies of food,* to weather, to the season. The consequence was a temporary and fantastic specific (not, of course, individual) prosperity of mechanical man. Mechanical or machine-minding man became numerous out of all proportion to the supply of food within the range of action of individual machine-minding men. Among the consequences of this destruction of balance were the American dustbowl and the British Empire.

*

The argument which informs the following two historical studies is that man, over a very great part of the surface of the earth, has become a disease of soil communities, and that this catastrophe derives quite as much from his past relations with the soil, as it does from his present ones: either he has reacted from past practices, or he has failed to learn from them, or he has transferred practices which succeed in one environment, to soils where they are pernicious.

Fleas are parasitic upon men: if they are few they cause him minor discomfort, but no serious harm, so that his vitality and power to continue functioning are not impaired. If the fleas become excessively numerous, they may so weaken their host by their depredations as finally to destroy him and, in the absence of any other host, themselves. A few men can live parasitically upon a soil, without destroying it, but should they become too many they inevitably and invariably destroy it unless they find means to enhance its annual increment of fertility. For, as fleas suck men's blood, so men suck the fertility of soils.

Before examining the way in which this has happened time and again in the past, it will be as well to give some attention, in general terms, to actual examples of two regions of the world in which, from being at worst harmlessly parasitic upon the soil, man has become or is becoming a disease of the soil community.

NATIVE AND ALIEN TECHNIQUES

When a people grows up as a member of a soil community, its agricultural or pastoral practices grow out of the conditions of the country, and are consequently adapted to it, just as the life-maintaining practices of other native species arise out of, and are adapted to, the ruling conditions.

When peoples intrude into a virgin soil community, at an early and primitive stage of their own technical development, the soil community will impose upon them, by its superior strength, modifications of their agricultural practices which suit its own well-being. The intruders are allowed in, but by no means on their own terms. The terms are laid down by the stable community into which they are trying to thrust themselves.

People whose farming (and sometimes even industrial) practices derive from either of these beginnings have a past—that is they possess a continuum of traditions which joins them to their origins as members of their particular soil. Such a past is of enormous practical value: it may mean, for example, being able to take 30 cwt. of wheat from an acre of land which has already yielded crops in two or three thousand seasons, instead of a wretched 8 cwt. from an acre almost barren and dead after only a century of cultivation. The farmer who works land similarly worked by his spiritual, if not physical, ancestors during a score of generations, need not be stupidly conservative: he may employ new methods, grow new crops, and use new tools. But he will, by a sort of intuition which rises out of his organic relationship with his land, test each novelty before he adopts it, by reference to a code of morality in his relations with soil, a code which he has inherited. He will respect the land as a life, never exploit it as a mineral.

But when a people at a very high technical level intrude upon a virgin soil community, or upon an old artificial soil community, they possess the means to impose their will: they will offer no terms, make no adjustments in their native practices, concede little or nothing to the invaded soil. They will probably introduce their own native practices at that level of efficiency which they have reached at home, and which, perhaps, their own soil has been adapted to during hundreds, even thousands of years. Or they may, by their scientists, devise, intellectually, new practices, with an insufficient understanding of the conditions in which these practices are to be applied.

Both these catastrophic things happened when white men took control of Africa; and, what is worse, the methods evolved by the native inhabitants, out of the conditions of their environment, were made impossible to practice.

TROPICAL AND SUB-TROPICAL AFRICA

The functioning of a tropical soil community, as compared with a temperate one, resembles the functioning of a busy commercial centre as compared with that of an agrarian community. The total amount of wealth may be the same in both cases, but the money of a commercial society circulates much more rapidly than that of an agrarian community, as the fertility of a tropical soil circulates more quickly than that of a temperate soil.

In a temperate zone, the tempo of life being relatively slow, the capital of the community, that is the fertility of the soil, is largely tied up in the soil itself, the earth. This is so much the case that when a virgin soil is broken, particularly in semi-arid steppe country, it is possible to obtain crop after crop without manuring, simply out of the stored fertility of the soil. Such a proceeding is, of course, criminally stupid; morally, it is as if a family of children opened their mother's veins and lived by drinking her blood until she died. It remains true that the thing can be done, has been done, and is being done.

In a tropical soil community, however, owing to the great speed with which plants and animals grow and decay in favourable conditions; to the absence of a winter season of rest; and to the density of animal and vegetable populations, the greater part of the fertility of the soil will, at any moment, be found not locked up in the soil itself, but working in the living members of the soil community. This is perfectly satisfactory provided that nothing happens to prevent the quick and steady return of this capital to the soil-bank, so that it can be re-issued to support more life. This return is achieved by the deaths, where they stand, of as many creatures as lived upon the soil. In fact, in a tropical soil, the fertility capital is being turned over more frequently than in a temperate soil, a state of affairs which good economists would approve, but which, in view of the want of reserves, might cause some dubiety in circles where thrift means savings in cash, not investments.

When men make clearances in tropical jungle, for their cultivated crops, they drive away the animals, cut away or burn off the vegetables. By so doing they destroy a great part, probably the greater part, of the soil fertility. The earth which is cleared carries only a small reserve, and it is therefore incapable of yielding more than three or four cultivated crops without showing signs of exhaustion. If too many crops be taken from such a soil, it may be so exhausted that, when abandoned by men, the jungle cannot return to do its work of restoring the fertility and recreating a balanced soil community; there may not even be enough nourishment and moisture left to enable some very humble and undemanding pioneer plant to begin that work. In that event, the soil dies and erosion occurs.

From this it should be clear that it is particularly easy for men to become a disease of tropical soils. But the indigenous humans of tropical and sub-tropical African soil communities, in so far as they were farmers at all, did contrive to live without damaging their environment. They practised shifting agriculture, like our own Neolithic ancestors. In some places they still do so. Shifting agriculture entails clearing a small part of the jungle, planting a food crop, and continuing to do this until returns show signs of failure due to soil exhaustion. The whole community then moves on to a new site, leaving the jungle to return and restore the health of the cultivated section.

Men practising this kind of agriculture can, of course, make no progress in the development of their own potentialities as vessels of consciousness. But given some sufficient stimulus, it is probable that the Africans would, sooner or later, have started to evolve a more efficient agriculture, from these primitive beginnings, and that the evolution would have been slow and steady enough to be conditioned by the nature of the soil, to grow out of that nature, and to be adapted to it. What would have happened then, would have been something like this: as the methods of culture changed and improved, so would the soil itself have been altered, until ultimately, like the soil of Europe, it would have been as much changed as a stone is changed by being taken out of the ground and dressed and built into a cathedral.

Men practising shifting agriculture cannot be said to be fitting themselves to a balanced community without disturbing its equilibrium; nor are they creating artificial soil communities to replace the natural ones which they cannot help destroying the moment they become efficient farmers. Such shifting farmers are parasitic upon their soils, and must therefore be classed as a disease of those soils; but a disease in so mild a form that it causes only a few quickly healed and non-septic sores on the earth's face.

The mildness of these Africans considered as a disease organism, like the mildness of any other disease due to an organism, is a benefit derived from their relative weakness in the face of the strength of their environment. Such tribes of wandering soil-scratchers have a very high infant-mortality rate, a low vitality, which makes them victims, in their turn, of disease organisms; and above all a proneness to warfare with other tribes very useful in keeping their numbers in check. What a pity that the bucolic military genius of a Tchaka, a Dingaan, a Cetywayo, protecting the soil of Africa by encouraging thousands of Africans to cut each other's throats, should all have gone for nothing! Because while the white overlords of Africa will not allow the blacks to fight each other any more, they will do nothing else to check the destruction of African soils by overstocking with men.

For when a rule of law is imposed upon these African farmers, preventing warfare, their numbers increase. Provided with medical care, they grow even more numerous. The more numerous they become, the more frequently must they, of course, return to a patch of soil which they have already cultivated, until soon they are returning to it before the jungle has had time to restore its balance and rebuild its fertility. What for thousands of years have been nothing worse than ephemeral and insignificant sores on the face of the earth, become permanently septic sores. The sickness spreads. Man, from being a mere source of irritation, like lice on a dog, has become a mortal disease, like *Pneumococcus* triumphant in the human blood-stream.

Where it is not a question of the pressure of the whites upon native practices, but of the introduction of European methods into the African soil communities, the consequences are as bad, perhaps rather worse. The structure of European soils, as I have already said, is artificial: that peculiar and so pleasant granular texture of a loam in good heart is as much a work of man as *Hamlet*, or Durham Cathedral, or the Rockefeller Centre. It has taken longer to make than either of those other works: approximately five thousand years in fact. It is adapted to agriculture, not to wild nature; it is enormously more fertile, enormously more resistant than any natural soil. If a natural soil is treated as if it were a European soil, it just cannot take it: it dies. Vast areas of African soil have been killed off by the *Afrikander* variety of the disease *Homo faber*.

The following is a quotation from G. V. Jacks' and R. O. Whyte's *Rape of the Earth*:

> European influence has been responsible for the rapid, and in places now uncontrollable, biological deterioration of the land. Whatever European plans for the future of Africa may have been, whether their object was imperial, commercial, educational, religious or military, they included no provision for the safety of the soil. At the time when Africa was being colonized there was no apparent reason and little precedent for caution. The luxuriant tropical vegetation suggested immense wealth to be had for the taking; it seemed only necessary to introduce scientific technique and to substitute a settled agriculture for the inefficient shifting cultivation of the natives. But the soil has yielded up its wealth too readily, and its apparent boundless fertility disappeared under European agricultural methods before the damage done was realized.

THE SOUTH AMERICAN STEPPE

The principal natural soil communities of South America are of two kinds: those in which the dominant species are grasses, and those in which the dominant species are trees. On the whole these soils have hitherto resisted the relatively weak attacks of the disease organism *Homo faber*, but the overstocking of grass soils with immense herds of cattle and sheep for slaughter and export as meat, is causing a debility of these soils which can have only one end.

This particular manifestation of man as a disease of soils has not yet been considered. But the grazing of maiden grass soils can be just as damaging as the ploughing of such soils.

Grass soils can, of course, support, as one of their members, a population of graminivorous animals, but the numbers of such animals must be so checked by the natural dangers and disorders of the flesh, that the work of the grasses in turning solar energy into fertility is always more than adequate to supply the body-material of the animals which, in any case, should return their carcases, made of borrowed nutrients, whence they came. When men stock grass with their tame cattle, they protect this valuable property (Latin for *cattle=pecunia*) by the driving away of predatory species, and by veterinary care. Then, the number of beasts which the soil is made to carry depends upon the will of the herdsman and the condition in which his cattle are maintained. Since the herdsman has neither the means, nor, until very recently the inclination, to measure the consumption of soil fertility and compare it with the natural annual increment, he can (and frequently did and does) so overstock the ranges, that his beasts are not simply eating part of the usufruct of productive labour done by the grasses, but gobbling up fertility capital. In a few seasons the grass, having used up stored energy, begins to deteriorate and die, and the soil community is threatened with extinction.

Could a knowledge of, a true derivation from, some pastoral past of mankind, have guided these modern shepherds and cattle men into a wiser course? Could it have enabled them to avoid becoming diseases of their soils?

It is possible, even probable, that if the enormous new pastoral economy of the twentieth century had developed on the Eurasian *steppe*, this error might have been avoided. Not because Eurasians are morally or intellectually superior to Argentines or Guatemalans, but because they have in them, in their bones and blood, in the very atmosphere which they breathe, a knowledge of the *steppe* on which they live, out of the substance of which they are made. The *steppe* remained, for thousands of years, a healthy and vigorous soil community despite the activities of its numerous human members. It began to die when an alien people of farmers, the Russians, conquered it and brought in the plough, or cattle upon a relatively modern, European scale. During thousands of years grass, and man as herdsman, had co-operated successfully; and then, in tens of years, man as farmer did so much damage to the *steppe* soil communities, that the government of the U.S.S.R. is spending, and must long continue to spend, milliards of roubles and countless quantities of human energy in trying to create a new and artificial organic balance.

The vast herds maintained by ancient peoples, herds of horses in the case of the Tartars and Mongols, the peoples of Jenghiz, of Timur, of the Golden Horde; of Attila, and of their remote ancestors, were only relatively vast. The horses and other cattle were grazed over very great regions, for ever shifting across hundreds of miles, indeed right across central Asia and eastern Europe, the herdsmen adapting their culture to their moving economy. By this means the grasses, the grass soil communities, were never overtaxed. It does not in the least matter whether the herdsmen knew, intelligently, why they acted as they did. But in the absence of knowledge, rational knowledge, of the real nature of their environment, an intruding people who have not grown up out of their adopted countryside, have no tradition of conservation, no respect for the life of the soils off which they propose to live. The South American cattle men had no tradition from which to derive wisdom. They had only the ethos and the example of the great Republic to their north, and this they adopted. Industry and application are certainly virtues which the American peoples possess almost to excess. The South American ranchers saw that the thing to do was to work hard and make money. They stocked the *steppe* of their countries without regard to the consumption of a soil fertility which they did not even know was consumable. They bartered the future of their soils for Packards, mistresses, electric light, palaces in their capitals and apartments in Paris. They did not begin to make a culture out of their soil: they bought an alien one with their soil's fertility.

Not only do modern cattle men destroy the fertility of their *steppe* soils and thereby put the life of the grass soil communities in danger. They sell it oversea.

Between 1920 and 1950, that is in thirty years, the Argentine alone exported to Britain 11,683,000 tons of beef, not to mention other meats. This represents approximately 50,000,000 head of cattle. The average age of these beasts would be 3 years.

In 3 years a steer consumes 10 tons of grass. A ton of grass represents, in terms of plant nutrients taken from the soil, perhaps 1 cwt. Such nutrients can, of course, be replaced as artificial fertilizers; whether they are so replaced is another matter. In any case, the texture of the soil is none the less not restored. An immense quantity of organic material has been removed. A small proportion of it can be restored by manuring with steers' dung, but there is a steady and continuous loss. What then, has happened as a result of this export of meat? A quantity of top-soil equal to about a million fertile acres has been sent away from the soil community to which it belonged, eaten by the English, assimilated into their flesh, or, by way of their sewers, thrown into the sea.

If it were literally true that every atom of energy borrowed from soil by animals living on and off it, must be returned whence it came, then man, as a semi-parasite, could not live at all. The factor left out of account is the usufruct, the annual increment of fertility won by plant-populated soils. It would be perfectly sound to kill and eat so many cattle as could feed off the Argentine *steppe* without breaking into soil-fertility capital. But no more; or not until the cattle men had done what the farmers of Europe have done, made an artificial soil capable of yielding far more than a natural soil.

*

So much for the two examples of man as a disease of soils. They are by no means the only cases, nor even the worst. Both have their origins in a fatal breach with the past, in the inability of the men concerned to understand their environment, since they did not grow in it, were not native to it. Yet not even men native to a soil community have always, or often, avoided the destruction of their soils. But at least they have generally gained much from that destruction: the glorious civilization created by Athens was paid for by the loss of the soil of Attica, indeed came into existence as a by-product of that loss.

CHAPTER VIII

THE SOILS OF ATTICA AND THE RISE OF ATHENS

THE soil communities of Attica were not always of that austere simplicity which has characterized them in historical times. They were, anciently, for the most part forest soils, and although mountain soils are commonly composed of fewer and hardier species than forest soils in lowlands, the protection afforded to the earth by deciduous trees and what falls from them as dead matter, creates an environment favourable to the prosperity of many species.

The top-soil upon rocky mountains is precariously lodged, and only the presence of trees permits it to accumulate as a basis for a soil community. The fall of dead leaves and other rubbish deposits an annual layer of vegetable matter, with the texture of a sponge. This, together with the trees' function in absorbing enormous quantities of water, and then sweating it out again at the leaves, so governs the water cycle in forest countries, as we have seen in the case of Sind, that instead of rainfall running off and carrying with it earth and the raw material of earth, flooding and silting rivers, and causing erosion, the process is reduced to a gentle, steady and beneficent motion.

Although this water-controlling function of trees is only now being applied in practical soil conservation, it is not newly discovered. Of one of its aspects Gilbert White says,[39]

> ... trees are perfect alembics; and no one who has not attended to such matters can imagine how much water one tree will distil in a night's time, by condensing the vapour, which trickles down the twigs and boughs so as to make the ground below quite in a float....

The force of rainfall is broken by trees, the water absorbed by the spongy leaf-mould, and filtered slowly through to the top-soil.

Forest soils also soften the climate in another manner. Anyone who has experience of flying light aircraft over forest country knows that as the aircraft crosses the frontier which separates grass or arable soils from the forest, it rises sharply. This rising current of warm air draws in air to replace it from the surrounding atmosphere, thus maintaining a constant circulation. As we have already noticed, the temperature among trees will often be as much as 20 degrees lower than it is in the open, while in cold weather the air among trees is relatively warm. Forest soils in short, tend to reduce violent extremes of weather, to create an equable climate, to soften seasonal changes into a slow and gentle rhythm.

Such soils were common to most parts of mountainous Greece in prehistoric times, and some endured well into historic times: the country described by Polybius, his native state of Arcady, was such a soil at least as late as 160 B.C.

If, however, the trees are cut down, a mortal blow is struck not only at the soil community, but at the soil itself. The leaf-mould is soon consumed, the loose, forest soil, differing greatly from grass-soils in texture, and extremely erodable, is dried to dust by the sun; washed away as mud by the rain; blown off the rock to which it is no longer bound by living roots, until the bare, stone bones of the landscape are exposed.

The deforestation of Attica was begun at an early date, for much before the time of Pericles few trees remained, and wood for ship-building had to be imported. Historical Attica inherited from prehistoric Attica one of the poorest and thinnest soils in Hellas: and it was probably this misfortune which made Athens, in the magnificent phrase put into the mouth of Pericles by Thucydides, "the education of Hellas".

*

The position which the people of Attica adopted *envers* their soil community, their refusal to play the humble part in

Hellenic affairs which living in equilibrium with their wretched soil would have entailed, cannot be considered as an isolated phenomenon, but only in the body of an ecological account of the Hellenic world: however, by concentrating upon Attica and glancing at other States when necessary, some impression of what happened can be given.

We know very little, by direct report, of the natural soil communities of Greece before men began to destroy them. By the time of Thucydides (*c.* 465-400 B.C.), erosion had in many places quite destroyed the soil, while in other places artificial soil communities had been created and stabilized (e.g. Boeotia, Thessaly). Thucydides says:

> The country which is now called Hellas was not regularly settled in ancient times. The people were migratory, and readily left their homes whenever they were overpowered by numbers. There was no commerce, and they could not readily hold intercourse with each other either by land or sea. The several tribes cultivated their own soil just enough to obtain a maintenance from it, but they had no accumulations of wealth and did not plant the ground; for being without walls they were never sure that an invader might not come and despoil them.[40] Living in this manner, and knowing that they could anywhere obtain a bare subsistence, they were always ready to migrate; so that they had neither great cities, nor any considerable resources. The richest districts were most constantly changing their inhabitants; for example, the countries which are now called Thessaly and Boeotia, the greater part of the Peloponnesus with the exception of Arcadia, and all the best parts of Hellas. For the productiveness of the land increased the power of individuals; and in turn was a source of quarrels by which communities were ruined, whilst at the same time they were exposed to attacks from without. Certainly Attica, of which the soil was poor and thin, enjoyed a long freedom from civil strife, and therefore retained its original inhabitants. And a striking confirmation of my argument is afforded by the fact that Attica, through immigration, increased in population more than

any other region. For the leading men of Hellas, when driven out of their own country by war and revolution, sought an asylum at Athens. And from the very earliest times, being admitted to rights of citizenship, so greatly increased the number of inhabitants that Attica became incapable of containing them, and was at last obliged to send out colonies to Ionia.[41]

Here is a first example of the poverty of Attican soil beginning to work towards the greatness of Athens, by enabling her to recruit to the city "the leading men of Hellas". And it is probable that the greater part of that soil poverty was man-made.

Late Neolithic men were able to cut down forest trees with their beautifully made stone axes. The Mayas of Central America, indeed, who never passed, technically, the Neolithic level, created their whole high culture in tropical forest clearings with nothing but stone tools. Nevertheless, a want of metal did, by a merciful dispensation, impose upon Neolithic peoples a relatively slow pace in their work of deforestation. There seems almost to be a Providence in this, for when a community of men is to grow up in a soil community, and must therefore substitute for the natural equilibrium of the plant and animal species, an artificial one, the work must be done very slowly, the pace must be accommodated to the rates of biological and organic change. Stone tools do not permit of such fast work as will destroy, instead of changing, what may, perhaps, be called the metabolism of soils.

The appalling destruction of soils wrought in less than a century in North America was due simply to the fact that it was technically possible. Virgin soil communities were invaded by men from a neighbouring high culture, equipped not only with steel, but very soon with machine tools. Moreover, it is important to realize that this destruction was also *psychologically* possible: the natural environment of primitive, native societies is, to some extent, protected against its human members by the mythology and traditions which these men have accumulated in their contacts with trees and animals and herbs, and which each new generation inherits as a lore and a feeling. But the sophisticated intellectuals who are the men of high civilizations, products of their particular "Socratic revolution", uninfluenced by Orphic feeling, are not inhibited in their assault upon a soil community. They do not feel themselves to be merely members of it, even though dominant ones, but are outside nature, God's tenants, given a free hand with the landlord's property.

Now it is clear that before the ninth century B.C. an amount of damage had been done to the mountain soils of Hellas out of proportion to the powers of stone-equipped peoples to commit. No doubt the grass-soils of Lakedaimon, Boeotia and Thessaly were still virtually intact; but it is clear that the hill soils, particularly those of Attica, had long been deforested, partially exhausted, and gravely overstocked with men. I suggest that the rapid, and perhaps rather sudden destruction of Greek mountain forests, and consequently of soil fertility and equable climatic and topographical conditions, was due to a cause very similar to that which has had such hideous results in the United States, in Africa and in Australia: the intrusion of peoples technically much too advanced for the slow work of healthily transforming natural into artificial soil communities. For Greece was the goal of numerous immigrant hordes from the north and east, as well as civilized colonists from the south.

In this connection, here is a short passage from an article in *The Times* (23 October, 1950), describing results of excavation in Samothrace:

> ... The diggers unearthed a burnt layer of sacrificial debris about two feet thick containing huge quantities of animal bones and masses of pottery of the period 700–650 B.C. *The pottery consists mainly of two sharply contrasting groups; extremely fine and thin Greek vases,* mostly huge, double-handed drinking cups of a hitherto unknown variety, embellished by a subtle and consciously sparse use of ornament, and plump, *native "prehistoric" cups, made of grey clay* without the potter's wheel, and without any ornament at all. Both groups were clearly

used together in the sacrificial banquets by the Greek immigrants who first settled on the island and by the natives who fused their civilization and religion in due course. The contrast between these hitherto unknown ceramics reveals the immense superiority of Greek cultural tradition over the primitive surrounds that it had begun to penetrate in the age of Greek colonization.

Something like this must have happened in what became the nuclear Greek communities, in the preceding age of Greek immigration. The men who came in from the north, Achaeans (in their later waves called Dorians), were not farmers, but herdsmen and soldiers. But they were equipped with bronze, and so, of course, were the ultra-sophisticated colonists from Crete, from the *Thallassocracy of Minos*, who created the Mycenean civilization later to destroy its parent. It is surely possible that relatively efficient metal tools came to Attica too soon and too copiously for the good of Attican soils? Left to themselves, the makers of those grey clay vases, or their congeners on the mainland, would have worked so slowly in transforming their environment that they might have created an artificial soil community as stable as that of England or France. Their state of mind probably resembled that of the native inhabitants of North America, who had such a profound respect for the earth that one chieftain refused to obey an order to plough his soil on the grounds that to do so would entail cutting open his mother's breast. Such a thing would be an atrocious impiety. Without, perhaps, following this native American to his conclusion, it can certainly be said that the total want of feeling that the soil is alive led the invading Europeans to kill North American soils unwittingly.

But not even a deeply ingrained mythology of respect for life in all its forms, and for the patterns in which it manifests itself, will long restrain men with an intellect, of which they have become conscious, to "corrupt" them, from withholding their new, shiny, power-conferring axe from the bole of their neighbour trees.

Hesiod's poetry fixes for us the conditions of Greek agriculture (Hesiod was a Boeotian) nearly three thousand years ago. The Greece of which he wrote was already a country of peasant farmers to whom the poet, in *Works and Days*, addresses advice:

> Get a house, and a woman and an ox for the plough. . . . Make everything ready at home so that you may not have to ask of another and he refuse you, and so you are in lack, the season pass by, and your work come to nothing.

Men, he says, are born to misery, and to avoid the worst consequences of this state, there must be hard and orderly work throughout the season. In October, hew and shape timber, make your plough from a suitable tree, procure oxen, and buy or hire a ploughman not less than 40 years old. . . .

No younger man will be better than he at scattering seed and avoiding double sowing; a man less staid gets disturbed, hankering after his fellows.

For every month there is hard work, and in all the year very little rest, and that accompanied by no diversion. Nothing could be further from the state of mind evoked by Homer's poems. We are made aware of a people who have given up the youthfully heroic way of life depicted in the *Iliad*, and who have got down to the brass tacks of careful and systematic cultivation. There is a feeling of a worked countryside densely populated, in which only application and skill can keep a man from straits.

*

Before the eighth century B.C., then, the pressure of immigration into Greece, and of natural increase throughout the Peninsula and the Islands, was such that the soils of Hellas could not support their inhabitants. We have already seen that the meagreness of Attic soils, although a grave economic handicap, was also a source of social and political advantage. Many of the Greek cities went to war with their neighbours in order to conquer living room, but Attica was not worth conquering. Other states, and even Athens, began movements oversea, planting in Italy, Southern France, Sicily and Spain, south in Libya, east in the Islands and in Anatolia. These movements, if drawn as a series of charts at ten-year intervals, and projected as a moving cartoon, would give the impression of a violent explosion outwards from metropolitan Hellas. And the energy manifest in that explosion was to maintain that outward pressure until the whole Mediterranean world and the parts beyond were Hellenized.

The ecological and population problems which confronted Attica were even more difficult than those which confronted most of the other Hellenic states. Her energy was so much absorbed in solving them that her people were unable to accumulate wealth and buy that leisure in which her creative minority could have begun the making of a culture. Sparta and Corinth, to name but two cities, were practising the arts and crafts, Ionia the sciences, at a high level of civilization, while Athens was producing nothing but the means of subsistence.

*

When a people finds itself upon a thin and stony soil, the product of natural erosion, or of the tactless mauling of the natural soil community by the people's predecessors, it may, in certain climatic and economic conditions, save itself by the ingenious exploitation of its subsoil. Such a people may, even in the absence of a fertile top-soil, create a balanced soil community, but one which will be of a peculiarly artificial and precarious kind. For one of its "members" must be a foreign market.

Subsoil is less fertile than top-soil, differing from the latter in being composed largely of mineral particles, with a lower proportion of organic matter and of living organisms. The life of subsoil moves at a slower tempo, for the bacteria are few and those deprived of both air and food. Nevertheless, the essential plant nutrients are present in subsoils, indeed often plentiful, since soluble salts are continually leached out of the top-soil by rainfall. Plants of at least two very different kinds can be cultivated in such semi-barren soils with economic advantage: these plants are either such as have adapted themselves, in nature, to living off mean and austere soils; or they are such as, native to rich soils in nature, and accustomed to grow rampantly, if severely checked in their habits by transference to meagre conditions, compensate for the stunting of their body growth by a generous production of fruit. That they can make this change in their nature is partly due to the distinction between the uses which plants make of their various nutrients: nitrates, always in short supply, but relatively plentiful in rich soils, relatively rare in poor ones, are plant body-builders. But the ripening of fruit-bearing wood in such plants, and therefore the formation of flower-buds, and hence the production of fruit, is stimulated when the intake of phosphates and potassium salts rises relative to the intake of nitrates, until they are disproportionately high by natural standards. Thus, it is a common practice in market-gardening to graft fruit-tree varieties on to stocks which starve the tree; another practice is to constrict the flow of nutrients by bending the fruit-bearing branches, by cutting away rings of bark, or by constricting ties. Equally effective, within certain limits, is to plant the tree in soil poor in nitrates and relatively rich in phosphates and other elements. This can only be done safely when the natural vigour of the plant is excessive, from the cultivator's point of view.

The fig tree, the olive tree and the vine belong to one of the classes of plants which can be used to exploit poor soils. By the large-scale planting of these three trees, but particularly of the olive and the vine, the people of Attica solved, within certain limits, the problem of creating an artificial soil community. But this was such that it could only serve them, only hold them steady in the opposite scale of the balance, on conditions which were not only artificial, but which were not even agricultural in their nature: they were mercantile and military. The Athenian response to the challenge of their miserable soil drove them to become, from one of the most backward of the Hellenic states, the "education of Hellas"; from one of the most conservative, the most radical; from one of the poorest, the richest; and from one of the most pacific, the most warlike.

*

The antiquity of the culture of the vine is such that we have little knowledge of its origin, and it is therefore difficult to assign it an original habitat. Some species of the genus *Vitis* occurred, in remote times, in many parts of Europe and near Asia, for archaeologists have disinterred, botanists identified and classified, fossilized fragments of vines. The wild plant is a dioaecious deciduous one, *Vitis vinifera* ssp. *silvestris* Gmel. This plant, once native to a large part of Europe, the Near East and Transcaucasia, is still to be found in the latter region and in parts of Turkey. The cultivated vines developed from this species are, for the most part, hermaphroditic; they are classified as a sub-species, *V. vinifera* ssp. *sativa* D.C., whose polymorphism is so remarkable that description is only possible by varieties, which number about three thousand. The sub-species has been developed by selective breeding and by the selection and propagation of bud mutants, often in conditions of isolation from other vine populations which have made possible the externalization and conservation of Mendelian recessive characters.

Probably it was a South Caucasian people who first cultivated this plant. Their behaviour will have been like that of the British Colonists of North America, who very quickly learnt to go out into the autumn woods of Virginia and Maryland, gather the wild muscadines from the native vines, and make wine with them; thereafter, they brought vines into their gardens, in some states compelled to do so by law, and cultivated them; finally, they attempted to acclimatize the better European vine to their climate and soils. Yet these colonists were not of a people accustomed to viticulture as a commonplace. No doubt the people who first began to cultivate the vine about 4000 years B.C., somewhere in what is now Azerbaijan, Georgia or Armenia, acted in much the same way.

The first inscription recording the cultivation of vineyards was made by the *Patesi* Gudea, of Lagash in the Tigris–Euphrates country, and it has been dated by archaeologists *c.* 2400 B.C. But the cultivated vine did not reach Greece until at least a thousand years thereafter, coming by way of Lydia, through Thrace, and under Semitic, perhaps Phoenician auspices, for the Greek word for wine—and the product always precedes the plant—is οινος which is a Semitic loan word (Hebrew, Arabic, *yain, wain*). This, at all events, is the probable route of the vine into Greece, for Lydia was famous for vineyards at an early date, and was long associated with the Hellenic peoples. There is an alternative route, however. Phoenicians may have introduced wine and the vine to Crete, whence it would have come, by way of Mycenae, into Attica and other Greek states. But since the spread of viticulture can be closely associated with the cult of Dionysos, and since the principal known primitive shrine of that cult belonged, according to Herodotus, to the Satrae, a Thracian people, it is probable that the vine came down into Greece, rather than across the sea from the south.

The vine is a forest plant, supporting itself, as a seedling, on trees and, grown large in the course of its very long life, capable of uprooting its support. Forest soils, although acid, are rich and generous, and vines in nature are grossly fed, their immensely long and wandering root systems enabling them to gather moisture and nutrients at great distances from the stock. But despite this character, the vine is admirably fitted to go into partnership with men. Transplanted to grudging and stony soils, its habit of rampant growth is severely checked, it grows more soberly; skilfully pruned and supported, it becomes very fruitful.

The ruined soils of Attica were, in part, reclaimed by planting vineyards.

The olive tree (*Oleo europaea* L.) is native to South-western

Asia, according to Victor Heyn.[42] It was cultivated and improved by a Semitic people. The olive prospers in poor, limestone soils and, like the fig, prefers to be near the sea. The Greeks of the heroic age made much use of the olive wood which is, indeed, excellent, taking a high polish. The haft of Pisander's axe, the club of the Cyclops, the marriage bed of Odysseus were of olive. On the other hand oil, although familiar to the Homeric Greeks, seems to have been something of a luxury, probably an import, and perhaps used chiefly as a cosmetic. If this is the case, the olive tree, in the ninth century B.C., was known as a forest or wild tree, unimproved as to fruit, but not as an orchard tree; or, if planted in some gardens, was something of a rarity, perhaps with the status of the mulberry in England. In Britain, in our own time, the walnut, although found here and there in plantations, is not an object of any considerable cultivation, although it matures its nuts well, and is widely planted in parts of France as a source of valuable oil. The case of the walnut, in England, is closely analogous with that of the olive as it appears in the Odyssey, where it is an orchard or garden tree, grown for its fruit, not its oil, along with apples, pears and figs.

There is no sign of the cultivation of the olive in Hesiod. Herodotus says that,

> ... at a time not long past there was not an olive tree in the world, except at Athens.

This is obviously nonsense, but it is possibly true that olive trees of a fruiting variety, improved out of all recognition on the wild plant, were brought into Hellas, and specifically into Attica, from Asia. Heyn says:

> It may be the fact that wild olives grew on the rock of the citadel, and that one of them was grafted with a fruit-bearing olive from over the sea. ...

It is certainly the fact that the olive was associated with Athene, was regarded as her special gift to her favourite city, and was unquestionably the spring of Athenian wealth, power, and civilization.

*

Although grapes and olives, wine and oil are excellent and wholesome foods, it is perhaps not possible to sustain life on them alone, and certainly no community of men has ever tried it. Where these foods are available, the rest of the diet can be much reduced without disadvantage; nevertheless, a staple is necessary, bread, meat, or preferably both.

The Achaeans were enormous eaters of meat; but when historians throw up their hands and utter loud cries over the idea of some Achaean hero consuming the whole back of an ox, or half a pig, they are perhaps thinking in terms of the size of modern meat cattle. The art of breeding cattle was not, of course, unknown to antiquity; Isomachus, in Xenophon's *Oikonomikos*, discusses it with Socrates. But this art was perfected by the British inventors of high farming, in the eighteenth century A.D., men like Bakewell and Coke of Holkham: they, and their successors, gave us meat-cattle and pigs upwards of four times the size of the earlier breeds. However, it is certainly true that the Greeks of the eighth century B.C. regarded only meat as real food, everything else as a relish, including wheaten bread which, however, figures importantly in most of the meals described in the Homeric poems.

But even before the time of Pericles meat had fallen to an insignificant place on the Attican menu, and bread had become the staple. Yet this rise of bread as a principal food of the Athenians, coincides with a further decline of their corn lands, the expansion of olive-orchards and vineyards. At a time when the population of Attica, citizens, metics and helots, judging by Pericles' statistics for the armed forces of the Polis, can hardly have been less than 300,000, the total Attican production of bread corn, that is of wheat and barley, in a good year, was 675,000 bushels. This is enough to supply 75,000 people with bread.

How were the Athenians able to eat bread? In the answer to that question is also to be found the reason why Athens became "the education of Hellas". Since the Athenians could not live by eating olives and drinking wine, they were forced to undertake the exchange of these commodities for bread corn, notably wheat. There were, in the Mediterranean and surrounding countries, a number of markets where this exchange was possible. The Scythian farmers grew vast quantities of wheat for export in the still famous wheat-soil, the black earth country of the Ukraine. Sicily had become, and for centuries remained, a wheat exporter. The fertility of Egyptian soil was, despite having to support a teeming population during some thousands of years, maintained by the unique phenomenon of the Nile floods, whereby the rich top-soils of an enormous tract of Africa were annually deposited in the Nile valley of Egypt. This region was, perhaps, the country of origin of the cultivated cereal grasses. It was certainly a granary throughout the whole period of Hellenic civilization. And Athens might trade for corn even in some of the islands—Euboia, Lemnos, Imbros probably had wheat or barley surpluses for sale. And most, if not all of these markets were open to import the excellent wines and olive-oil of Attica.

But the export of wine and oil entailed the development of ancillary industries. Both commodities had to be packed and carried in jars, so that the manufacture of ceramics must have become increasingly important. And since the topography of Greece, the position and remoteness of the corn markets, put land-transport out of the question, the trading of cash-crops for a living meant the growth of a ship-building industry and of a merchant marine.

When a people still in the dynamic, creative phase of its genius, engages in some form of manufacture on economic grounds, the products of that manufacture are nevertheless liable to be objects of art. General Tilney told Catherine Morland (*Northanger Abbey*), when she remarked upon the elegance of his breakfast-table china, that,

He was enchanted by her approbation of his taste, confessed it (the china) to be neat and simple, thought it right to encourage the manufacture of his country; and for his part, to his uncritical palate, the tea was as well-flavoured from the clay of Staffordshire, as from that of Dresden or Sevres. But this was quite an old set, purchased two years ago. The manufacture was much improved since that time. . . .

Jane Austen's General Tilney was referring to a new industry, founded by men of enterprise, with the object of filling a practical demand for crockery, and of making money out of it. But the objects they produced were works of art—the china of Rockingham, Derby, Coalport, Spode and others which, today, we seek in antique shops and at auction sales and pay for, if we have the means, at a price which takes into account not the utility of the purchase but its rare beauty and fine workmanship.

When Athens developed her ceramics industry in order to carry her wine and oil abroad, she made her potters rich, and they were able to create works of art in clay which, in their turn, became valuable exports. Attican pottery had long been good and had competed with that of other peoples all across Greece. Athenian country-gentlemen and ex-soldiers did not, perhaps, "encourage the manufacture of their country" quite as General Tilney did, but nevertheless the cases are analogous. When the buyer has taste, the craftsman can supply him with objects of vertu for his domestic needs: when the buyer has no taste, the manufacturer can supply him with objects of the same utility, but which, like the domestic china of the Carthaginians or the modern English, have no aesthetic attributes at all.

As it was with Athenian pots, so it was with Athenian ships. The case is less interesting, because whereas it is possible, and indeed easy, to make teacups or oil jars which are sufficiently usable, but are vulgar and hideous, the beauty of a ship depends much less upon the taste of the ship-builder. A ship is a machine which has to work under the pressure of certain natural forces. The design of an efficient ship is dictated by laws beyond human control, and it so happens that if the design of a machine derives from the natural forces with which it must work, it will have some of the beauty of a natural object. Thus, for example, between 1900 and 1950, an age of declining taste, aeroplanes have become steadily more beautiful.

Towards the end of the nineteenth century of our own time, conditions of world trade made the survival of the merchant prosperity of Boston and Salem, New England, dependent upon American ability to carry goods, and especially tea from China, faster than they could be carried in English bottoms. Money was poured into ship-builders' hands, and they, with astonishing daring, turned the bows of their ships inside-out, altered the conventional rigging, and created what was, and perhaps still remains, the most beautiful machine ever made: the Clipper.

The Athenian ship-builders and sailors became, under the stimulus of the oil and wine trade, incomparably the most skilful of all Hellenic seafarers, and more than a match for the Phoenicians, for it was essentially a Phoenician navy which they defeated and destroyed at Salamis. The importance of sea power became so great that, towards the end of the Peloponnesian war, with Attica a ravaged and desolate land, the Delean League broken up, famine and plague in the city, all military Hellas and the Great King against her, and, worst handicap of all, the ruffianly and treacherous Alcibiades to plague her, Athens could only be defeated when her enemies took wholeheartedly to the sea. They learnt the lessons she had taught herself, mustered an overwhelming naval force, and destroyed her fleet: if Athens was "the education of Hellas", the fact was never more strikingly demonstrated than at Aegospotami.

For, of course, the creation of a merchant marine had entailed the creation of a fighting navy: it was not very likely that the rising commercial importance of Athens would be watched with indifference or applauded with generosity by other Hellenic powers, dependent for their own prosperity, if not, at least to the extent of Attica, for mere subsistence, on sea-borne trade. Corinth, Aegina, perhaps Carthage, must do all in their power to cripple this belated but formidable rival, she, in her turn, to destroy or dominate them. This is not the place to reiterate Athenian military history in detail: the city was driven into fighting commercial wars. She was forced, by the ancient ruin of her original soil communities, and the consequent spoiling of her top-soil, to conceive, build, man and master the art of a navy. The men were found, as, in growing and dynamic communities, the men always are found. Above all, in Themistocles, Attica had a man who combined the navy-making talent of an Alfred or a John Hawkins, with the fighting seamanship (within the terms of his time), of a Nelson.

Themistocles' opportunity was made for him by the men who cut down the virgin forests of Attica.

*

The spectacle of Athenian superiority in the arts, sciences, philosophy and literature: and her pre-eminence in war and politics, until ruined by her arrogance with the allies, by the implacability of her enemies, and by the irresponsibility of her leaders, is a curious one.

There is no reason to suppose that the peasants and gentry of Attica were a people of genius naturally superior to their enemies, or their neighbours. Claiming that their ancestors alone had withstood the Dorian invaders, although it is more likely that Attica was not worth conquering, and that they were therefore "Ionians", the Athenians built much on this alleged racial difference. We are familiar with nonsense of this kind. The Spartans, to consider only one other Hellenic, and Dorian, people, were before her in the arts of civilization until the middle of the sixth century, and it happens that in the case of the Spartans we have a singularly simple instance of soil shaping history, though in a sense opposite to the Athenian case.

The Spartans were among the first of the Hellenes to practise fine arts. Their poets were renowned, and their pottery and other craft-work, although clearly of oriental provenance in the matter of style, begins to show signs of a native character in design, the typical promise of cultural and intellectual creativeness. Then, in the middle of the sixth century B.C., the progress of Spartan culture comes to an abrupt stop.

Sparta, originally an agglomeration of five villages, stood in *Lakedaimon the Fair* (Laconia), in the Peloponnesus. Menelaus was one of their kings. The soil was a rich and deep one, and therefore coveted. Moreover, when the malthusian crisis came upon Hellas, the Spartans added to their territory more land of the same quality, by conquering Messenia and enslaving the Messenians. Thus, instead of being forced into adventures and radicalism, they were, by the great value of their soil, forced into a sort of miserly conservatism: *their* object was not to trade for a livelihood abroad, but to keep jealously the soil which they had, and which, as an artificial soil community of some stability, was capable of supporting them.

The Spartiates themselves, that is the land-owning citizens, were anciently of Achaean stock, later Dorian. They were greatly outnumbered by the aboriginal inhabitants of the land, whom they had turned into Helots. These Helots were slaves, owned by the community, not by individuals, and hired or loaned out to the land-owning Spartiates to till their holdings. This was not quite plantation slavery of the kind which later ruined Rome and inflicted an incurable wound on the United States, for the tillage was subsistence farming, not cash-crop farming. A third class of the Spartan community was that of the Perioaeci, free but not enfranchised peasants; the origin of this class is uncertain, but they may have been of Dorian stock of some tribe other than the Spartiate.

The Spartans came to depend, for their subsistence, simply upon holding their rich, artificial soil community, founded upon a deep top-soil, in balance. They had at once to defend and to work it, and to keep it isolated from all commercial contact with the outside world, for that would have upset the balance and forced them to change their ways. They might, given their beginnings, have adopted a more dynamic,

> *A bit too simplisticly materialist*

centrifugal system, but they were tempted by the security offered by their soil into a conservatism which then became increasingly necessary. The interest of the Spartiates became vested in the maintenance of the slavery of the Helots, and the labour of the Perioaeci.

This state of affairs engendered in the Spartans, but particularly in the Spartiates, a state of mind in which fear and suspicion dominated, fear which seems to have reached such heights that one is tempted to call it psychopathic. It led them to commit atrocities against their culture, their Helots, and their own human nature. As an example of what their state of mind, the product of their ecological situation, could do: about 424 B.C. the Ephors of the city issued a proclamation inviting all Helots who claimed to have given good service to the state in the recent war, to give in their names. Two thousand responded, were crowned, honoured, and thereafter secretly massacred. The Spartiates did not dare to allow their subjects to possess self-respect, as if they were citizens, nor to feel that they had rights.

But long before this spectacular horror, the Spartiates had demonstrated the lamentable consequences of one stable artificial soil community having to maintain its isolation in the midst of a civilization variously unstable in that respect. About the middle of the sixth century they became so acutely aware of the delicacy and precariousness of the equilibrium they had made, so afraid that their Helots, the Perioaeci, their neighbours, might upset their system, that they devoted themselves, with horribly ant-like ignobility, simply and solely to maintaining and defending it. They instituted a system of permanent and unremitting military service for *all* citizens. The details of their organization into this hive-like commune are very nearly incredible.

Herodotus, who has a taste for what is called "firm" government, says that the Spartans managed their affairs very badly until one of their leading men, one Lycurgus, considered by modern historians to be mythical, happening to be at Delphi on a visit to the Oracle, was greeted by the Pythoness, when he entered the Temple, with:

> Oh! Thou great Lycurgus, that com'st to my beautiful dwelling,
> Dear to Zeus and to all who sit in the halls of Olympus,
> Whether to hail thee a God I know not, or only a mortal,
> But my hope is strong that a God thou wilt prove Lycurgus.

This somewhat fulsome greeting was followed up by advice upon a suitable constitution for Sparta.

The device of attributing the more frightful manifestations of political ineptitude to God is, of course, familiar. No doubt bishops will be found to bless atom-bombs. The fact is that the Spartans, instead of being challenged by their soil into making a creative response, were cosseted by it, by reason of the possession of fertile soil and a Helot population, and then found themselves compelled to devote all their energies to defending their own psychological bondage. By the constitution attributed to Lycurgus, no deformed or weakly child was reared; boys were taken from their mothers at seven, and raised in barracks, to cunning, theft, war and hardship. From the age of twenty the men lived in military messes, and if allowed to marry could only see their wives by stealth. A peculiar kind of homosexual relationship was formed between novice soldiers and veterans. The possession and use of money was forbidden, the medium of such exchange as there was being iron bars. The Spartan women were trained as gymnasts, but they seem to have possessed more sense than their men, who had achieved the remarkable and sterile *tour de force* of creating a community with a single trade, a single art, a single science: war. It is hardly necessary to add that poetry, design, all art and craft and philosophy abruptly ceased. Bismarck said of the military machine created by the father of Frederick the Great, and called Prussia, that it could produce nothing but *Kartoffeln und Soldaten*. In point of fact it produced, among other things, Immanuel Kant. But Sparta's eminent men were the generals and diplomats who, when sent abroad on missions, were prone to betray their country for a bribe.

Sparta, then, like Athens, was the product of her soil. It is clear enough that the challenge of her wretched top-soil made Athens a great manufacturing, mercantile and naval power. But was it the same cause which drove the city to surpass rival states which had taken to industry and trade? Surely their superiority was, indeed, a product of the same causes; was, at some removes, as much the consequence of the destruction of the Attican soil community in ancient times, as were those steps which the city first took towards it.

The manners, intellectual freedom, and ethics of a society organized as a commercial oligarchy depend for their quality very much upon the origins of that oligarchy. That of Athens, like that of eighteenth- and nineteenth-century Britain, had to rise in conflict with, and be constantly challenged by, the formerly dominant class of land-owning gentlemen. The Isomachus of Xenophon would have been perfectly at home among such eighteenth-century Englishmen as Coke of Holkham, intent upon improving their property in land, and the methods of working it. Pericles, like Walpole and Washington, was a gentleman. Cleon was a tanner; Samuel Whitbread and John Wilkes were the sons of brewers, and even the Pitts might, in Jane Austen's phrase, be described as "of low origin, in trade, and only very moderately genteel".

An aristocracy of the Athenian or English type, rooted in soil, creates, by reason of its leisure, its education and its touch with soil, high standards of taste, and sometimes even of behaviour. And a bourgeoisie intent upon supplanting it in power finds itself forced, at first, to live up to those standards. Few social forces have been as useful, in English social life, in educating the upthrusting middle-class in humane manners, as that of snobbishness. It is not clear, even from Aristophanes, whether this same force worked for the good of Athens: that satirist's bourgeois political grafters are presented in all the grossness of their commercial manners. Cleon shows no signs of having been influenced by the manners of the Alcmaeonidae or other gentle families. But then, Aristophanes was an outrageous Tory.

The social organization of Athens, then, before and during the rise of the city to a world power, somewhat resembled that of England before the industrial revolution. The great landowners lived on and off their estates and governed the country. And, as in Britain, the creation of industries and navies entailed the creation of new classes, traders, ship-builders, chandlers, and sailors, all men engaged in enterprising and even dangerous occupations, hardly likely to fit them for a place of mere obedience in the State. Such men will not consent to remain disenfranchised: they feel their importance in and to the commonwealth, and insist upon a part in its government. And they cannot be prevented from enriching the domestic culture, out of their experience, and with their vitality; enriching it, but, until the influence of the tradition-fostering aristocracy of the soil fails, not cosmopolitanizing and corrupting it.

Nothing, in short, is more stimulating to a community than a struggle, even a violent one, between an ancient but still able landed gentry and a rising bourgeoisie and proletariat. It was such a struggle which made England in the seventeenth and eighteenth centuries, the education of Western Civilization, as it made Athens the education of Hellas. It is beside the point that non-Englishmen, non-Athenians were perhaps more numerous and gifted exponents of the European, of the Hellenic cultures respectively. These two countries created, by means of their aristocratically inspired, democratically-tending commercial oligarchies, those conditions in which the potentialities of their respective cultures could be realized to the full.

The Athenian democracy was the creation of the new Athenian bourgeoisie pressing against the governing aristocracy. These Athenian radicals were the products of the new Attican industries and trades. Those industries and trades were forced upon the Athenians by the poverty of their exhausted and eroded soil. The culture of Athens was the product of the radicals and the aristocrats in creative conflict, and therefore of that same soil poverty.

*

For the community which has been unable to create, in its country, an artificial soil community of which its people are fully contributing, not particularly parasitic members, there is an ever-present danger. Athens had been unable to do other than she did, once wanton and ignorant deforestation had ruined a large proportion of Attican soils. She had created an artificial soil community of some stability, but of a type which could not find her people in subsistence unless she traded its products abroad. The maximum subsistence crops she was capable of producing, to make bread and fatten cattle, might support 100,000 people. But at the outbreak of the Peloponnesian war her population cannot have been less than 300,000.

One of the major psychological dangers of a highly developed commercial economy, is that of losing sight of a fundamental and vital truth: that the products of industry, whatever their nature, ought, for the health of the community, to be valued as subsistence-substitutes. In Jacquetta and Christopher Hawkes', *Prehistoric Britain*, Jacquetta Hawkes says:

> A most dramatic find made recently at the bottom of the Grimes Graves (flint mining) pit leads on to the whole question of the magico-religious beliefs of prehistoric times. Enthroned on a ledge sat the chalk-carved image of a fat and pregnant woman, looking down on a very perfect chalk phallus and a great pile of deer-horn picks which had been laid as offerings at her feet. Here, in fact, was the shrine of a fertility cult, but one apparently intended to serve a curious and unexpected purpose. This particular shaft had failed to strike the usual rich flint bed, and it seems reasonable to suppose that the shrine was set up to counteract the sterility of this pit, and ensure the abundance of the next.

It would be difficult to find a more striking example of a healthy state of the mind and spirits of men as members of a

soil. Everything touched by and serving living beings must either be adapted to the fact that the user's life is organic; or must corrupt the user by withdrawing his attention from this fact.

It is not, as the world was and is organized, safe to forget that trading for food which your land will not afford directly, is a precarious and vulnerable expedient, however effectively it may stimulate thought and feeling and develop the domestic culture. The mortal weakness of having a member of your artificial soil community outside your control generates fears in proportion to what you have to lose. Athens had an empire to lose, an empire largely created by her fear-inspired arrogance, out of the Delean League of originally free and equal allies. Her poor soil and relatively large population had forced this empire upon her. Her victory at Salamis showed her of what she was capable, and upon the ruins of her old and humble respectability, wrought by the Persians, she built greatly.

But that greatness required the support of relatively enormous food imports. Athens *dared* not be anything less than the mistress of Hellas; and not even the genius of Pericles, the unscrupulous diplomacy and naval talents of Themistocles, the shrewd boldness of Cleon, could save the city from the trap which the poverty of Attican soil had set for its human parasites.

Nor could the attributes of these leaders do other than involve the country they wished to serve in the defeat of Aegospotami, and in the disgrace and decline of the power, the name and the culture of Athens.

CHAPTER IX

SOIL AND THE
HANNIBALIC WAR

ALL members of soil communities are conditioned, within the limits of adaptation possible to them, by their soil. We have noticed that the grape vine changes its habits to suit the soil, and men are far more adaptable than vines. But the character and behaviour of men can, in this context, be even more closely compared with that of plants: in soil, both are shaped by soil. Out of soil entirely, plants wither, and so, perhaps, do human communities. At all events something mortal happens to the spirit of civilizations when their relationship with soil becomes one of exploitation. Cosmopolitanism, and the disappearance of local character is, in a large measure, due to the breaking off by men of intimate contact with soil, and their consequent divorce from the influence of soil character. Thus, for example, the citizens of London, New York, Paris, Johannesburg and Sydney are, excepting for some superficial mannerisms of speech and habits, interchangeable. But it would not be possible to interchange a Lincolnshire fen-farmer, and a Guatemalan *Gaucho*.

The influence of soil community character is by no means confined to effects upon the physical ways of life. The character of people is even more supple than their brains and muscles. To take extreme cases as examples, for the sake of clarity, men living on exceptionally simple and austere terms with their soils, the Arab as presented by Doughty or Lawrence, the *Gaucho* as presented by Hudson, the French Canadian pioneer as presented by Hémont,[43] all these show, so clearly that explanation would be superfluous, that the character of men is profoundly modified by the nature of their relationship with their soil.

It is a curious fact that men shaped by poor soils, like vines in similar conditions, have a more stimulating, finer "flavour" than the members of rich soil communities. The manners of moor and mountain farmers are sometimes uncivil, but they seem to behave more "nobly" than their valley brethren. One can contrast, within a single country, the character of the Norman farmers as depicted by de Maupassant; and that of their Provençal cousins as depicted by Daudet. And one can eliminate the subjective element, confirm the objective observation of these authors, by personal experience. The English in India became enamoured of such peoples as the Pathans and Sikhs; and grew contemptuous of the members of such rich communities as Bengal.

These observations might seem to lead to the absurd conclusion that men cannot be both prosperous and admirable. But, of course, soil is not the only influence upon men to form their character, nor is that character formed only by environmental forces. Moreover, the *nature* of the relationship which men make with their soil is quite as effective in modifying character as are the attributes of the soil itself. A subsistence economy and a cash-crop economy produce, respectively, strikingly different results, both upon the soil itself, and upon the men who work it.

The expression *artificial soil community* has been much used above, more or less explains itself, but has not yet been defined. This definition can conveniently be given here, associated with an examination of the effects of subsistence farming upon both soils and men.

An artificial soil community is an agricultural region, large or small, but in either case integral, in which the natural balance of a wild countryside, which sustains and enhances soil fertility, has been successfully replaced, as a rule over a long period of time ,by an artificial balance of cultivated instead of wild plants, domestic instead of wild animals. Such a community must, of course, include men as members, men living not off the soil as capital, but off the increment of fertility which they themselves are engaged in producing. The community is self-contained and self-supporting in essentials, so that although part of its usufruct will perhaps be employed in purchase abroad to raise the standard of living of the community's members, the community can be isolated without suffering any material privation.

It was noticed by Jacks and Whyte, in *The Rape of the Earth*, that "economically efficient" farming, in a cash-crop economy, is far more liable than "inefficient" subsistence farming to destroy soil fertility. That this should be so is not surprising: the advantage of subsistence farming in terms of soil fertility inheres in the relationship between the soil, and the needs and interests of the men who work it.

A man subsistence farming five acres[44] must get all the needs of his family off that plot. He will probably grow a cereal, or cereal substitute such as potato; some garden stuff; some crop, such as flax for making fabric; or a crop which can be exchanged for yarn with a neighbour; some fruit. Subsistence farming rarely enables the farmer's family to eat meat, but he may keep a pig, and poultry. In the north, he will devote an acre to grass, and feed a cow. In the south he will have a small vineyard to yield him wine, and some olive trees to provide the oil which is the substitute for the northerner's butter. Instead of vines, the northerner may grow some barley for ale; oats, perhaps, for animal feed, or porridge. Obviously the crops grown vary with latitude and custom. The point is that a subsistence farmer is *unable* to practise monoculture, a system pernicious both for the soil itself, and for the farmer's character as a citizen.

Furthermore, a subsistence farmer on a small plot will soon find it necessary and beneficial to adopt a system of crop rotation, to make use of dung as manure, to attend to drainage. In short, he is forced by his own needs and the demands of his soil, to practise true husbandry: husbanding his land, he slowly transforms the natural soil into an artificial one, the texture, the fertility reserves of which will enable it to supply his family generation after generation.

The term subsistence farming should not be applied too narrowly. Surplus crops will be sold or exchanged. It is quite possible to practise cash-crop farming *in the spirit of subsistence farming:* it is what English farmers have been doing for generations, and it entails a profound sense of unity with the soil, and of responsibility for it. Above all, it entails close and continual contact between man and soil, a personal relationship whereby the farmer's senses are never out of contact with his land, so that he comes to react to its condition almost as if it were a part of his own body. Obviously, a farmer equipped with a certain amount of machinery can form such a relationship with a larger piece of land, than a farmer without such machinery. For the alternative, the use of slaves, will not do. This being so, the five-acre plot which a family might manage with hand tools, becomes, with light machine tools, a fifty-acre plot.

It should be said that although the hand-worked plot ought not to be so large that it entails the use of hired labour or slaves, except casually at harvest time, it ought not to be so small that the farmer is forced to overcrop the soil in order to live. As we notice, the Roman smallholding before 393 B.C. was only two *jugera*, or $1\frac{1}{2}$ acres (see Note 44). The consequence of this, added to the fact that the same Roman territory included large feudal estates worked by the lord's feudatories, resulted in a disastrous exhaustion of the Roman soils. If the optimum size of plot has been arrived at, it is important that a system of primogeniture in inheritance should maintain it. The sharing of the plot among the farmer's heirs entails its subdivision, and is pernicious.

The post-revolutionary breaking up of the large estates, in France, among an excessively numerous peasantry, however desirable from the point of view of equity, resulted in the progressive pauperization of certain populations, and the exhaustion of soils. The identical phenomenon, but with aggravating circumstances, creates the most serious problems in southern Italy today.

In nature there are very few and exceptional soil communities which are not composed of numerous species. For the health of artificial soils it is necessary that as many kinds and as different in their feeding habits as possible, should be present. Monoculture constantly drains one particular series of nutrients from the soil, until the latter is first unbalanced and finally exhausted. Crop rotation maintains soil balance and thus helps to maintain fertility, since, from the soil's point of view, it is as if several species were present. The small Roman farmers were clever at crop-rotation, particularly in the use of nitrogen-fixing plants such as clover, alfalfa and other legumes. But in large-scale cash-crop farming, for example the "bonanza" wheat farming of the middle western United States, monoculture is more profitable to the exploiter, whose aim is to enrich himself and live in a city, not be a farmer, in the proper sense of the word.

*

The basis of Roman life in the fourth and third centuries B.C. was one of small, freeholding, subsistence husbandry. But this system had first to be made. In making it the Romans made their own character, learnt the arts of law and order and government, and created their citizen armies. In so far as they maintained that system, they were virtuous; and need never, perhaps, have quarrelled with Carthage. In so far as they were unable to maintain it, they lost their virtue and were *forced* to quarrel with Carthage.

From ancient Etruria down to Naples, the soils of western Italy were formed, in the river valleys and especially that of the Po, by alluvia on a bottom of clay. And on the hillsides and plains, by volcanic ash deposited during a long period of great intermittent volcanic activity. As evidence of this, there are fifty extinct volcanoes within 25 miles of Rome, alone. Volcanic ash is rich in several plant nutrients, notably in the salts of potassium, phosphorus and sulphur. But even when mixed with sand or clay subsoils, volcanic ash is not, in our sense, a soil; however, it is an excellent matrix for one.

In the intervals of volcanic quiescence the land was invaded by forest trees, but as these were subsequently overwhelmed by another volcanic outburst, they were buried too deep to become available as vegetable matter for the formation of that top-soil which the first human settlers were to find. All, that is, except the last forest invasion: after the last fall of ash, the trees again invaded the hills and plains of western Italy, and there began the establishment of a balanced soil community. Much of this timber (but not nearly enough for soil security) remained standing well into historical times, so that in the third century B.C. even, Theophrastus could write:

> The plains of Latium bear the laurel, the myrtle and remarkable beech trees. Trunks are found that singly suffice for the keel beams of the great Tyrrhenian ships. Fir and pine grow upon the hills. The Circaean promontory is thickly overgrown with oaks, laurels and myrtle. . . .

We have already noticed that such forest soils create their own equable and gentle climate and keep a firm control over the water-cycle. The climate of Latium under trees would have been humid and equable compared with its present climate. This ancient west Italian climate, coincident with the forest soils, would have extended at least from Praeneste to Monte Genaro, and would have included the once wooded, now naked, and (therefore) eroded Volscian range.

Unhappily, trees were not the dominant species in these regions for long enough to enable them to make a deep top-soil. Perhaps there may have been Palaeolithic and Neolithic communities in the Latin forests at a very early date, but they would not have been the people to harm the trees.

Italic peoples began to come down into Italy over the Alps, about 2000 B.C. These first immigrants had no more than a limited equipment in metal, it is true, but their stone axes and other tools were greatly superior to those of the aborigines, and so were their spirit and vitality. They soon became capable of relatively "efficient" deforestation. But at that time how long had the trees had in which to do their soil-making? Professor Tenney Frank suggests,[45] that the last layers of volcanic ash were deposited during a volcanic outburst throughout this region, post-dating the Egyptian pyramids. If the pyramids were built between the third and twelfth dynasties, Frank can only mean that this volcanic eruption post-dates the *first* pyramids: that is, that it occurred after 3000 B.C. In that case the trees had a good deal less than a thousand years to rule in Latium and the adjacent soils, before men began to replace them as the dominant species. It is by no means long enough, and as a consequence the forest soils of western Italy, although volcanic and therefore fertile, were very thin. The clearance of these soils was begun by the Neolithic Italians from 2000 B.C. onwards; and the process began to be greatly accelerated when, between 800 and 700 B.C., Etruscan immigrants, and Greek traders introduced the use of iron.

Other things being equal, the aridity of a soil climate is proportional to the number of trees present. As the early Italians cut trees to clear soil, they were unwittingly engaged in changing the climate of their country in an unfavourable sense. This process has been continuing ever since. Varro[46] (116–28 B.C.) says that the wheat harvest of Latium was made in July. Today it has to be scrambled in in June, to save it from the withering sun and drought. Probably some hundreds of years before Varro's time, in the hey-day of the feudal estates and two *jugera* smallholders, an August harvest may have been normal, as in south-eastern England today.

The soil of the Campagna was thin and fertile: the settlers burnt off the forest and scrub, a vicious practice adopted some three thousand years later in North America, with lamentable results. The cleared soil yielded great wealth under intensive farming, and as population increased proportionately to the availability of food, the human members of the Roman and Latin soil communities became not only excessively numerous, but very prosperous. This at the expense of soil fertility which was simply being dissipated. They became, in fact, a disease of their soil, which very soon began to show symptoms of grave debility. The destruction of the plain forests was beginning to cause aridity, and when high-farmers have to take to dry-farming the consequences are usually fatal for the soil. The felling of the hillside trees, for the export of timber to Hellas, a growing industry, bared the hillsides. The water-cycle was disturbed. Torrential run-off of the decreasing rainfall carried away the hillside soils, silting up streams and rivers, causing flooding, and creating malaria-infested marshes; the most mortal symptom of soil disease, gulley-erosion, appeared on the hillsides.

But the Latin farmers were not immediately defeated by this threatened failure of the source of their life and wealth. They realized that every inch of their arable soil was valuable, and they made a magnificent effort at soil conservation, an effort hardly matched until within the last few decades of our own era. They saw the damage done by rain-water run-off on the eroded hillsides, and they cut an immensely elaborate system of drains into the tufa, covered them, arranged dams of massive masonry, and generally took control of the water, carrying it under the remaining soils and draining it into the Pontine marsh. A similar system was installed at Veii. The most extraordinary lengths were gone to in order to avoid using arable soil for anything but agriculture. For example, the artificial outlet to the Alban lake was cut into solid rock over a long distance, in order to save an acre or two of soil for the plough. The amount of labour involved in these soil conservation works must have been out of all proportion to the value in money of the extra crops obtained. But the soil was not thought of as money, but as life; a subsistence farming community is saved from falling into the error of thinking of soil in financial terms. Soil is sacred, and must be saved.

That the sixth century Roman system was some kind of semi-feudalism is deduced from these difficult and costly works of agricultural engineering. Whether the deduction is sound is another matter: Tenney Frank[47] has a typically American distaste for admitting that although smallholders could not each, individually, have carried out works which pass beneath hundreds of plots or farms, they might have done the work by means of some communal or co-operative arrangement. Orthodox historians are prone to fight shy of this idea, being afraid to be accused of the jejune error of attributing socialistic ideas to ages which had not conceived of such; and perhaps, of admitting that co-operation can achieve anything. As a matter of fact there are plenty of instances of communal works of large magnitude being carried out by ancient civilizations. But all things considered, it is probable that much of the Latin and Roman land was in the hands of large landowners, and worked by persons who owed them service, and who also held, in their own right as free men, plots of two jugera ($1\frac{1}{2}$ acres). Varro[48] says that the ancient Roman families were supported by such plots, and this, before the onset of soil debility, is not impossible among a frugal and industrious people.

But as soil exhaustion and erosion continued, which they were bound to do when crop after excessive crop had to be wrung from the *ager Romanus*, from such soils as those of Latium, until the great majority of smallholding "villeins" were in shocking distress; famine and pestilence became commonplace, and there began that agitation, among the Plebs, first for some relief, later for power, which was to recreate the Roman character and the Roman state. The soils of Rome and Latium were soon forcing the Patrician party to modify their claim to engross the political power of the city.

That this was exactly so, Livy, it must be admitted, does not make clear: from that historian's references to famine and pestilence, and the social and political consequences of these evils, one would deduce a series of unfortunate accidents, rather than a chronic ill. But with modern knowledge of what happens when men become a disease of their soil it is justifiable to deduce from Livy's early books that social evolution was being forced on at an almost revolutionary pace, by Roman and

Latin soil debility. There are frequent references to famine, followed by pestilence, followed by government settlements of the consequent social uproar, generally entailing purchases, by the Consuls, of wheat, *abroad*. Soils in the condition of Rome and Latium by the middle of the fourth century do not recover when neglected: they grow waterlogged and foul, they provide breeding places for the anopheles mosquito. Was malaria the pestilence which usually accompanied Livy's famines?

That the soils were increasingly neglected is clear: in the Consulship of T. Geganius and P. Linicius, "whilst all abroad was undisturbed by war and the civic dissensions at home were healed, the commonwealth was attacked by a much more serious evil: first, dearness of food owing to the fields remaining uncultivated during the Secession (of the Plebeian party) and following upon this a famine such as visits a besieged city. It would have led to the perishing of the slaves in any case, and probably the plebeians would have died, had not the Consuls provided for the emergency by sending in various directions to buy corn".[49] Again, in 451 B.C. there was famine. In the Consulship of P. Geganius Macerinus and L. Menenius Lanatus, "The misfortunes began with the famine, owing either to the year being unfavourable to the crops, or to the cultivation of the land being abandoned for the attractions of political meetings and city life".[50] In this year things were so bad and the Government's relief measure so inadequate that, "Many of the Plebs lost all hope and rather than drag on a life of misery, muffled their heads and threw themselves into the Tiber".[51] Pestilence and famine again occurred a few years later, and yet again in the Consular year of Q. Fabius Ambustus and C. Furius Pacilus. There are far too many famines to be due merely to normally recurrent bad seasons. The soil was failing, and the Romans adopted both the Attic and the Spartan solutions.

They planted olives and vineyards, e.g., on the Alban hills; and they conquered neighbouring territories (Veii) to get more land. Both measures, in the long run, helped to destroy the Roman character.

During two centuries, from the driving out of the Tarquins and the establishment of the Senatorial oligarchy, the Plebeians, including the two-jugera smallholders, had struggled for relief and for political and social advancement as a class. The establishment of the Tribunate, the Tribunes being magistrates whose duty was to represent the Plebs against the Patricians, was their first major triumph. But the first great practical triumph in their campaign came in 393 B.C. In that year territory was won in war from the Veii, and this territory was distributed among all the citizens, including the two-jugera smallholders. As a consequence these now became seven-jugera holders, that is freeholding farmers working five acres of land.

The results, excepting no doubt for the unhappy Veii, were satisfactory. A depressed and disaffected Roman peasantry became a substantial and self-respecting and patriotic yeomanry, men with the rights which go with property, and with the confidence to demand more power in the state. The Licinian-Sextian law of 366, which threw the Consulship open to the Plebs, also forbade the state to rent more than 375 acres to any single tenant.

The Roman of the middle fourth century was, then, a free, smallholding, fully enfranchised yeoman; and this pattern endured, with various modifications and reverses, for two centuries. Such a citizen is hardy, self-reliant, prolific and patriotic; and an obstinate and formidable soldier in a cause which represents his interests. But although the proletarianized peasantry of the city had, by conquest, and the Licinian law, been partially returned to the land and to self-respect, the population was still too large to be fed off the five-acre smallholdings which, in any case, were primarily subsistence farms only secondarily interested in cash-crops. Nor were the large plantations of the rich aristocrats chiefly concerned with wheat growing, although there were such farms. The slave-manned plantations were of two principal kinds, and *both were direct products of soil erosion or exhaustion.*

The eroded hillsides, such as the Alban, were of no use to

the small farmer; capital and time were required to make them pay as vineyards or olive groves. In the plains, where exhaustion had gone so far that the only thing to be done was to regrass the soils; and in those parts where nothing but a few inches of turf had ever covered the tufa, ranching could be practised. Both of these industries demanded far more capital and perhaps far too long a wait for a return, to interest the smallholder. They were exploited by rich individuals, and later, perhaps not until imperial times, although Mommsen puts it earlier, by joint-stock corporations. These corporations were either Patrician or they were made up of Equites, the new class of financial tycoons which rose as the empire grew larger.

Meanwhile, Rome needed wheat.

One way to get wheat was to drive the Carthaginian colonists out of the granary of Sicily and appropriate it for Rome. It is not suggested that the origin of the First Punic War was merely economic. There were other causes; Rome was finding herself forced into the position of Hellenic champion, and various Greek states were for ever quarrelling with Carthage. But there is no doubt that the conquest of the Sicilian wheat-lands did solve Rome's food problem for a time. Her land-distribution policy had assured her of a formidable citizen army of men with a stake in the country. That this was so had long been well tried and tested; of the influence of this agrarian policy upon Rome's fighting potential, Tenney Frank wrote:[52]

> That Rome bore so well the shock of the Gallic invasion, that she passed without bloodshed through the broils of the class-struggles, survived the revolt of the Latins, and had the prudence to devise the liberal and flexible constitution which enabled her to unite Italy in an effective federation, all this seems now in no small measure due to the habit of providing by land distribution a solid and interested citizen-body from the proletariat.

This same policy, and therefore the soils which were its origin, had made Rome, soon deeply involved in foreign affairs throughout the Mediterranean region, capable of withstanding the strain of her protracted struggle with Carthage, a struggle for what neither power then knew was to be the mastery of the world. True, Rome and her virtues were hideously warped by the strain: yet a Rome of a kind survived, whereas Carthage was destroyed.

*

Husbandry may develop into what is carelessly called scientific farming, a term commonly used to mean intelligent farming. But *real* scientific farming is usually imposed upon the country by the city, and is not necessarily "good" farming at all, but merely profitable, for a time, to the farmer or his bank.

Something must be said concerning the confusion over the use of this word *scientific*, in connection with farming.

One of the most significant symptoms of our present unbalanced state of mind in the West, is that the adjective *scientific* has become one of uncritical approbation. True, there has been some reaction away from this state of mind among a few intellectuals, a kind of uneasy, if wholesome, *trahison des clercs*. But we are concerned with the majority of the people for whom *scientific* means *good* and who commonly use certain expressions, signifying approval, which have, in fact, atrocious meanings, e.g., *scientific warfare, scientific crime;* or employ the adjective, again as one of praise, in contexts descriptive of socially dubious activities, e.g., *scientific salesmanship, scientific advertising*.

By means of this same perverse use of language, the expression *scientific farming* has assumed the significance *good farming*. And so, in certain conditions, it may be. Science in agriculture is good when the approach of scientific specialists to the subject is controlled by an ecologist, or by an ecological point of view; when it is biological rather than mechanical; when the scientist's respect for husbandry is profound; his education humane and philosophical; his methods controlled by empirical trials. Such a scientific agriculture has only come into being in the past two or three decades. But scientific farming until recently has often been, and still often is, very bad farming indeed.

Pure scientific agriculture entails an approach to the soil very different from that of the husbandman. The latter, no doubt unconsciously, is aware that he is a symbiont in an elaborate and delicately balanced union of species, the artificial soil community. The scientist too often approaches the soil in the spirit of an industrialist: here, in this dirty stuff underfoot, is material to be transformed into food by an efficient application of chemistry and mechanics to problems of production. Such a state of mind may, and frequently does, lead to the *consumption* of the soil, and that at a rate vastly increased by scientific efficiency.

It would be tedious to keep making reservations in favour of the new ecological scientific agriculture, whenever, in what follows, the term *scientific* has to be used pejoratively, in the sense of a scientific abuse of soil. I shall therefore define my terms as follows: for the old scientific agriculture I shall henceforth use the phrase *industrial agriculture,* while retaining the phrase *scientific agriculture* to mean the proper application of biologically biased knowledge to soil problems, with all the integrity, detachment and imaginative understanding which belong to a branch of philosophy.

The agricultural industrialist regards soil as an inexhaustible source of wealth, requiring only sufficiently powerful machines and quick-acting chemicals to extract it. For him a field of wheat is a machine for transforming certain chemicals, which he feeds to the roots, by means of photosynthesis and some later processes, into loaves of bread worth money. Such a point of view cannot arise in the countryside itself: the state of mind from which it derives is one peculiar to highly sophisticated urban communities.

The first treatise on industrial agriculture, that is the first treatise to apply an essentially urban, non-attached analysis to soil problems, although the work is not "scientific" in the most pernicious sense, is that of Mago, a Carthaginian.

*

Perhaps no community has ever created a more purely intellectual and artificial relationship with soil than Carthage.

The Carthaginians did not grow out of, or grow up with a native soil: having long practised commerce and shipping for a living, they finally turned to the exploitation of the soils they had acquired by trade and by force. Their approach to their soil was industrial because it could not possibly be anything else. For, vigorous as an individual community, Carthage nevertheless belonged to a long moribund culture; incapable, therefore, of an activity which could properly be described as organic. The Carthaginian community gives an impression not of a living entity, but of a kind of machine.

Carthage was not an Hellenic city by right of birth, but because she found herself in the ambience of a dynamic culture which happened to be Hellenic, and, having no soul of her own, was compelled to make a spurious one by imitation. Formerly, she had done the same thing in Egyptian terms.[53] Carthage was politically, commercially, and to all outward appearances, an Hellenic city state. But the Carthaginian could not feel or think, carve stone, paint pictures, worship, sing, act, dance or reason like a Greek. Nor, however, had Carthage any valid style of her own: the creative phase of the culture to which the Carthaginians really belonged, that of Phoenicia, had been over a thousand years before the Punic Wars. The products of her manufacture are without any native style, they are debased copies of Egyptian or Hellenic styles. The physical appearance of the city was not Punic, it was Hellenic. The greatest public building, the artificial commercial harbour and the inner naval harbour, the Cothon, were the work of Greek architects and engineers, or at the very least of Greek designers. But that Carthage could not, in the things that matter, be Greek, any more than Turkey can be Western Christian, is very apparent, not only in the state of mind which the actions of her Government constantly revealed, but in the atrocious rite, still practised in that Hellenically gracious city, of sacrificing the first-born of noble families by hurling these infants into the furnace burning in the brazen belly of the god Eshmun.

Carthage, like a score of other such places, was founded by Phoenician merchants as a trading post, perched on the African shore, without anything whatever to do with African soil. Such, in spirit, Carthage remained, even when she had become perhaps the greatest, certainly the richest city in the Mediterranean, with a population of two or three hundred thousand, perhaps half a million. Grown thus great, however, she ceased to pay rent to the Berber landowners, which she had long been doing, and conquered the surrounding country for her own. The soil which thus became Carthaginian was not of large extent, but it was fertile. From Mago, and some other and casual notices, it would appear to have been what is called a semi-arid soil, that is a grass soil with a deep top-soil, which has to be dry-farmed, and in which the major farming problem is that of water conservation. (Cf. the United States Middle-West, parts of Spain, and Italy.) The cultivation undertaken by the Carthaginians could not, of course, be husbandry. There were no husbandmen. It had to be industrial, and in any case the Carthaginian state of mind would have made this so, even if the social organization of the people had made another solution possible.

The intensive plantation cultivation which the Carthaginian plantation-owner undertook, and which was subsequently imitated by the Roman conquerors of the land, had the long-term effect of letting in the desert. Conceivably, the original forest—and grass—soil communities might have acted as a barrier to the advancing sand, might even have pushed slowly southward, carrying a more humid climate with them as trees invaded the grass, and colonized the Sahara. But cultivation which took no account of soil as such, and was concerned with getting the largest possible crops out of the soil, had the opposite effect. The Sahara began its northward march; it has been on the move ever since; it has already invaded Europe, by way of Spain, an old African trick.

Carthage, then, instead of growing up out of a soil and with it, grew simply as a centre of commerce and a base for war, on a piece of land acquired by tenancy, and to which she was indifferent. Already in a high and corrupt phase of a soulless civilization, she seized upon some soil by force, and proceeded to form with it the only relationship possible for her, one of industrial exploitation.

Urban Western men, accustomed to being flattered as uniquely powerful in material matters, by newspapers whose advertisers need the goodwill of their readers, are prone to ignore the massive achievement of past civilizations in the manipulation of matter. It is commonly thought that mechanical science has conferred upon us powers of manipulation different in kind from those possessed by our predecessors, but as a matter of history we have yet to achieve, with all our machines, any feats of agricultural engineering to surpass those of certain ancient civilizations.[54] We shall come to that phase in due course, no doubt. Meanwhile it should be realized that there is no significant difference between a flint or bronze digging tool and a bulldozer. Almost unlimited slave power can achieve quite as much as mechanical power. The Carthaginians applied to the exploitation of their soil the device of plantation slavery upon a very large scale.

The device is one of the most vicious means of expressing power yet tried. It was the ruin of Rome, who imitated it. And it was the destruction of Carthage when she came into conflict with a Rome which had not *yet* imitated it upon a serious scale.

The truth is as Goldsmith saw it: the insight of the poet is, as usual, more immediately effective in arriving at the truth than the careful experiments of science and economy:

> Ill fares the land to hastening ills a prey,
> When wealth accumulates and men decay.
> Princes and peers may flourish and may fade,
> A breath can make them, as a breath has made.
> But a proud peasantry, its country's pride,
> When once destroyed can never be supplied.

And Carthage had never even had a peasantry, proud or otherwise. Few Carthaginians had any working relation with the soil at all. To whom was Mago's technically admirable book on farming addressed? Principally, it seems probable, to such leading Carthaginians, men like the Barcas, who tended to withdraw, with their millions, from the coarse world of trade, to acquire an aristocratic point of view, to settle, supported by hundreds of slaves, in their great villas, there to improve their property and their gardens. Their relationship with soil would be almost as artificial, as ephemeral, as phoney indeed, as that of our own company promoter or cinema magnate, with his farm in Surrey or Sussex, purchased as a weekend toy, a source of butter and eggs for his family, and a means of avoiding income tax by setting his farming losses off against his city gains.

Greek visitors and Roman conquerors exclaim over the wealth of produce and stock from the Carthaginian soils. The application of industrial agriculture to virgin soils is, in fact, extremely productive of wealth for the exploiters. Orchards, cornfields and cattle pastures crowded each other on the North African littoral. But where are the farmers, the yeomen? There is nothing here which resembles a true artificial soil community, but rather the wheat factories of the Middle West, the orange factories of California. Carthage remained, what she had always been, a trading post.

A state so founded, or rather unfounded, existing as a community of negotiators merely, of buyers cheap and sellers dear, a nation of Trimalchios, seems to acquire no substance as a nation, a people. In reading of Carthage one experiences a vague, uneasy feeling that one is reading of something unreal. As soldiers and seamen the Carthaginians had great qualities, yet their acts do not seem to count. There is something offensive, squalid and slightly incredible about a community which seems always and invariably to have acted shrewdly, coldly, unscrupulously. The foreign policy of the Punic government of millionaire business men is so consistently unchivalrous and calculating, that it has the air of something "ideal" rather than real.

This haunting, chimerical and depressing attribute of the city was seized upon by Flaubert, with the result that *Salammbo* is one of the rare books in which poetic insight has been used to invoke a scene from the past. It is a book informed with a sort of utterly un-Hellenic, un-Occidental semi-mystical sensuality; and at the same time with *accidie*, a profound and terrible *cafard*. Perhaps *spleen* is the English word for this. That this is due to no warping of the poet's vision is clear from the fact that a shade of the same feeling falls across the reader's mind, though the book in his hands be not *Salammbo* but the most sober of Punic histories.

The fact is that, for its salvation, a human community must, like a community of any other creatures, be founded in a soil. When Carthage fought Rome there was no clash of two valid nations: there was a struggle between a nation and a vast and powerful cartel of joint-stock trading concerns which happened, among other properties, to own and work some agricultural land. When, at the head of an army of mercenaries and impressed colonials, supported by trained fighting elephants, and by a gorgeous and devoted bodyguard of young Carthaginians of good family, Hannibal went out of Spain into Gaul, over the Alps and down into Italy, he there performed the most incredible *tour de force* in military history: in the teeth of his own government, almost without supplies or reinforcements from home, he stayed in the enemy's country for sixteen years. He made half Italy Hannibalic, thus assuring that when he did withdraw the Romans themselves would, by furious punitive measures, wreak havoc even where he himself had not done so. He consistently defeated Consular army after Consular army, for there was no man living anything like capable of matching his military talent. The armies of Rome were citizen armies, they were Goldsmith's proud peasantry, under arms. With the slow, obstinate, unspectacular heroism of their class and nation, they got themselves massacred by thousands. They were irreplaceable; the land which they worked could not spare them if the Roman character was to be spared. Half the farmlands lay derelict, during nearly two decades.

At a certain moment in the course of this war, Hannibal could have taken Rome. There can be no question of that: he did not do so, and that refusal to do what every soldier aims to do, capture the enemy's capital, is one of the major mysteries of military history. To the question which this strange behaviour on the part of Hannibal propounds, Captain Liddell Hart once gave a very suggestive answer. In a brilliant essay on the subject of Hannibal's career, he wrote that Hannibal did not take Rome because to have done so would have been to end the war too soon: before his god he had sworn to destroy Rome and, like Shylock, he might have said:

> An oath, an oath, I have an oath in Heaven:
> Shall I lay perjury upon my soul?
> No, not for (Rome).

Hannibal, Captain Liddell Hart suggested, had devoted his life to revenge, and that revenge must be satisfied by making sure that Rome died in agony and by inches, not still half intact.

It is a very possible answer: Hannibal's people and his father had been shockingly wronged by Rome. The Carthaginians were notoriously vindictive and ruthless, and their religion one of the most frightful, in its rites, of which we have knowledge. Had Hannibal taken Rome when the city lay open to him, he must have ended the war, and thereafter have been the instrument of making a rational peace, dictated by the commercially-minded Carthaginian Senate. He preferred to make sure of the destruction of Rome.

In a way, he succeeded.

It is true that he had, although undefeated in the field, to withdraw at last from Italy; that he was beaten in battle, in Africa, by Scipio; that he witnessed the humiliation of his city; that he had to fly for his life from Roman vengeance; that that vengeance caught up with him; that he was sold by the king with whom he had taken refuge; and that he died by his own hand rather than fall into Roman ones. Meanwhile he had made sure that the subsequent career of Rome, instead of being a great and splendid triumph of civilization and culture, was a slow agony of decline and degradation into the worst manifestation of slave-supported imperialism.

The foundation of the Roman character was the Roman soil community. Hannibal destroyed it, and with it Rome's power to act with generosity and charity. She was no longer capable of making what, in her beginning as a great power she seemed to be making, a Commonwealth. She could only make a spiritually barren, aesthetically contemptible, socially decadent monstrosity.

*

To analyse in detail the nature of Hannibal's triumph would require a large volume. On the other hand it is hardly enough merely to assert that Rome was ruined in her very foundations by the Second Punic War.

Here are two quotations from Tenney Frank's *Economic History of Rome:*

(i) The Second Punic war which was fought on Italian soil wrought terrible havoc upon the chief industry of the people and thereby accelerated the processes that we have already noticed.[55] For more than twelve years the battle lines swept back and forth over the villages and fields of central and southern Italy. . . . Whatever contestant retreated, grainfields were burnt for military reasons, vineyards and orchards cut, and cattle driven off. The inhabitants who escaped scattered to the four winds, many abandoning Italy permanently for Greece.

And, during the period of reconstruction:

(ii) Vast areas of devastated lands . . . could not be catered for at present. These the State took possession of, partly because they were without claimants, partly in accordance with *the new theory of sovereignty recently adopted in Sicily*,[56] because they were forfeited in battle to the conqueror.[57] What was to be done with these vast areas, aggregating a total of at least two million acres, at least half of which was arable? Obviously the State pursued what seemed a reasonable course in offering it in large leaseholds to Romans who had the capital requisite to make use of it. . . .

The spirit of the old Rome had been made by men who believed, with Alexander Pope (incidentally at the age of twelve!) that:

> Happy the man, whose wish and care
> A few paternal acres bound,
> Content to breathe his native air
>   In his own ground.
> Whose herds with milk, whose fields with bread
> Whose flocks supply him with attire;
> Whose trees in summer yield him shade,
>   In winter fire.

Whether the remaining Romans still had these sentiments is uncertain: that they could no longer live in the manner described is only too certain.

In Cato, in Varro and in Columella we have three monographists from whose writings the new, evil and inevitable soil policy of Rome can be examined. Beloch[58] estimates that the *ager Romanus,* the Roman soil, was, by seizures and expropriations, raised from a pre-war approximate ten to a post-war approximate twenty million *jugera*. Columella says that unimproved land in Italy sold for about £10 (Gold par. say £30 1952 value) per *jugerum*. In that case the *ager Romanus* was worth about £570m. at 1952 values. Before the war there were about 250,000 Roman *citizens,* i.e. landholders of one sort or another. The average size of a holding therefore becomes not about 10, but about 62 *jugera*. And the average capital in land per farmer no longer about £200, but about £2000.[59] But many thousands of Roman citizen smallholders had been killed in the long war, others had flown abroad, others been proletarianized. There must have been many fewer citizens after the war, than before it. Yet the land held by citizens was doubled, and its value per head multiplied by ten. There is only one possible inference. Despite the persistence in some places, of the old, sound system of soil-man relationship, of the smallholding subsistence farmer, Roman soil had become primarily a vast Slave-manned Plantation, the slaves, of course, being provided by Carthaginian prisoners-of-war.

Thus, the whole nature of the Roman *polis* had been shockingly and mortally changed, in such a sense as to bring upon Rome, inevitably, the Gracchan revolution, the Social War, the Civil Wars, the failure of Republicanism, the transformation of Democracy into the totalitarian monster-state of Augustus and his successors, and the economic decline of the Roman Empire into the vicious and ridiculous system desperately imposed by Diocletian.

CHAPTER X

OKLAHOMA: DEATH OF A SOIL

ONE of the symptoms of that decadence of the spirit which overtakes a great civilization before its failure or when it is about to give birth to a new one, is an outbreak of territorial expansionism late in its career: thus, for example, the violent Hellenization of the known world between the times of the adventure of Alexander and that of his aged and heroic emulator, Trajan. Thus also the European conquest of the world for Western Civilization late in the nineteenth century, a conquest which has the superficial air of a dynamic and creative act, but behind which one can detect that fear and despair at the failure of the spirit which accounts for its violent and predatory character: it is as if, for the loss of moral and aesthetic "goods" at home, there was an attempt to substitute success in arms and trade abroad. Dazzled by the gaudy feats of successful military men, orthodox historians have consistently failed to perceive that Imperialism is a symptom of despair, of a deep self-distrust in the soul of the imperialist culture.

Imperialist adventures in the past have tended to ruin the home soils of the imperialist powers, since those soils have provided the wealth wasted by the soldiers. Only Hannibal contrived to ruin rather the enemy's soil than his own, but then he can hardly be said to have had a soil. And when invaded soils were laid under contribution by the successful imperialist, the latter was, as a rule, no more "efficient" a farmer, and therefore no more dangerous to the soil, than his victims.

The nineteenth-century Western expansion was peculiar in that the men who constituted its forces, its civil rather than its military expression, were equipped with steel tools and very soon with machinery, capable of carrying soil exploitation to unprecedented lengths. Very fortunate were those soils which could interpose between the invaders and their own integrity, a golden armour. In the spiritually very different invasion of South and Central America by Europeans in the sixteenth and seventeenth centuries, the wealth of the victim countries was there, in gold and silver, to buy off the *conquistadors,* and the fertility of the soil was damaged but not ruined, however the working of it was interrupted and disorganized.[60] But the case of North America was very different.

That sub-continent was inhabited not by men of high civilization, with gold to offer, but by tribes of savages, some in a Palaeolithic stage of culture, with a matrilinear, exogamous pattern of social behaviour; others in a Neolithic phase of development; a few, for example the Five Civilized Tribes as they were significantly called, were at that interesting stage in which food-gathering and hunting gives way before the rising efficiency of semi-sedentary agriculture.

These tribes of Red Indians had no negotiable wealth to offer the fierce and determined invaders of their soils; those soils, their hunting grounds, were their only asset. But these hunting grounds were potential farms, and it happened that the invaders of North America were not arrogant and predatory Spanish soldiers to turn in disgust from the idea of a life of agrarian toil, but a people who esteemed the idea of each man as an independent farmer on his own freehold as the most desirable of ideals; they were land-hungry, would-be peasants inspired by an unsuitable, dangerous and powerful mystique drawn not from their native culture, which was failing, but from the records of the settlement and rise to prosperity of such another and earlier horde of land-hungry migrants, the Israelites of the Bible.

The settlement of the European North Americans upon the virgin soils they overran took place with fatal rapidity. It is almost true to say that whereas in A.D. 1800 North America west of the original thirteen colonies was empty but for a couple of hundred thousand, if so many, Stone Age tribesmen, by 1900 this vast country was already full of white farmers at a level of material culture comparable with that of Europe and in some ways surpassing it. Only the most massively stable soil could stand the sudden and exhausting draft upon fertility which is represented by this meteoric rise in material wealth. But it should be emphasized that the farmers in question were not conscious of doing any damage: they were simple and honourable men with a worthy purpose, that of keeping their families in bread and independence by the sweat of their faces—of religiously fulfilling the terms of the curse laid upon Adam and Eve. In order that they should do this it was deemed necessary that each family hold a farm of 160 acres, although how this figure was arrived at seems to be obscure.

The American pioneer peasants were not seizing made-land but virgin soil. Faced with a choice between park-land, forest and *steppe*, they naturally swarmed towards the latter, for it offered few natural obstacles to the plough, and seemed to have been made for just such a contingency as the sudden arrival of men far advanced in agricultural techniques. But land which, in semi-arid conditions and in a state of nature, offers few natural obstacles to the plough, is land which will not long stand ploughing; and ought not to be ploughed.

The case of the soil of Oklahoma is of particular interest because in that case we have an example of men, considered as a disease of soil, reaching a mortal stage of virulence within half a century.

*

As the boundaries of Western Civilization were pushed westward from the limits of the original colonial territories, and especially after the Louisiana Purchase, it became necessary to make provision for the Indians, other than the laborious and distasteful one of slaughtering them which was favoured by the rougher sort of United States citizen. In the history of the relations between European and the American Indians, both civilized and savage, the intention and behaviour of European governments has been uniformly good, those of the free and enterprising citizens of those governments almost as consistently bad. The United States government set aside a very considerable tract of territory for the exclusive use of the Indians, and seemed to understand the desire of these Red men to maintain the integrity of their tribal economy, to remain in their Garden of Eden rather than leave it voluntarily to share the laborious exile of the white men. The territory thus set aside included the present State of Oklahoma, and was populated by a number of small bands of various tribes of Indians, as well as by the Five Civilized Tribes, that is the Cherokees, Chickasaws, Choctaws, Creeks and Seminoles. It is worth remarking that in the Choctaw tongue, Oklahoma means *Home of the Red Man*.

Although the Indians might practise a shifting tillage, as well as hunting, their attitude to the soil was still that of its other animal members: it was a place to wander in, moving about in search of game, of wild vegetable food, of fertile soil patches. It is clear that the nineteenth-century Cherokees and kindred peoples were on the way to establishing a settled agriculture. It is equally clear that in the absence of European interference, the inferiority of their tools would have assured a very slow and steady exploitation of their land, which would have given the soil a chance to change gradually into the artificial tilth which is the basis of permanent man-made soil communities like that of north-west Europe. It is, finally, probable that had the Central American culture not been destroyed by the Spaniards, the northern Indians would have come under the influence of that high civilization, and would have learnt from the Mexicans the techniques of advanced agriculture, although at the same time they would have had to pay for this by contributing thousands of victims to the reeking altars of the abominable Aztec war-god Huitzilopochtli. But none of this had time to happen, and to the sedentary farmers of the eastern United States, that is of European, tradition, who became continually more numerous all along the periphery of the Indian Territory, the Indian mode of life must have appeared as a shameful waste of land, and perhaps too as a blasphemous defiance of the curse of Adam.

These Europeans were not, for the most part, unreasonably hostile to the Indians: they were very willing that the Indians should be treated on exactly the same terms as themselves, that is that each Indian family should be allowed 160 acres of good land, and should, as enfranchised citizens of the United States, live on and off that land exactly as the white men did, or proposed to do, themselves. And feeling themselves perfectly fair and reasonable, they considered that the laws which restrained them from settling Indian territory were not sensible, and therefore were not respectable. And when, in a democracy, a law fails to obtain at least the tacit support of the citizens, there is no way of enforcing it. A government which feels itself to be simply the representative of its citizens can only with enormous difficulty employ military force against its own people, its own employers, *itself*, in fact.

During several decades the pressure applied to the United States government by the farmer-citizens and by commercial and industrial interests, to open up the Indian Territory, was unremitting. And it is eternally to the credit of several United States governments that they so respected the objections of the Indians to this course, although what was proposed seemed very fair and just, that they resisted pressure to the point of risking insurrection and civil war. They did not hesitate, time and again, to use military force against their own people in order to keep their pledges to the Indians, and that in the teeth of the angry violence of their constituents. Nevertheless, they were, in the long run, forced to break every promise they had ever made to the Tribes.

The real difficulty in this situation inhered in the fundamentally different attitudes towards soil, and particularly towards land-tenure, of the two conflicting peoples.

The white people were the heirs of an ancient high civilization which had passed its cultural and spiritual zenith some time before. They were, even in their simplest and humblest members, sophisticated, in fact corrupt, in their attitude to land. A symptom of this intellectual corruption was, and is, the degradation of women and soil to the status of personal chattels. It seemed to the European colonists of America right and proper that each head of a family should own a piece of land, and should exercise upon it a patriarchal right. In short, these people had sunk into the same condition of spiritual blindness, in the matter of man's place in the living world, as afflicted the Romans towards the end of the Punic wars.

The Indians, on the other hand, had no conception of soil as property. Such an idea must have seemed to them immoral and irreligious; land tenure among them was not several but tribal, not personal but communal. There is no clearer nor more final answer to those who still believe that there is something "natural" about the idea of each man as a freehold smallholder, than the persistent, obstinate and despairing resistance offered by the Indians to the apparently reasonable suggestion, often reiterated, that land should be distributed among them in severalty, that every adult Indian should receive 160 acres of good land together with enfranchisement as a citizen of the United States. The Indians were implacably hostile to the idea that land could be held as private property, could be bought, sold, given away or bequeathed.

This ecologically invaluable instinct was, of course, debauched. It was probably among the half-breeds that the idea of soil as property first gained admittance; then the more sophisticated Indians consented to it; and lastly the mass. But it is significant that the earliest tribes to accept land-holding in severalty were the smaller ones, whose tribal organization had long been breaking down under the pressure of the white invasion. The Indian Territory was at last deprived of the protection which native human customs, grown up within its influence, had extended to its health and integrity. It lay open to disease.

The nature of the pressure which the citizens applied to their government to achieve this end is not without interest, and an important aspect of it has been vividly described in one of the most admirable short novels in the English language: Frank Harris' *Elder Conklin*. Across the boundary of Conklin's land lies empty, virgin soil, unworked, uninhabited, part of the Indian Territory. The Elder plants in it a crop of corn, for he needed extra money to indulge the expensive plans of an adored daughter. A military detachment is sent by the government to throw down the Elder's fences, and destroy the corn he has planted on Indian land. The military are opposed by a formidable band of farmers, the Elder's infuriated neighbours, who consider the legalistic attitude of their government wholly unjustified. The Elder holds himself aloof from these violent courses: he is prepared to use violence, but alone, without involving anyone else. But the story should be read: it describes one of the most significant stages in the Westernization of the world, and it describes what was happening on the frontiers of Oklahoma between 1878 when illicit settlements in the Territory are first noticed and the United States Army had the unenviable task of ejecting the settlers, until 1889, when the Territory was thrown open to settlement by law.

This is not the place to describe the activities of David L. Payne and his "Boomers" who forced the opening of the Territory. They constantly invaded Indian land and settled on it; they were as often ejected by the military. Payne was probably a crook, or at least an opportunist, who exploited the land-hunger of would-be settlers to build up an ugly racket. But the criminal cynicism of the leader must not be allowed to impugn the good faith of the led. There were rogues, no doubt, among the *boomers,* but for the most part they were honest and respectable men.[61]

The settlement of Oklahoma, then, took place in 1889, by the extraordinary device of a land-rush:

> Between the middle of March and the middle of April several thousand persons gathered in the neighbouring states,

ready to make the race for the homesteads or town lots. Before the day set for the opening, they were allowed to pass through the intervening Indian country and form on the borders of the district to be opened.

Additional soldiers were placed on guard as a precautionary measure. On April 22 a force equal to two regiments was in the field. The cavalry, nearly half of the total force, was stationed along the border to hold the settlers back till noon. The infantry was placed at important points in the district, especially at two places where land offices had been established. . . .

Promptly at noon the settlers were given the signal to start, and the run began. Men raced on horseback, in carriages, and in wagons. Five trains entered the district from the North. The first of these reached Guthrie, twenty miles south, at one-thirty in the afternoon, but the passengers found that United States deputy marshals, together with settlers who had slipped by the border patrol, had already staked out a town site. Other persons had been busily engaged since noon making entries for adjacent farms. Those who entered in this way before the appointed time were known as "sooners". Purcell, where the Santa Fé railroad crossed the Canadian, was the starting place for most of the settlers entering the South. Many of these reached Oklahoma station, where the Santa Fé crossed the north fork of the Canadian, midway between Purcell and Guthrie. Rivalry between Guthrie and Oklahoma City began at once. Other towns were staked out and occupied, and by nightfall many of the homesteads had one or more claimants.[62]

On that day at least twelve thousand, and perhaps as many as forty thousand, entered the virgin territory of Oklahoma. No exact figure is known but it was probably about 20,000 and these mostly men, the heads of families which might number on an average three persons. Thus we may estimate that the population of the new territory . . . it was not yet a State . . . was about 60,000 people a few weeks after the opening race for land.[63]

In 1890 drought destroyed the growing crops of these first Oklahomans, and Congress was forced to vote them aid.

By the end of 1890 all the new territory was occupied, some plots were claimed by more than one family of settlers, and new land had to be made available in 1891. This pattern of events repeated itself several times. The methods of adding to the territory were two: either an Indian reservation was taken over by the Government, 160-acre allotments given to the head of each Indian family, and the rest of the land sold to settlers at about a dollar and a half an acre—for example in the case of the Cheyenne and Arapahoe tribes in 1892; or, as in the case of the Cherokees in 1893,[64] the Indian land was bought outright from the Tribe, and the distribution of the purchase price left to the Tribal council.

As we have seen, the population of Oklahoma towards the end of 1889 was about 60,000. In the following years new land was added to the future state, new farmers settled on it. By 1892 the population was 130,000, but by 1900 the figure had reached 389,000. Towns had been built, trades and industries flourished, railways crossed the country, coal and other mines had been opened and were being worked. In ten years the soil community of the Oklahoma territory had been transformed from a state of nature into an artifact, and one which was being elaborated at a tremendous pace.

The community which had thus come into being in a single decade represented considerable wealth, but it is the nature rather than the amount of that wealth which is significant.

When a community of Europeans colonizes virgin soil its members are neither willing nor able to go through the whole process, requiring some hundreds of years, which transforms a natural soil into an artificial one of great fertility and stability, such as that of north-western Europe, capable of supporting a very high standard of material wealth. The aim of the colonists is to live at the same standard as the people of the motherland, or rather to live at a higher standard, justifying their emigration by surpassing the stay-at-homes in material prosperity. Thus almost as soon as they settle on their virgin soil, they begin not only to farm it, to exploit the soil fertility stores of centuries, but to build at once factories, railways, public utilities, and cities, and very soon to write and print books, paint pictures, build and man opera houses, theatres and bourses; in short, they try to establish *at once* the outward signs of a wealth which, in the "normal" way, would be the accumulation of centuries of toil upon the land. This can only be done by purchasing goods and services beyond the frontiers of the new soil community, and in return its members offer some valuable consideration. Central and Southern America were stocked with the material of European culture in exchange for gold and silver. But the consideration sent abroad from Oklahoma and similar North American soils in payment for the materials of high civilization *was soil fertility*.

Today it would probably be possible to turn the soil fertility of an area as large as the Dust Bowl into some other form of wealth, or into cash, in about ten years, with the aid of the enormously powerful machinery now available for soil-fertility mining. It would probably take no longer than that to turn semi-arid steppe, subject to drought, into a desert, and to possess in exchange a few hideous cities, a few hospitals, a research institute, a few art galleries and theatres, some libraries, half a hundred factories, a score or two of rich men, and a population of depressed proletarians. Fifty years ago the process, although far too rapid for the welfare of the soil, was not quite so fast. The Oklahomans, who presumably supposed that they were founding farms which would have the longevity of those of Europe, could anticipate, had they but known it, at least on the most easily ploughed and readily yielding of their soils, only *one generation* before those soils died beneath their feet and left them in the hideous predicament of the protagonists in Mr. John Steinbeck's *The Grapes of Wrath*.

The very rapid development of Oklahoma into a country with all the appurtenances of an old European state would not have been possible without the aid of the most efficient, and therefore in certain conditions destructive, machine for soil-exploitation ever devised: capitalism, with credit banking. Europe did not have to stand the strain of this device until at least 600 years from the beginnings of her native culture.[65] But the Oklahomans were able not merely to sell their soil fertility out of the State as fast as they could sow and reap; they could also make large drafts on their future activities as farmers, anticipating what they supposed to be the inexhaustible fertility of their soil by borrowing money at interest. And the bankers' interest was paid out of soil fertility.

The men of European culture and with European techniques who exploited the grass soils of the region which has since become known as the Dust Bowl, naturally applied to those soils the methods they knew and understood and which had answered so well in Europe for centuries. It seemed to them that they were in a peasant's paradise, for the soils were rich in plant foods, and had the appearance and texture of the best agricultural soils. But North-west European rainfall is hardly anywhere less than 20 inches a year and in most parts nearer 40 inches. The soils of the Middle West had a mean rainfall of nearer 10 inches a year, and it was their grass cover alone which enabled them to maintain their stability during thousands of years in such arid conditions. Every drop of water was absorbed and held in the vast sponge of the grass-roots. But once ploughed the soil had no means of retaining water. In years of subnormal rainfall, the crops simply perished: in other years they might flourish by virtue of unremitting cultivation which conserved some water about the roots by means of a dust-mulch. Such cultivation, in arid conditions, helps to destroy the granular texture of the soil. If two or three inches of top-soil are reduced—nowadays it is done with the disk-harrow—to a fine dust, the soil immediately below that dust remains damp, the dust forming a kind of natural "capillary tubes" which are the products of soil porosity, and by way of which soil water is drawn to the surface. Such a method is only safe where manuring with organic material is consistent and ample, and where some kind of crop rotation avoids the withdrawal from soil of a particular group of elements year after year.

But in Oklahoma not only were artificial fertilizers made available to the farmer a decade or so after the settlement of that state, but monoculture very rapidly became the commonplace of the region, a monoculture which was perfectly in accord with the American trend towards a thorough industrial specialization in all walks of life.

Moreover, less than twenty years from the land-rush of 1889, American farmers were offered an unprecedented opportunity to enrich themselves, or at least their bankers, by exporting American soil fertility in vast quantities to feed Europeans too busily engaged in mutual throat-cutting to tend their own soil. And in due course, when the United States joined in the throat-cutting, even larger profits became possible. In order to supply the Allies with grain, forty million acres of virgin soil were ploughed and cropped, ploughed and cropped to exhaustion, without regard to the consequences. Today, according to Jacks and Whyte,[66] much of that land, the majority of it, is either quite barren, or marginal.

Less than 35 years after the settlement of Oklahoma, on a day of high wind from the west, a strange dark cloud hung over the city of New York and all the coast north and south of it. The phenomenon was to be repeated, but on this first occasion of its occurrence its novelty helped to impress the ten or twelve millions of people who saw it hang like a red veil over land and sea with its portentous, threatening, warning quality. The cloud was dust, and the dust was the top-soil of the Middle West, including vast areas of Oklahoma, on its way to be lost in the Atlantic. A combination of monoculture, dust-mulching, a couple of drought years in succession and a couple of weeks' high wind, had had its inevitable result. The soil of the Middle West was blowing into the Atlantic at a rate which, combined with water-erosion in other parts, could reduce North America to a barren Sahara in a matter of about a century.[67]

When, between 1889 and 1900, thousands of farmers were

settling Oklahoma, it must have seemed to them that they were founding a new agricultural civilization which might endure as long as Egypt. The grandsons, and even the sons of these settlers who so swiftly became a disease of their soil, trekked from their ruined farmsteads, their buried or uprooted crops, their dead soil, with the dust of their own making in their eyes and hair, the barren sand of a once fertile plain gritting between their teeth. They went west, to pick fruit in California, in single families, in groups of families, in whole caravans of families, riding in ancient "jalopies" and everywhere scowled upon, harried forward lest they become a charge upon some other State. The pitiful procession passed westward, an object of disgust—the *God-dam'd Okies*.

But these *God-dam'd Okies* were the scapegoats of a generation, and the God who had damned them was perhaps after all a Goddess, her name Ceres, Demeter, Maia, or something older and more terrible. And what she damned them for was their corruption, their fundamental ignorance of the Nature of her world, their defiance of the laws of co-operation and return which are the basis of life on this planet.

PART FOUR (I):
THE MARGINAL CASE

*

CHAPTER XI

EURASIA AND CHINA

OVER vast tracts of Asia and Eurasia men have reduced their soils to a state of debility by a process of slow exhaustion. In these regions they have not, with greed served by scientific efficiency, totally destroyed soil fertility in the course of a few generations; the recurrent famines and crop failures of today are due rather to many generations of men acting as semi-parasites upon soils which have neither been improved nor absolutely ruined, but just barely maintained in working order.

Such is the case upon the yellow-earth *loess* of North-west China. But why is it *not* the case on the Black Earth *loess* of Eurasian Russia, another soil of aeolian origin and similar structure, and which, like the Chinese soil, was originally a soil community of grass species, a *steppe*? The answer, of course, is not in the nature of the soil itself, but in the histories of the men who lived on it. In one case agrarian civilization came into being very shortly—that is on the sort of time scale which the long life of a soil demands—after the deposition of the *loess* was complete; in the other the *steppe* found, in the nomadic pastoral cultures of central Eurasia, protectors who prevented the ploughing of the grass cover. The quite modern and relatively trifling soil exhaustion and erosion problem of the U.S.S.R. today, on the Black Earth, is as nothing when compared with the shocking condition of the Chinese Yellow Earth country.

Of Northern China in our own time, G. V. Jacks wrote:

> ... the destitution which reigns in the North-western loëss region ... the birthplace of Chinese civilization. The

wind-blown loëss is one of the richest soil materials known, similar to that which has formed the black soils of the Russian steppes. It is also the most easily eroded when deprived of its natural grass cover. Once erosion has started it proceeds with great rapidity, and processes of natural revegetation are slow to keep pace with it. . . . The gigantic gulleys formed by the torrential streams continually undermining the gulley walls present some of the most striking pictures known of the power of erosion. The great blocks of loëss broken off by the streams are rapidly disintegrated, loading the rivers with silt and causing catastrophic floods. Like the Mississippi, the Yellow River, which drains the loëss region, is now largely a "raised" river, flowing for long stretches above its densely populated plain.[68]

The process of destroying the stability of this *loess* soil has been going on for rather less than 4000 years, and it is only today that the disease of this soil has reached such an advanced stage, that the *loess* region is threatened with death. Professor J. Thorp[69] has made it clear that only a revolutionary change in the method of soil exploitation from arable to animal husbandry, entailing the restoration of the grass cover, can save the *loess* from its alternative fate of slow depopulation.

Today, one hundred million human beings, at the mercy of the Yellow River floods which are due to past soil-man relationships of an unsatisfactory kind, owe their recurring miseries to the ancestors they worship. On the *loess* soils was made the civilization of China; the same soil will fail to support the heirs of that civilization tomorrow unless today the people do one thing for which the past gives little warrant, and to which they are, in consequence, strongly averse.

Dr. Lin Yutang pointed out that, with the exception of one great group of foodstuffs, the Chinese are omnivorous.[70] The exception is dairy food, particularly cheese, which is apparently considered unclean: the ancient Chinese[71] had no milch cattle and were forced, like the ancient Peruvians, to make their civilization without the aid of milk and milk derivatives.

What is not in their past they will not readily admit to their present, and perhaps their aversion to milk products may have been reinforced by the fact that the pastoral enemies of their arable order, the horse-herding nomads of the *steppe* to the west of them, lived on milk and cheese.

What was the beginning of a relationship between soil and men which has resulted in the men of the present being faced with the need to break sharply with their past in order to assure their future?

*

Man lived in Northern China before the *loess* soil was laid down and in places he continued to maintain some sort of life and industry throughout the whole period of the deposition of the *loess*. Such, at all events, is the opinion of Dr. Gunnar Andersson,[72] who found the remains of Palaeolithic communities of hunters and gatherers who had inhabited the pre-*loess* country in small and perhaps rather isolated bands. There existed, at a time coinciding with the Ice Age of Europe, a North-western Chinese soil the nature of which we do not know, but which constituted a complete and mature countryside, a soil community inhabited by men and beasts and in terms of which Neolithic man would, no doubt, had he ever had the chance, have developed a suitable agrarian culture. Then came the dust-storms from the west, blowing during hundreds, perhaps intermittently thousands, of years. The ordinary irregularities of the country were in time completely covered up beneath the wind-borne soil which made the *loess* —it was, to use Dr. Andersson's own figure, as if a snow-storm had filled the valleys and bottoms and made a level plain where formerly had been rolling country. So deep and complete was this coverage that even the ancient rivers were filled in, and at the end of the process a vast, flat *steppe* had come into being, covered with grass and without rivers.[73]

Trees do not readily grow in *loess* soils, especially where rainfall is low. In some regions, however, forest belts did come into existence, and given time these would have raised the rainfall in their vicinity, creating the conditions for their own spreading. Possibly the whole region might have become afforested, and had this been so, and had the forest enjoyed a couple of thousand years of dominion, the newly made soil might have been stabilized. But man, in the precocity of Chinese civilization, stepped too soon out of his place in the natural soil community, began to dominate and change it.

In China, archaeology is yet young, and not a great deal is known of her antiquities, but what is known is sufficient to give us a familiar picture. Some surviving Palaeolithic community must have initiated the Neolithic revolution—there is little evidence for the immigration of Neolithic aliens and, on the other hand, a good deal to show that Neolithic industry and agriculture in China were native, however influenced by foreign contacts. Palaeolithic communities survived the dust-storms and doubtless had to modify their economy to suit the new conditions:

> In the whole Choei–Tong–Keon basin the loëss contains numerous traces of an absolutely homogeneous Palaeolithic industry left by a population which appears to have inhabited the district during the whole period of the formation of the loëss.[74]

The latest products of this Palaeolithic community are comparable in excellence of workmanship, taste, and finish with the European work called Magdalenian—and these are still below the top level of the *loess*. In fact, the deposition of the soil which the first "Chinese" farmers were to exploit was barely complete at the time when that Neolithic revolution whereby men change from soil-membership to soil-parasitism, was about to occur. By 1500 B.C. the Chinese Yellow Earth was supporting, as we shall see, an advanced and elaborate Bronze Age, urban culture, great cities and a sophisticated society with a fine literature and evolved graphic arts. The Yellow Earth yielded up its wealth very quickly, very readily, and to its great cost.

Certain, naturally very much later but still very ancient, writings, and the evidence of animal remains, make it clear that proto-Chinese inhabited the *loess* in climatic conditions warmer and wetter than at present, and in parts, as has been said, densely forested. At the next point of Chinese pre-history revealed by archaeology we find ourselves in a similarly warm, humid climate, but among very different people, men of a late Neolithic culture, inventors of the rectangular stone knife, of the earthenware cooking oven, and of a village layout, which are still in use today, but for some trifling changes in the materials. There were already other tools, which are still, as to design, in use; for example the bow-drill. These inventors were an agrarian people, without cattle, practising shifting tillage, rapidly exhausting the top layer of the *loess* wherever they settled, causing the small beginnings of erosion. They passed on to their descendants the earthenware stove and the bow-drill and the oblong knife, indeed, but also the grotesque country-side of the eroded *loess*, in which the then tiny gulleys have become tremendous ravines, some of them comparable with the Grand Canyon, and which cut up the whole landscape into vast, cliff-sided plateaux, like huge slices of yellow cake, the dividing clefts going down to the very bottom of the *loess* and revealing, here and there, the ancient land which lies beneath it, soil of a flora and fauna differing very greatly, and perhaps entirely, from that which covered it, and of which perhaps only one member, man, almost infinitely adaptable, survives.

The primal Chinese farmers attacked their vulnerable and unstable soil with digging-sticks and foot-ploughs of stone, hoed their crops with stone hoes, and reaped their harvest with sickles bladed with mussel shells. Their milling-stones and rollers were of basalt, granite or even, to the great detriment of their teeth, sandstone, which mixes its grit with the flour.

If, in the first well-documented pre-civilization, the first urban culture of China, one seeks for traces of the agrarian primitive culture which gave rise to it, one would be inclined, at first, to deduce that never was there a people among whom women were less important. There is hardly a sign, in what we know of the civilization of The Great City Shang, in Anyang, Bronze Age successor of the late Neolithic cultures, that women played any considerable part in Chinese economy, and this is disconcerting, for these people were, in the beginning, cultivators without cattle. True, the people of Shang had herds, but their ancestors had had none, and it was among their ancestors that their social habits would have been formed: however great the change in these habits, induced by a change in economy, some trace would remain. The only animals domesticated for eating by the Neolithic proto-Chinese, were pigs and dogs, neither of which can be the objects (though dogs are the instruments) of a pastoral economy.

However, at a second glance the picture is not quite the same: in the Neolithic remains; in the modern "Neolithic" communities of Indo-China; and in one other important particular, there is evidence that proto-China had her matriarchal period, when the Great Goddess received honour; and that the pattern of developing soil exploitation did not differ there from that with which we are familiar elsewhere.

Carl Whiting Bishop observes:[75]

> That the latter (Neolithic Chinese) traced descent through mothers, and that women played an active, and even leading part in institutional life, seems fairly certain.

Witches, female mediums, and priestesses dominated the spiritual life of the Neolithic community, in the service of the universal goddess, here known either as *The Mother of All,* or as *Ruler of the Soil,* but, singularly, never depicted in human form. Society was organized on matrilinear, exogamous, tribal lines:[76]

> Some interpreters (says Creel) have held that the family organization and even the sexual morality of the Shang peoples were very loose indeed. They go so far as to say that the men of that time knew the identity of their mothers, but not of their fathers.

This refers to a relatively late and advanced culture and its significance in our context is obvious.

The principal work of the fields among these same Anyang peoples was done by men, but women had sole care of the mulberry trees, the silk worms and the weaving of silk. This may be another relic of the feminine economy of the past, as may the fact that when a good harvest was in question, the propitiatory rites and sacrifices were addressed to the female ancestors. And there is a yet more significant case: the ancient Chinese included, in the ceremonial name of persons, the name of a day of the week, and when sacrifice was to be made to an ancestor it was so made on that ancestor's name day. But the day chosen for sacrifice when two ancestors of opposite sex were to be invoked in the same cause, was that of the female. We can hardly attribute this to mere chivalry!

There is, moreover, evidence of a very interesting nature, for the dominance of proto-Chinese society by women engaged in tillage: this society was an important province of the ancient (and modern, for that matter), almost ubiquitous, and astonishingly persistent cowrie-shell culture.

Species of *Cypraea*, the cowrie-shell fish, occur in many parts of the Pacific, the Indian Ocean, and in the Mediterranean. The species of primary cultural importance are *C. moneta* and *C. annulus*. Shells of these are found in Palaeolithic grave goods; but they are also still in use today, are important in some Nigerian and Indian burial rites in 1952 as they were important, in these and other rites, over the greater part of the world, five and perhaps six thousand or more years ago. The cowrie-shell motif is common in Bronze Age Chinese art; it occurs in modern Chinese craft-arts. Strings of cowrie-shells were the ancestors of strings of *cash*, the cowrie-shell was the first current "coin" of China, possessing, however, a value so high that it can have been of no use for the ordinary transaction of petty commerce. A string of cowries was ample reward from a prince to a statesman for some important public service. Cowrie money was and is common over a vast Pacific area, perhaps the largest area in which a single money was ever current. Cowrie-shell amulets, cult objects, occur in graves from Britain to Peru, from China to Germany, and over thousands of years in time. As money, cowrie-shells were so firmly established in China as a tradition, that the first metal coins of China were imitations of cowrie-shells in copper. In the province of Yunnan, cowrie-shells were not demonetized until the sixteenth century of our era: they were still current coin in Siam in the late eighteenth, in Indo-China in the nineteenth centuries. Where they were once in use as money they tended to survive after demonetization, as the ornaments or cult objects which they must have been *before* monetization. The species in most common use was *C. moneta*; after that comes *C. annulus*, and where neither of these was to be had, some other *Cypraea* was employed.[77]

All this and a great deal more is well established, as it is that China was formerly a cowrie country. But why *cowries*? They have no mechanical properties making them superior to more easily obtained shells: why not mussels, whelks, clams?

In early Chinese, and other usage, cowrie-shells are closely associated with women, especially as an ornament or amulet. There are exceptions: for example, among the Kado of the Hausa country we read that the shells are commonly worn by men, and perhaps an anthropologist might be able to show that where these exceptions occur, the culture contains other examples of the inversion of social-sexual rôles. Generally, however, the cowrie belongs to women, and in the Lacadive and Maldive islands, as probably elsewhere, the fishery of cowries was peculiarly and sacramentally feminine, undertaken at certain phases of the moon, the men of the tribe being barred from any participation in the work, or even from onlooking.

The fact is, according to Professor Elliot Smith, that primitive men saw in the cowrie shape and pattern a resemblance to the female vulva, focus of the whole Fertility Cult idea, and therefore of primary and incomparable importance in agriculture.

From Elliot Smith, from J. W. Jackson,[78] from Adamson,[79] it is very clear that this was so. And indeed, the generic name of the species comes from *Cyprus*, or *the Cyprian*, who was Aphrodite.[80] In short, cowries owe their importance to being fertility cult objects, they belong to that complex of ideas associated with the primal predominance of female values, itself based soundly on social and economic causes, one of the most important being the initiative taken by women in inventing and practising the cultivation of plants for subsistence. And since the cowrie was so important in proto-Chinese cultures, it is likely that proto-Chinese agrarian civilization, like the rest, was feminine.

Concerning the tillage practised by what must, in late Neolithic times, have become a considerable population, and its effect on the Yellow Earth, the *Huang-tu*, a good deal can be deduced from the Bronze Age culture of The Great City Shang, and from the early writings. First of all, then, a glance at this first of the Chinese urban cultures, created out of the wealth of the foregoing generations, and out of the fertility and endurance of the unstable loess soil.

Between primitive Neolithic Chinese civilization and its sophisticated apogee and emergence into the high culture of the Bronze Age, there were, of course, a number of intermediate stages. Few sites have yet been excavated, and much of the literature of the subject is in Chinese, but some examples are available to us. There are the remains of a late Neolithic society still practising some hunting, primarily dependent on agriculture, and with considerable herds of swine and edible dogs, but no other cattle.[81] The cereal basis of this tillage was millet, and that this was the oldest grain cultivated in China is clear in that it is the only cultivated plant of the North Chinese which was the object of a cult.[82] The next stage is represented by the Black Pottery culture of Ch'êng-Tzu-Yai: the people at this stage built walled enclosures of stamped earth and had added to their farm stock both oxen and horses, and possibly the water-buffalo. The presence of the latter animal, and the fact that elephants were among the game hunted throughout this period, are further evidence of the relatively warm and humid Chinese climate in the second millennium B.C.

After Ch'êng-Tzu-Yai come the people of Great City Shang who settled on the Huan River, which probably means that this first Chinese urban culture (*c.* 1400 B.C.) owed its sedentary character, the semi-permanence of its settlement, to an alluvial soil. The pace of development is relatively extremely rapid, and surely attributable to the ease of soil exploitation on the Yellow Earth. The wealth of Great City Shang was such, evident in the extent of the city, in the sophistication and the quantity of the metal work, and the advanced stage of its letters, that soils over a wide region must have been laid under contribution. The ruin of the Yellow Earth, however, would have been even swifter had the Shang people, and others who must have reached much the same stage of development (for we hear of relations with neighbouring powers), been dependent on tillage only. But the Shang folk, like their predecessors of Ch'êng-Tzu-Yai, had important herds of oxen, as well as pigs and edible dogs. The grass cover of considerable areas must have been preserved as pasture. Perhaps the rising importance of stock-raising is connected with the degrading of women to a very insignificant place in the social and political life of Great City Shang. But if the removal of the soil's grass cover, and the onset of erosion of which the Chinese suffer the consequences today, were somewhat delayed by the need for pasture, deforestation had gone so far, that the builders and carpenters of Shang had to fetch their timber from the mountains. The want of trees was having its effect in transforming the whole nature of the soil community by modifying the climate: rainfall was decreasing, fauna changing; towards the end of Shang's career, the elephant and the water-buffalo were becoming rare, and may already have disappeared. It is also possible that the consumption of soil fertility may have been more rapid than we have supposed: it is known that the government of Great City Shang moved the site of the capital no less than five times in only four centuries: the reason may well have been military or political it may also have been economic.

For what we know concerning the Anyang civilization we are dependent on a peculiarly reliable kind of document, the *Oracle Bones*. This is not the place to go into a full account of these interesting relics, and it is enough to say that the Shang people consulted their Oracle by addressing questions inscribed on bones to the Ancestor Gods; the bones, being thereafter burnt, the answers were read by adepts in interpreting the cracks produced by heat.[83] The reason for the *writing* of the questions was that the early Chinese believed that whereas supernatural beings could not understand human speech, they could all read.[84] Questions inscribed on bones for this purpose, and in these conditions, would obviously be without bias and absolutely to the point. The history we can extract from them is peculiarly free from the warping given to historical documents by the prejudices of the historian, the interests of a party, or the fashion of a literary style.

The ideograms in which the Shang people wrote are not by any means the original Chinese writing: that has still to be found, and must have been devised and developed well before this time. The Shang scribes disposed already of 2400 characters (the modern total, however, is 70,000) and these were already considerably stylized, considerably evolved from the original pictographic symbols. Not only does the sense of what is inscribed on the oracle bones in this script tell us much concerning the life of the people of Shang, the form of the letters tells us what sort of things drew the attention of the makers of the characters great numbers of which are, in origin, drawings rural scenes and events.

The questions addressed to the Oracle in these characters are, however, even more useful in indicating the preoccupation of the Shang people: these relate very often to harvest estimates, and to weather forecasting. They refer to disputes with neighbouring peoples over pasture rights on the Shang frontiers, and to other farmer's matters, and that in such terms that we get a fair notion of the conditions in which farming was carried on.

One of the most important things which can be learnt from the oracle bones is that the climate was almost certainly taking on that eccentric character which is so trying on deforested, *loess* soils; this change must have been, at least in part, due to tree felling, perhaps in the foothills rather than on the plain, on a very large scale. The question of rainfall is the subject of religious rites. The oracle bone questions ask, "Will rain fall?" Such a question reveals that the region was becoming arid. But then we find the question: "Will rain fall *painfully*?"[85] Why painfully? Probably rainfall was becoming too little in general, and torrential at times: torrential rain on ploughed *loess* of the Yellow Earth kind means catastrophic gully erosion and dangerous river flooding.

Millet, wheat and possibly rice were cultivated. Probably paddy-fields were not made, for certain varieties of rice can be cultivated dry, and from imprints of rice grains on pottery from Yang Shao it is possible to deduce that rice was being grown at a time when irrigation works on a large scale can hardly have been undertaken.

We have already noticed that traces of the primal female domination of economy and social life were very rare by Shang times. The Shang princes were not succeeded by their sons, however, but by their brothers, the son being heir only in default of brothers. This is said by anthropologists to be a mark of clan domination, and may be a relic of the conquest of a sedentary agrarian people by a tribe of warriors, possibly by pastoralists.

If the importance of stock-raising, the brother-inheritance, and the insignificance of women in Great City Shang were due to an earlier fusion of agrarian and herding peoples, the latter were probably not western immigrants, nor, in the ordinary sense, nomadic. The *She King*[86] contains many agricultural figures of speech, but no pastoral ones: there is nothing equivalent to our Lamb of God, our Good Shepherd, the Peruvian

Michec, the Turkish *rahiyeh*. The Chinese did not, and do not, as we have seen, eat dairy foods. But the very mark of the central Asiatic nomads is their milk economy. Yet the Chinese aversion to milk foods was so strong that it might almost be the result of an ancient tabu; there is a story of a Chinese coming back from a visit to the west and passing himself off as an outland barbarian nobleman of the *steppe*. His pose was suspected, he was led to a table set with butter, cheeses, yoghourt; rather than eat of these unclean foods he gave himself away, and fled in shame.

Our argument is, then, that on and out of their relatively new *loess* soil, the Chinese had developed far too rapidly for the well-being of that soil, a very advanced and sophisticated urban civilization. How advanced? The hunting-poems of a period only just after that of Great City Shang tell us much. In societies developing agrarian economies out of a hunting past, hunting long retains the signs of its communal, its ordinary economic importance. In societies which have advanced beyond the memory of their earlier economy, hunting is not seen in the same light.

Unlike any former Chinese civilization Shang was completely dependent upon agriculture and stock-raising; the Shang folk had divorced themselves altogether from the natural soil community, and had become soil parasites, even, in so far as they may have practised irrigation, soil-makers. Hunting was still common, but it had become an aristocratic pastime, had ceased, as in England today, to be an important source of food. The spirit and the nature of hunting in such conditions is totally different from the same attributes of communal hunting for the larder: for example:

> Shu has gone hunting
> Mounted in his chariot and four
> The reins are in his grasp like ribbons
> While the two outside horses move (with regular steps) as dancers do.

> Shu is at the marshy ground,
> The fire flames out all at once,[87]
> And with bared arms he seizes a tiger
> And presents it before the Duke.
> Oh Shu, try not such sport again,
> Beware lest you be injured.[88]

And again:

> A lucky day was Keng-wu
> We had selected our horses;
> The haunts of the animals,
> Where the does and the stags lay numerous,
> The grounds of the Ch'i and the Chu,
> That was the place for the Son of Heaven to hunt.
> We have bent our bows;
> We have our arrows on the string.
> Here is a small boar transfixed
> There a large rhinoceros killed.
> The spoil will be presented to the visitors and guests,
> Along with the cup of sweet liquor.

These poems, and others, from a period succeeding that of the Shang, but representative of it none the less, depict hunting as an upper class sport, not a business. We are reading the literature of a people who were far in spirit, but not far enough in time, from the beginnings of their soil-exploiting career. The wealth of Great City Shang and its successors can only have come out of a soil which was of comparatively recent origin. It is very obvious that the price of this rapid accumulation of wealth was gully erosion: not only could the vast ravines of the Yellow Earth of today not have been made in a few centuries, but there is reason to believe that not much less than 4000 years ago engineering genius was being used to check it. Terracing, for example, is of enormous antiquity in North China, and something like contour ploughing. But none of these ancient methods of soil conservation could do more than slow up the pace of soil destruction.

For reasons connected, no doubt, with the Chinese aversion to milk, tillage must have grown in importance at the expense of stock-raising, with the exception of swine-herding. Possibly, also, a system of land-tenure and inheritance tending to break up the land into small holdings, may have had some similar influence. Had the descendants of the Shang people made more and more of their cattle, less and less of their cultivation, the consequences would have been different. The preservation of the grass would have saved the soil, and the necessity for more and more pasture would have preserved the grass. As it happens, there is a case in point: had the farmer Russians been able to exploit the Black Earth *loess* of Eurasia in peace and quiet, as the Chinese were able to exploit the Yellow Earth *loess*, the scenery of South-west Russia today would be as grotesque as that of North-west China. Fortunately, in this case, there were the *steppe* people, the horse-herding nomads who, during two thousand years or more, protected the grass of the *steppes* from the plough. That story is a repetitive one, a counter-point, as first farmers, then nomads, swing across the *steppe*.

As to the condition of Eurasian *loess* soil today, it is not intact. Two centuries ago, the farmers having triumphed over the protectors of the *steppe*, exploitation began in earnest. According to the survey made by Jacks and Whyte:

> The Soviet Union is affected by sheet and gulley erosion on agricultural lands in Central Russia and Ukraine. . . . One of the worst eroded areas, by reason of its steep and broken relief, is the south-west steppe region. A survey of the Russian literature leaves the impression that erosion as an imminent menace is mainly confined to the intensively cultivated zone, although it is prevalent and increasing, in milder forms, over much larger regions, particularly in the "chestnut soil" areas, which correspond ecologically to the short-grass country of North America.[89]

The mass of the U.S.S.R. consists of the Eurasian *steppe*, which is bounded on the north by the Arctic Sea, on the south by Turkestan, the Caspian and Black Seas, the Caucasus and the Crimean mountains; in the east by the Altai, Tartagatai and Shan-Tien mountains, and in the west by the Carpathians, the Baltic, and the rocky spine of Finland. The only geographical feature of this vast *steppe* is the Ural range which forms no climatic nor ecological barrier, the *steppe* being identical to east and west of the range excepting that, in the far west, the influence of the Atlantic is felt upon the climate. The result of this influence is that the orderly succession of climatic belts from south to north, each with a characteristic flora and fauna extending uniformly along almost the whole length of the belts, is slightly but significantly displaced in the west, so that, for example, deciduous forests occur further to the north in the extreme west, than anywhere else in the lateral extent of the country.[90]

Roughly coincident with the region between the 45th and 47th parallels of latitude is an arid, grass soil with a mean annual rainfall of less than ten inches. This is the *steppe* proper, the native soil of nomad peoples, capable of supporting them and their beasts without serious flagging where the population does not exceed three to the square mile.[91]

At its northern limits this *steppe* proper merges, through a gradation of soils changing through light brown and chocolate to very dark brown, with the *chernozem* soil, the famous Black Earth. This also is *steppe*, in that it is a treeless, grass soil community. But the grass is more lush, the rainfall generally higher, and the grass, rotting down through thousands of years, has mixed with the top layers of basic *loess* a high proportion of organic material, to form a very fertile loam. Nevertheless, as a natural grass soil, the *chernozem*, if ploughed, is not, in the absence of trees and the special precautions taken by man, stable, and it can very easily be lost by erosion. The rivers of this region have carved and eroded deep valleys in the *loess*, so deep that irrigation entails lifting the water by the use of power. Yet irrigation is necessary, for the rainfall is unreliable, a fact which has frequently caused total failure of the crops and consequent famine.

The northern limit of the fertile *steppe*, drawn as a line, wanders as far north as 54° and as far south as 49°, touching Sarastov on the Volga, Kishinev, Poltava and Kharkov. Northward of this limit occur park-land soils, open Black Earth country stippled with hardwood trees, and coppices, a border land between farmers and herdsmen. It was at one time believed that this thinning of the trees into open park-land was the result of the desiccation of a formerly densely forested region. Mirsky, however, believes that[92] until man took a hand the trees were advancing, not retreating, continuing a process of colonizing the soil begun in post-glacial times. This is very probable: the mean annual rainfall being less than twenty inches, the progress of the trees would be relatively slow, the rate of their increase rising as their larger numbers tended to raise and stabilize the rainfall. South of Moscow the width of park-land is great, but further east it turns into dense forest.

Further north again, in the central and eastern sectors of the east to west vegetation belts, deciduous trees give way to conifers, to arctic forests of Siberian type, and still farther north come the tundras, soil communities harsh and treeless but which, in glacial times, when they extended all over Europe, supported a numerous fauna of great herds of herbivores, ample for the support of the splendid Palaeolithic culture of hunter-artists.[93] Tundra soils are unsuitable for exploitation, and demand membership of their species; tundra people, accordingly, are always hunters, never farmers or herdsmen.[94]

In the west, as we have said, the gentling influence of the Atlantic allows deciduous trees to grow farther north: consequently, in the north-west of the European *steppe* there is, thrust into the characteristically Russian pattern of soils, a typical European soil salient, of exactly the kind which gave rise to the stable agricultural soils of North-west Europe. Within this region, Russian history, in so far as it is "European" in character, began, and the fact is solely due to the nature of the soil. The Baltic, in the west, connects this region with North-west Europe. Elsewhere it is bounded by the *steppe*, the nomad's country.

Russia, then, provided two very distinct opportunities for soil exploitation. The North-west soil was capable of being turned into a very fertile and stable "European" soil, the perfect agricultural soil with which we deal in Part V. The *steppe*, on the other hand, rich though it is in the *chernozem* regions, naturally invites the creation of a pastoral culture, with no change from the natural to the artificial soil community but that entailed in replacing the wild fauna by herds of tame horses, or other cattle; moreover it cannot be ploughed without danger to its continued existence.

Russian history is primarily a long and brilliantly colourful account of the struggle between farmers and horse-herders across the park-land country, the farmers trying to drive their ploughs out into the *steppe*, the horsemen trying to push their pasture rights up towards the forest. While these two forces held each other in balance, the soils in question were protected from abuse: the peasants checked the over-stocking of grasslands by making war on the herdsmen; and the herdsmen protected the grasslands against destruction by the plough. Consequently, the consumption of soil fertility, instead of being a galloping progress, a catastrophe, as in North America, and even North-west China, has been slow, and only now begins to call for measures of conservation.

Strictly agricultural cultures appear very early on Russian soils. That which is known as the Tripolye, not the earliest, but the earliest which is fairly well documented, may have been related to the Danubian agrarian civilization of Central Europe,[95] but if this was so it was more advanced, at least aesthetically—in its ceramics, for example; according to some archaeologists, its painted pottery is more akin to the Chinese of the period, than to the less evolved European. The Tripolye people flourished towards the end of the third millennium B.C., and were perhaps the heirs of a thousand years of shifting agriculture, although they themselves had settled into a sedentary way of life.

The great struggle between farmers and herdsmen begins very early. In high Palaeolithic times there was a people of hunters in Russia whose culture was characterized by a certain burial rite: they removed the flesh from the bones of the dead, and painted the skeleton with the blood-surrogate, red ochre. Accordingly, they are known as the Painted Skeleton people. While agricultural experience was producing the Tripolye farmers, the Painted Skeleton folk, who hunted the horse in Palaeolithic times, had learnt to herd it instead. As the first great horse-herding people of the *steppe*, of whom we have knowledge, these probable descendants of the Painted Skeleton people flung themselves upon the Tripolye settlements about 2000 B.C., and utterly destroyed them. There followed perhaps a thousand years during which Russian agriculture was confined to the forest, while *steppe* and park-land were dominated by the triumphant horse-herders, developing their specialized techniques and economy to that level of perfection which had been attained when these formidable people burst into history.

About 1100 or 1200 B.C., it was again the turn of the farmers. We know little of the Cimmerian people, except that they were sedentary peasants, as well as soldiers, and that their culture was western in character. They extended their settlements, and enjoyed several centuries of prosperity on the Black Earth. But in due course the horse-herders, having learnt to ride and to fight from horseback, poured off the *steppe* and drove in the limits of the cultivated land. These horsemen were the Scythians of history.

The Scythians were a gifted, indeed brilliant people. Mounted, and armed with iron, their impact upon the sedentary states, and upon the imagination of Greek, and later, Roman writers, was terrific. They had developed a highly formalized but lively style in the graphic arts, especially in depicting animals.[96] They either absorbed and dominated the peasantry of the Crimea or themselves took to farming, establishing important centres of commerce on the Black Sea, coming under the influence of the Greek colonists, and exporting grain to Attica.

It is tempting, if rather too fanciful, to see in the fate of the Scythians a punishment for the betrayal of a trust. If they settled down to farming on so considerable a scale as to become exporters of wheat, unwittingly enabling Athens to become, despite, or rather because of her ruined soils, the "education of Hellas", they did so at the expense of the *steppe*. It was not the business of these horsemen to plough, but rather to check the advance of the plough. At all events, a more aggressively nomadic, if less gifted people, destroyed the semi-sedentary civilization of the Scythians, and allowed the grass to grow again in South Russia. It is possible that the Sarmatians, the new incumbents of the *steppe*, were descendants of those earlier horse-herding nomads who had wiped out the Tripolye farmers about 2000 B.C.

The Goths were the next peasant champions. They moved into the territory between Danube and Don, dominated the horsemen, formed an alliance, which became a union, with the Alani, a Sarmatian people, learned Alan techniques, and finally founded a Goth-Alan kingdom. It was a sort of League of Nations affair, governed by the peasant Goths and pastoral Alans, but including, as merchants and craftsmen, Jews, Arabs, Germans, and "Russians", although that name had as yet no meaning. This Don-Danube agrarian kingdom was overwhelmed by a people whose name has become a by-word for ruthless military ability: the Huns. Not only were the Huns terrible as soldiers, but they seem to have been so ill-favoured, and their manners so very uncouth, that they were thought of rather as monsters than as men, and were barely admitted by their victims to belong to the human race at all. At all events, they did humanity one service: they brought the Slav people into history, as their servants, as part of their *rahiyeh*, indeed as slaves, but still, it was a beginning. These Slavs were the antithesis of their Hun masters, a forest, agrarian people, and it is all part of the pleasantly stylized, almost artistic struggle over the *steppe* that it should have been so implacably pastoral and belligerent a people who brought to the notice of the world the peasant race which was to carry the arts of agriculture throughout the whole region of the *steppe*, and plough up the grass for ever.

There follows upon the Hun epoch on the Russian soils, one of chaos, during which rival nomad peoples founded and lost empires, and in some cases learnt to settle and to cultivate soil, although probably the cultivation was usually done for them by their subjects: such were the Bulgars and the Avars, the former a most gifted folk who bequeathed much to the Russians who came after them. Indeed, Russian national consciousness was perhaps finally crystallized only when the Byzantine Emperor Nicephorus summoned the Russians to his aid in his struggle with the rival Bulgarian Empire, some centuries later.[97]

In this same interlude of competing powers, the Slavs spread over Russian soils and formed settlements of peaceful farmers. In the east, at the same time, Turkish-speaking peoples, battening upon older sedentary settlements, made themselves nations, and the cultural work begun by them in East Russia was carried on by their successors, another people who learnt to settle and cultivate the *steppe*. These were the Chazars: their influence radiated from Astrakhan, and extended along the lower Don and Volga: their civilization owed much to the influence of another people once nomadic, now turned farmers and merchants, the Jews; and the Jewish religion was adopted by the Chazar princes and their noblemen, and perhaps extended to the principal classes of the whole nation.

While farmers and horsemen and rival nomad peoples wrestled for the *steppe*, to the north, in the wooded hinterland, there grew and changed and died, and grew again, a series of agricultural civilizations, between *c*. 700 B.C. and *c*. A.D. 300 Such, for example, were the sedentary cultures of Ananyino and Piany-bor. During that thousand years the predecessors of the real Russian people were learning agriculture the hard way, the way that brings into existence stable soils in forest clearances. Among such forest people were the Slavs, hidden in their woods until dragged into the light of history by the Huns. So difficult were the conditions in which agriculture could be practised on the forest soils, that the proto-Slavs never wholly emancipated themselves from mere soil-membership on their native soil, from hunting and gathering their food. They spoke an Indo-European language which reveals them as related to the Lithuanians and Balts. They brought into the common pool of Eurasian civilization not a culture of their own, it was inconsiderable, but the gift of learning from others, great energy, and great numbers. They did not, unaided, make the nations of Kiev, of Novgorod, of Muscovy; in those enterprises they were led by Swedish Vikings. Yet the character of those nations was not Scandinavian, it was Slavic; it was, quite soon, *Russian*.[98]

It was not until the end of the ninth century that Russia proper, the nuclear communities of that region of "European" forest soil thrust into Eurasia, began to show signs of life. The tutors of these farmers were the Bulgars and the Chazars, both become sedentary and agricultural, and therefore fit mentors for the people who were to drive the plough into the *steppe* and dispossess the nomads once and for all.[99] The first Russian nations, living by commerce and by tillage, were oligarchic organizations of land-owning boyars with a prince who was, in a sense, the land-owner of all his territories, yet was primarily a war chief. There were elements of feudalism in this social system but the Russians were perhaps the first post-Hellenic people to carry the idea of property in land to its logical conclusion, and at a time when in Europe land was, at least in theory, held but not owned, inalienable in the last analysis, it had become a chattel in Northern Russia. The reason is not hard to guess, and as usual it was the nature of the soil which shaped the institution; the agricultural land of, for example,

Kiev, was poor; the prosperity of the community was founded not upon tillage, which merely kept it alive, but upon trade, particularly in furs. Much of the food for the city was imported from the Niz, the territory of Moscow. A community of traders tends to carry the idea of buying and selling, of absolute property rights, to extremes.[100]

Nevertheless, these early Russian nations were peasant in their outlook, and such cities as Kiev and Pereyaslavl were constantly on the alert against incursions by the nomads, their neighbours of the *steppe*. While the farmers were vigorous and active, the plough was pushed out into the *steppe*, and the nomads of the border country absorbed into the sedentary community, either to change their way of life and settle, or to become borderers in the service of the peasant State, shock-troops against the deep *steppe* pastoralists less liable to corruption in their way of life by contact with settled peoples.

In the eleventh century the Cumans of the *steppe* put another end to agrarian expansion on to the *steppe* soils. This counter-offensive was effective, the plough was driven back, Pereyaslavl, to name but one city, became a mere outpost, a fort in the enemy's country instead of a centre and a market. During two centuries these Cuman and Kipchak horsemen dominated the *steppe* and the park-lands, and threatened the Russian states. Even Kiev, a great and prosperous city, cut off from her markets in the Byzantine Empire, and from the ports of the Black Sea, was much reduced in her circumstances. Nevertheless, the peasants were by no means inactive, they continued to skirmish into the *steppe*, to snatch a crop here and another there, practising shifting tillage and catch-cropping where, due to the raids of the horsemen, it was not worth making permanent settlements.

Under the leadership of Kiev the Russian states had come into a union which was the promise of an empire, and this union was not destroyed by the Cumans. In the course of time tilth and pasture reached a state of equilibrium, evident in the tendency of the Russians and the Cumans, the peasants and the horse-herders, to come to an understanding: but in such cases the attractive power of the sedentary social system is always the stronger: the peasant is rarely equipped or inclined to turn nomad unless unreasonably oppressed. The nomad, on the other hand, readily settles down. Cuman manners softened; like other pastoralists before them they began to betray their trust, to tolerate the advance of the plough on to the soils which must suffer if the grass cover were destroyed.

As, formerly, the Huns had taken over that trust from the relaxing hands of the Sarmatians, so now the Tartars took it over from those of the Kipchaks. In the thirteenth century the armies of Jenghizkhan overran and dominated the whole of Eurasia, and subsequently all China as well, and a single nomad people ruled the great land mass of Eurasia from the Pacific almost to the Atlantic.

The Tartar Mongols[101] were not savages, but a highly evolved, clever and disciplined people with remarkable gifts for bureaucratic organization which they may have owed to their Uigur clerks, for the Uigur seem to have been a singularly advanced and polished tribe, with a gift for office and book-work.[102] The reproach of savagery which is commonly addressed to the Tartars—and the very name has become a synonym for intractable brutality—has been due to their deliberate, and highly "civilized" use of terrorism as a political and military device. Where resistance to their arms made necessary for their policy the administration of an unforgettable lesson, they not infrequently massacred whole populations, although they had none of the facilities for carrying out such a policy as were available, for the same purpose, at Hiroshima and Nagasaki, to the most civilized nations of our own time.

On the death of Jenghizkhan the unfortunate Mongol laws of inheritance operated to split the Empire, and the West fell to his son Juchi, the Tartars of his sub-Empire being known as Kipchaks—of the Golden Horde.[103]

Very broadly speaking it was Tartar policy to dominate the *steppe* soils exclusively, to leave the forest soils to the Russian peasants and to turn the intermediate park-land agricultural outposts into Tartar estates where the khans could play at settling down. The peasant and merchant principalities and republics, which had loosely combined to form an empire of sorts, were free to pursue their own way of life, but their princes and presidiums had to submit to the Great Khans, and their economy had to support a very heavy tribute.

The need to pay the tribute could only be met by lowering the Russian standard of living, or by increased trade in such articles as fur and amber, or out of soil fertility. The Tartar period was, accordingly, one of increasing soil exploitation but largely within the forest region where the soil could be exploited without danger to its stability, and tree felling could be undertaken without much risk of causing aridity. The period also saw increase in trade along the trade routes kept perfectly safe and well provided with rest-houses by the Tartar genius for maintaining order and for good organization. No way of economic growth could have been healthier. On the whole the *steppe* was still protected while forest was cleared and planted or tilled, and those Russian historians who have lamented the shame and horror of the Tartar yoke are quite beside the point. Moreover the Tartar impact broke up the Russian union into its component parts, giving each principality or republic a new lease of national life before the establishment of a Universal State of all the Russias.

The first peasant powers to take the offensive against the Tartars for the reconquest of the *steppe*, were the Lithuanian and Muscovite. Throughout the second half of the fourteenth century the Lithuanians had been building their strength, and skirmishing into the *steppe*. At the accession of Duke Vitowt (1388–1430) the Tartars were relaxing their hold on the park-land and *steppe* fringe, while the Lithuanian farmers were ploughing grassland. The ploughman pioneers were followed by the Duke's soldiers, and suzerainty was established over several border khanates. Vitowt invaded the Crimea, conquered the *steppe* all along its frontier with the forest, went beyond the reach of the Golden Horde Tartars into the sphere of influence of the new Mongol power of Central Eurasia; that of Tamerlane, or Timur. The Lithuanians were a match for the declining Golden Horde, but they were not in the same class as Timur's men, and Vitowt was stopped and defeated. Nevertheless, the *steppe* from Dniepr to Dniestr remained Lithuanian and was devoted to tillage until the fifteenth century, when the next wave of *steppe* trustees, the Krim Tartars, drove in the limits of the peasant advance and in some places pushed the farmers back to the forest fringe, retook the *steppe*, captured and sold into slavery thousands of Russians, and allowed the grass to grow again.

The Muscovite princes increased their territories mainly by purchase and sharp-practice, remarkable in a people with such a contempt for western bourgeois ideas. They were very humble before the Khan, and attracted, by their abilities, the attention of the Metropolitan Patriarchs, whose policy it was (like that of Pope Gregory VII in the west), to create an oecumenical great Russian state whose frontiers would coincide with the religious frontiers of the Orthodox Russian Church. Moscow was, as it were, chosen by the spiritual director of all the Russias to make the Russian Universal State.

As soon as the great church leaders were sure that the Tartars were growing weak, they encouraged their people to become aggressive and advance again into the *steppe*. This opportunity occurred when (1359) internecine strife split the Golden Horde. The Muscovite Grand Duke Dmitri, supported by the peasant principalities of Russia but, significantly, not by the merchant republics (e.g., Ryazan), went out against the Khan Malmay and defeated him at Kalikovo on the Don.

The last really serious threat to the rising prosperity of the peasant Russians by the nomads of the *steppe* was due, first, to the pressure put upon the Tartars by the Mongol power of Timur farther to the east, a pressure which drove the western nomads hard up against their expanding agrarian neighbours and tributaries; second, the actual westward march of the formidable Mongol, for the chastisement of Bajazet the Turk, and in search of the central Orda of the Golden Horde, whose Khan had offended him.[104]

Malmay, the Khan defeated by Dmitri, had been at civil war with Toktamish, a claimant to the western Khanate, who had Timur's support. Dmitri's victory over Malmay was good warfare, but bad politics, for Toktamish became supreme head of a once more united Golden Horde, and on being refused tribute by the city of Moscow, sacked it, reaffirmed the Tartar dominion and set back the peasant advance. Toktamish, forgetting his debt to Timur, invaded the eastern *steppe* to recover Urganj, formerly Golden Horde property, but then in Mongol hands. He had some initial success, even threatening Timur's capital of Samarkand before he had to withdraw. Timur, certainly the most implacable, possibly the ablest captain in history, pursued, caught and defeated the Golden Horde, but Toktamish escaped, rallied the survivors of his Orda, and with incredible audacity raided across Timur's frontiers north of the Caspian. The Mongol Khan was again forced to move, and this time he smashed up the Golden Horde once and for all, burnt Sarai and moved down the Don after sacking and burning Astrakhan. Moscow, with good reason, was terrified, and her Grand Duke led out his army in a spirit of desperation rather than courage. It was fitting that a peasant people, defending themselves against a pastoral war-band, should have the protection of the Great Goddess, the Earth-Mother: the ancient image of the Virgin was fetched from Vishaigorod and to her the Muscovites prayed, "Oh Mother of God, Save Russia".[105]

The prayer would appear to have been effective. Timur passed by Moscow with hardly a glance. This wooden town of peasant people, sacked only seven years previously by Toktamish can, indeed, have offered little temptation to the master of Samarkand, and the final consequence of Timur's expedition was wholly beneficial to the Russian farmers: the Tartar dominion had been destroyed by the Mongols, and the *steppe* lay open, at last, to exploitation.

From the beginning of the sixteenth century until the present day, the peasants of Russia have made swift progress against the nomads, until it is inconceivable that the *steppe* should ever again find a nomad trustee; any conservation of the *chernozem* soils which is to be done must now be due to the sense of responsibility of the farmers, no longer to the community of interest between the horsemen and the grass species of the *steppe*.

Two peasant powers began the new and final offensive against the horse-herders: the Muscovites and Poland-Lithuania. The advance guards were frontiersmen or pioneers to whom was given the name of Cossacks, in Great Russia, of Kozaks in the Ukraine. The word comes from Kazak,[106] a Turki word meaning one who secedes, an outcast by his own will.[107] There is, ethnically, linguistically, no Cossack people or nation, and the Cossack communities were made up of all the Russian nations. They advanced into the park-land and even into the *steppe*, formed fortified camps, and having learnt the techniques of the nomads, raided Turk and Tartar, creating a sort of screen of skirmishers behind which the plough could advance.

The Cossacks, followed by the Lithuanian peasants reached the limits of the Ukrainian park-land by the end of the seventeenth century, supported, for the nomads constantly struck back at them, by garrisons and forts supplied by the government, and by their own militia. Their advance was thus similar in character to that of the Europeans in North America during the period of the Indian Wars.

With the passing of the Mongol threat and the dispersal of the Golden Horde conditions were created for the final crystallization of the Russian Universal State, and the advance of the Muscovites out of the park-land on to the *steppe*. The first major outward movement, however, was not against the nomads, but against the much more ancient natural soil community of the north, the hunting country of the northern forests and the tundra. Fur was the magnet which drew the Russians into Siberia, notably sable and ermine, and the soil communities of the hunting peoples were destroyed in little more than a generation. According to Mirsky, even the territory of Mangazeya,[108] extremely rich in sable and ermine, was completely cleared of those animals in thirty years. There are few, if any, places left in the world where such a wanton disturbance of the ecology of a region would now be tolerated by any government. Much the same sort of thing happened subsequently in North America, where now, however, men with a profound natural *tact,* a feeling for balance, are engaged in restoring the species of certain countrysides, repairing the damage done by their ancestors; for it has been recognized that a soil community is the working order of all its members.

This predatory raiding of Siberia for furs was followed by peasant settlement; after the trappers and traders came the tree-fellers and farmers, but the forests and tundra of the north were not without their protectors: the hunting tribes were helpless against the civilized Russians, but the Orda of the Altyn-Khan Tartars stopped the Russians at Kuznetsk, and the Manchus, a *steppe* people who had imposed their rule by conquest on the peasant Empire of China, checked the Cossacks and turned them back at the Amur.[109]

Although the general picture from about 1550 onwards was one of peasant advance and pastoralists in retreat, the processes were not steady; the farmers had their set-backs, the horsemen brief interludes of prosperity. Several Orda of Tartars, composed of fragments of the Golden Horde, were able to make themselves felt, and notably those of Astrakhan, Kazan and Krim. But the expansive force of the peasant peoples was, on the whole, irresistible, and where peaceful settlement was made impossible by the Tartars, the Black Earth was tilled by forced labour under armed guards, until the middle of the seventeenth century, when a fortified line—Belgorod, Voronezh, Tambov was established and held, behind which farming could be carried on by free peasants, or by great serf- and land-owners, in the usual Russian style. Soon the wealth produced from the fertile soils was supporting new cities in regions which had, until recently, been the frontier, towns such as Belgorod which from being an outpost became a metropolis.

This brief excursion into Russian history is intended to be an account of the struggle for certain soils between two different economies, and not of the methods used to exploit those soils. Nevertheless, it should be said that whereas the nomads treated these soils as pasture lands for their horses, on and by means of which they lived, the farmers, especially in the pioneering era, snatched wheat crops as fast and often as they could with little regard for the future of the soil which, in any case, seemed to be inexhaustibly fertile. The pastoral way of life does no harm to the grass soils at all; nomads are rarely so numerous that they overstock their pastures, even when, as was the case in the more prosperous Mongol and Tartar Orda, every man had at least twelve horses, for riding, baggage, milk and meat.

The great land-owners who were among the first to benefit by the advance into the *steppe* had absolute property rights in land and even, later, in the peasants. The process whereby free peasants became serfs, the "souls" of Gogol's novel, need not concern us.[110] Slavery was also a Russian institution, although it appears to have been of little economic importance. On the other hand its social importance was great, for when the distinction between the two kinds of bondage was abolished by Peter the Great, it was done by reducing the status of the serfs to that of the slaves, and calling all of them serfs.[111] Agricultural slavery leads inevitably to abuse of soil: the actual labourers on the land have little or no interest in its condition, while its owners look upon it merely as a source of personal, not communal wealth.

The free peasants organized themselves in communes, with equality and exchange of holdings, in order that each holder should take his turn at the best and worst land. They adopted, but not until *c.* 1500, the three-year rotational system of Manorial Europe. But this system, combined with exchange of holdings, also leads to abuse of soil and its deterioration. The two tried methods of land-holding which entail soil conservation and improvement are those of medium freehold combined with high farming, such as the English system of the eighteenth to the twentieth centuries; and national land-ownership with strict laws of soil management, such as the Incarial system of ancient Peru.[112] Probably the soundest farmers in Russia were the monks, and as the monasteries owned up to one-third of all the agricultural land the damage done by bad soil management was reduced, or at least slowed considerably.

The ploughing of the *steppe* on a grand scale began in the late eighteenth and continued into the nineteenth century. East of the Don, the Kalmouk and Qazaq nomads were dispossessed; Bashkir pastures east of the Volga were turned into farmlands. Between 1736 and 1791, a series of Turkish wars ended in the Russians occupying the *steppes* of the Black Sea, Crimea, and Caucasian regions, and Ukrainian colonists brought in first sheep and cattle, and later the plough. By 1835 the export of wheat from these new soils had become an important item of Russian trade.

The process continued and is continuing: the victory of the farmers over the pastoralists and the very rapid exploitation of that victory have had consequences tersely described in the quotation from *The Rape of the Earth*. The historical processes which entailed the double attack upon the Golden Horde by Dmitri, Grand Prince of Moscow, and Timur, Grand Khan of the Mongols, and the implacable will of the peasants' Emperor Peter the Great, have operated to check the efforts of the present Soviet government to raise the per capita production of foodstuffs above pre-revolutionary levels, and have necessitated, for Soviet agricultural scientists and Soviet farmers, a revival of the ancient sense of responsibility for soil, and the expenditure of immense sums of money, energy, labour, and time upon the restoration and conservation of the Black Earth.

PART FOUR (II):
THE MARGINAL CASE

*

CHAPTER XII

INDIA: LAND-TENURE AS AN INSTRUMENT OF SOIL DESTRUCTION

BAUDHAYANA, in his *Dharma Sutra*, lays it down that, "it is impossible for one to obtain salvation who lives in a town, covered with dust" (ii, 3, 6, 33).

And, indeed, the civilization which came into being as a result of the fusion of the ancient agrarian civilizations of prehistoric India, and the invading Aryan culture, was a peasant civilization organized in village communities, and one in which, at first, cities played small part, for the people disliked and distrusted urban life. Both in the *Grihya Sutras* handbooks of instruction for the proper conduct of domestic life and the correct relations of the members of a household with each other and in the *Dharma Sutras,* which give guidance concerning the relationship of a man with the State, the kind of civilization and social life which emerges is one in which the great majority of the population live in small, or at most medium-sized rural communities, practising tillage or one of the trades ancillary to it.[113]

Before and during the Buddhist period, and probably from late prehistoric times, a system of peasant proprietorship was in force all over Ayran India.[114] A typical Indian community consisted of a "brotherhood" of equal peasants organized as a self-governing municipal group under a headman, and occupying an amount of territory suitable to their numbers and roughly equivalent to an English parish. The number of peasant families might be as low as twenty, perhaps as high as a thousand. The brotherhood was founded on the belief in the common ancestry of all the brethren, and was therefore, in origin, a true kinship group. Probably this social system had evolved from an earlier, tribal one. The community managed its own affairs and disposed freely of its produce, provided that the annual tax on raw produce was paid to the central government. The peasants were each responsible for a share of this tax, which was paid by the village as a whole, and for which the headman was accountable. The whole community could be held liable for the share of a defaulting member. The obligation to pay this tax, like every other social duty in India, was enforced by religious rules, and failure to pay it was met by religious-social sanctions. At the same time, however, the central government, monarchical or republican, was under a religious obligation not to oppress the peasants and abuse the soil by burdensome taxation: the amount of tax permissible may originally have been a tithe, but in practice it varied, in the Buddhist period and probably before then, between at least one-twelfth and at most one-sixth of the crop, according to the government's necessities, and other conditions.[115] Such a tax would not be so heavy as to hamper good farming: the modern English farmer with an income of £1000, pays more than 25 per cent of it in direct and indirect taxation, and survives.

It is difficult to ascertain the exact degree of control which the individual peasant exercised over the land he worked. Subject to the payment of tax, the crop was his property. Formerly, if the organization was conventionally tribal, he might hold (but not own) a given plot during his lifetime, and work it in common with the holdings of the other villagers. In Buddhist times the peasant seems to have been nearly a freeholder, working his land and enjoying its produce as a small capitalist, and even possessing the right of alienation by sale, gift, mortgage or bequest.[116] It is probable, however, that there were customary limitations to this right, arising from ancient traditions. The consent of the headman and therefore, in most cases no doubt of the corporation, was necessary to any conveyance of land, since the community, the village, was responsible for payment of the tax, and must make sure that each peasant would meet his part of it. Moreover, as the community was based, at least in theory, on the blood tie, there may have been objections to the admission of aliens. Where land belonging to a village was unoccupied the community of the village, as landlord, could let it to a tenant farmer, and the rent he paid belonged to all. According to at least one authority, an inefficient farmer, that is, presumably, one who was not making a fair contribution to the pool, or who was abusing his piece of land, *could be expelled from the village,* after being deprived of his holding. This hardly looks like absolute property right in his land. On the whole it would appear that by Buddhist times the system of peasant land tenure was in a stage of development, or decline, from some sort of communal holding, to individual capitalist holding.

There is nothing in this system which would lead to abuse of the soil, and much which would have been conducive to its improvement and the conservation of fertility. The system, however, had grave weaknesses, or rather the Indian social system in general developed weaknesses which were bound to have an evil effect upon the soil. In the first place, the highest classes and castes in the land were, by religious law, forbidden to practise agriculture: farming was considered to be beneath the Brahman, or noble, and was allotted, by secular custom and religious rule, to the middle-class, the *Vaicya*.[117] True, the rule was broken, sometimes even without evil consequences for the backslider, sometimes to his cost. But the point is that the ruling castes had no feeling of attachment to or responsibility for the soil, nor was it in the least necessary to own land in order to establish one's gentry. It is possible that in this rather matter-of-fact or even contemptuous attitude to land there is a relic of the contempt felt by the invading Aryas of the Rig-Veda period for the Dasa, the agrarian inhabitants of the Indus valley. Although these warriors practised agriculture themselves, and that to an extent uncommon among herdsmen, yet herdsmen they primarily were, and the wealth and prestige of their great men was expressed not in fields, but in head of cattle. People of that way of life do not develop traditions of landed gentry.

Another weakness of the Indian land-tenure system may have been that inheritance by primo-geniture was not the rule. The *Dharma Sutras* lay down rules concerning a man's heirs. All his sons seem to inherit equally, or with some preference, but never exclusive right, for the eldest. In default of sons, numerous heirs at law are mentioned.[118] The system would normally have led to increasing fragmentation of holdings with the rapid soil exhaustion which tends to be a result of that practice. But since the Indian family was inclined to cohere, probably the heirs of an estate in land might continue to work it as a unit. Moreover, it seems probable that the headman of a village had the power to redistribute holdings in certain conditions, surely another survival of communal tenure, and in that case it would have been open to the municipal authority to repair the damage done by a bad law of inheritance. At all events, the village communities undoubtedly were in the habit of acting in concert, managing soil and crop problems in common, digging irrigation systems, erecting public buildings, and constructing and maintaining the roads of the parish. Such a community, and one in which it was considered a mark of degradation to leave one's responsibilities as a member of the brotherhood, lay down the burden of freedom, and take service as a paid man with some nobleman, would not have tolerated the inefficient husbandry which is one of the consequences of fragmentation of holdings. But despite joint family holdings, this fragmentation did become a grave problem enduring into the twentieth century.

The condition for the satisfactory working of this system, such a working as would tend to a slow and steady improvement of soil and not to its slow and steady exhaustion, was that every party to the social contract implied in it should be responsible and conscious of responsibility. Unfortunately, although this was very likely the case for quite a long time, it began to be very far from the case towards the end of the Buddhist period, and indeed long before the end. Governments began to break their part of the tacit agreement by demanding, in tax, amounts greatly in excess of that allowed by religious rule. But while the tax continued to be paid in kind, the peasant suffered more than the soil, although even in this case the soil began to suffer, for if Central Government took half the crop, the remaining half might well be inadequate to support the peasant's family and he would be forced to squeeze more and more out of his land without the knowledge or means of how to make good the fertility he was consuming. At first, no doubt, increasing pressure of taxation might result in the clearance and planting of new land, but this could not go on for ever, nor is soil which is simply cropped to pay taxes ever treated well: the farmer's object is to snatch a crop with which to meet the revenue officer's demands, not to build up the soil of newly tilled land to make it valuable in the future. Not only taxation can cause this kind of soil-mining, of course; greed is an even commoner cause, and necessity another.

Really serious soil-mining, however, could only be caused by the substitution of a money economy for payment of taxes in kind. At a certain stage in the growth of all civilizations this revolution takes place: it is one of the symptoms of urban paramountcy, and its logical conclusions are the regarding of money as a commodity, dealing in money as such, and, finally, instead of the production of coin to suit the amount of wealth in circulation, or the adjustment of prices to such a figure that the wealth and coinage balance each other in practice, the manipulation of real wealth to suit a financial pattern.[119]

When farmer's taxes are paid in kind as a percentage of the crop, the tax is as flexible as the crop, and the Fisc is bound to accept, with the farmer, part of the ordinary risks and chances of agriculture, profiting from good seasons and taking in its belt in bad ones. Where money is substituted for kind, this rule *may* apply; but it may not, and in India the amounts due from each village tended to become customary, by arrangement between the headman, or the chief of a number of villages, and the Fiscal authority. Such an arrangement was a great temptation to headmen and chiefs, who tended to become tax-farmers, and to abuse their power by forcing from the peasants, and therefore from the soil fertility, a contribution in excess of their powers of resistance. Moreover, since the headman and chiefs were the men to whom the Central Governments looked for their money, those governments would tend to allow the power of the headmen and chiefs to increase, to support these village and district officers in the assumption of powers far in excess of those which tradition allowed them.

Nevertheless, the system seems to have worked tolerably well during the long Buddhist period, and far worse abuses were to come under the Mughals.

*

The Mughals were of Mongol origin, and Tartars. For a people of such antecedents to learn a sense of responsibility to ploughed soil is a work of time and goodwill. For a very long time the Mughal government did not take any interest or make any changes in the Indian systems of land-tenure and cultivation. The principal source of wealth in India was the soil, and by so much, that the revenue from all the other taxes together was insignificant when compared with the land revenue. During the greater part of the Buddhist period the land tax probably rarely exceeded one-sixth of the crop; during the greater part of the Mughal period, on the other hand, the tax was rarely less than one-third, often as high as a half, and was assessed not yearly, but over longer periods, which meant that allowance could only be made for bad years as an act of grace on the part of the authorities, the peasantry having no actual right to tax relief when their harvest failed. Neither peasant nor soil could stand this; the *raiyats*, that is the once land-owning peasants, began to abandon the soil, taking to service or even to *dacoity,* that is banditry. This tendency became so general that it caused the government grave anxiety and even forced them, little as they understood the problem, to make concessions to farmers who would take up derelict land.

That the Mughal governments did not take that interest in

the land which implies a sense of responsibility towards the soil is very clear:

> Under Muslim rule large areas of the country are left in the possession of Hindu chiefs who had, at any rate, a claim to sovereignty but had submitted to the Muslim rulers on terms which preserved to them internal jurisdiction; these terms might include the payment of a fixed tribute, or merely the personal service of the chief with his troops, but in any case the Muslim administration did not ordinarily interfere with assessment or collection of the revenue so long as the terms were observed. If a chief defaulted, the result was ordinarily a punitive expedition and either his displacement or revision of the terms previously in force; but so long as he remained loyal, he enjoyed the revenue of his territories subject to the payment of the stipulated tribute, if any.[120]

This looks uncommonly like the relationship between the khans of the Golden Horde and the various governments of the several Russian nations. It implies not simply a change in the recipients of taxes, but an extra burden—whether cash tribute or the cost of military service. The contract between peasants and their central government is one in which the former purchase from the latter protection from foreign enemies, and from civil strife, police, order, intercession with the Gods where the church is established, and, in all modern and even some ancient states, certain other public utility services. Such was the implied contract between the Indian *raiyats*[121] and their chiefs, and it must have remained unchanged by the conquest; but now the chiefs had to meet in addition the cost of tribute or service. Hence, no doubt, the rise in the land-tax from an average of one-sixth to about one-third of the produce.[122]

The bad aspects of this method were made very much worse by the system of Assignments.[123] When the Emperor wished to reward an officer or promote a favourite, he *assigned* him a certain district, a group of villages, not thereby permanently alienating the land from the Crown, but giving the assignee full powers to collect the revenue in his district, and, after payment of what was due to the Crown, to keep the remainder; and this remainder constituted his *place*, his reward. Later this system was extended so that even where no assignment had been made to a soldier or courtier or favourite, the existing chief of the district became the Assignee, and these Assignees tended to become local autocrats, to whom the Crown looked for the revenue and who, provided the money was forthcoming, were left to do very much as they liked in their territory.

This system was pernicious: the Emperors easily dealt with their obligation to men who had served them by assigning them a district without any idea what taxes were in fact available for assignment. The Fiscal authority had to find the district and at the same time make sure that the revenue was maintained. The assignee had not, of course, access to such books and registers as were kept by the Fisc, and if he was assigned such and such a territory with the assurance that it would bring him in x lakhs of rupees, of which he must pass on y lakhs to the state, the assignee was forced to take their word for it. But, at their wits' end to find suitable assignments, the Fiscal authorities began to falsify the assessments, assigning territories as worth a certain sum in revenue which, however, could not possibly produce any such amount. The unfortunate assignee then, having squeezed his peasants and abused his soil until both were exhausted, would still find that not only was he making nothing out of his place, but could not even meet his obligation to the state, and was liable to penalties accordingly. The falsification of assessment became general, until, at last, the system having become unworkable, it was abandoned, or partially abandoned, for prospective assignees actually began to refuse assignments and ask for what was due to them in cash. Moreover, the falsification of assessments meant that the small amount of protection which the *raiyats* and the soil had enjoyed, was withdrawn from them: in theory, assessment was made on the area sown, and the nature of the crop, calculated in money at ruling prices.

But this was mere theory, and in practice an assessment having been fixed by the hard-pressed Fiscal officers, who had their own doubtless large and increasing cuts to consider, the Assignee was free to force the money out of the *raiyats* as best he could, the central government being perfectly indifferent to the misery of the *raiyats* and the abuse of the soil.[124]

The system became so corrupt that (in 1566) the Emperor Akbar virtually abandoned it, establishing in its place one whereby the government maintained direct contact with the village headman by means of salaried officials.[125] This might have been an excellent thing had not the very able minister in charge, Raja Todar Mal, been shifted to a new post, and another put in his place, bringing with him his own team of administrators. A period of corruption and extortion followed, instead of a period of development and prosperity. The soil was further drained of fertility, the area under cultivation shrank, and with it the revenue. In due course the system of salaried collectors was given up, the system of assignments restored, a new assessment register made; the falsification of assessment started again immediately, and for exactly the same reasons as before.

By the time of the Emperor Aurangzib the standard of assessment was 50 per cent of the crop, and, in practice, "tended to be the utmost sum the village could be made to pay".[126] In short the soil was simply being regarded as a source of wealth for the treasury, with the usual consequences for its fertility capital.

Towards the end of the Mughal period another strain was put upon soil fertility in India. The Mughals, no longer militarily supreme, were forced to pay a sort of *Danegeld* to the rising power of the Mārathās, and as the government itself could or would not conduct its business in a more economical manner, it was certainly upon the raiyats and the overtaxed soil that this tribute fell. It again became increasingly difficult to get assignments accepted, and the appointment of tax-farmers, with little or no regard to anything in their character but the ability to get money out of the peasants, became common. The tax-farms then tended to become hereditary properties and the tax-farmers to become virtually chiefs, either of villages or districts. These chiefs, of tax-farm origin, and also the remaining real chiefs, who also became farmers of the revenue in their districts, were called *zamindār*, a word which, whatever its original sense, came to have the meaning "land-holder". And the group of villages, or district, in the grip of the *zamindār*, was therefore known as a *zamindāri*.[127]

As the central authority weakened, more or less independent chiefs, many of them of the old Hindu families, emerged as virtual autocrats of their districts, collecting the revenue from the *raiyats* and keeping it for the operation of their own governments, instead of forwarding it to the Imperial treasury. Tax-farmers, princes, adventurers, ex-soldiers, powerful *zamindārs* set up small states all over the empire, still nominally, but only nominally dependent. It was this system of chaos which was inherited by the East India Company when, at the end of the eighteenth and beginning of the nineteenth centuries, it took over the administration of the land revenue, at first indirectly, by the company's power over the emperor's minister or cabinet, the *Diwan*,[128] subsequently by constituting the council of the company itself *Diwan* of the empire.

*

By the time of Clive the revenue system of what was to become British India was in much the state described above.[129] The *zamindāri* system was corrupt and oppressive, assessments bore no relation to the real productivity of the soil and powers of the *raiyats*, and the latter were crushed under huge burdens and almost enserfed. When, during the Governor-Generalship of Warren Hastings, the British were engaged in taking over and trying to work the revenue system, the officers appointed by the company could not even get such facts and records as were in the hands of the incumbents of the system, upon which to base their reforms. The company was willing and anxious to better the lot and lighten the burdens of the *raiyats*, and to give the soil of India a chance to recover and improve. They came from a country in the exciting throes of the immensely successful agrarian revolution which produced High Farming, and taught Europe and the world how to farm well. But at the same time, they had to produce the revenue, and they could obtain virtually no information concerning crops, land, fertility, agricultural practices, land tenure history nor soil productivity, upon which to base proposals. The *raiyats* themselves were illiterate and suspicious, as well they might be, and probably thought the devil they knew preferable to the devil they did not know. They gave no help to the British. The *zamindārs* were, of course, determined to block all attempts to interfere with the powers and profits which they enjoyed.[130] Verelst himself (President of the Council) wrote on the subject:

> The Company's European servants are left in complete ignorance of the real produce and capacity of the country by a set of men who first deceive us from interest and afterwards continue the deception from a necessary regard for their own safety.

The passive resistance to the company's well-intentioned supervisors came also from higher officials called *Kanungos*. The *Kanungo* was a sort of super-*zamindār*, or rather an overseer of *zamindārs*, whose duty it was to:

> register the usages of a district, the rates and mode of its assessment, and all regulations relating thereto. To note and regard the progress of cultivation, the produce of the land and the price current thereof, and to be at all times able to furnish government with materials to regulate the assessment by just and equitable proportions.[131]

The *Kanungos* had many other duties, and their records were, in fact, complete registers of everything relating to land-taxation within their *Parganas* (Districts). They, above all, could have denied the British a right knowledge of the facts.

... it was in the power of the Kanungos to expose the value of their (the zamindār's) *parganas*. This power the Kanungos availed themselves of, and it was the rod which they held over them, so that the apprehension of an increase of his rents kept the zamindār in very effectual awe of the kanungo ... in a word, the kanungos have an absolute influence over the zamindārs which they exercise in every measure which can promote their own interests. ... It now happens that the kanungos manage not only the zamindārs but the business of the province. There is not a record but is in their possession and so much of the executive part they have at last obtained that they are now virtually the Collector, while he is a mere passive representative of Government. They are the channel through which all his orders are conveyed ... instead of being the agents of Government, they are become the associates of the zamindārs and conspire with them to conceal what it is their chief duty to divulge.[132]

As is not unusual in commerce, and when tax collecting becomes a kind of commerce, the two defrauded parties in this business were the principals, the government and the wretched *raiyats*. The collectors could not find out what rights the *zamindārs* and the *raiyats* had, respectively, in the soil, and the *raiyats* had been manœuvred, over a long course of time, out of their status as land-holding and perhaps land-owning freemen, into, at best, rent-paying tenants, at worst bound serfs. They were wrung and wrung again for taxes which went to enrich *zamindārs* and *kanungos,* and which they had either to force out of their improverished soil, or abscond and turn *dacoit.*

The case of those *raiyats* who, by custom, still paid tax in kind, was particularly hard. The men who paid in money were at least considered to have some rights, if only tenant's rights, but those who paid in kind were now no better than sharecroppers on an annual tenancy-at-will.

A perfect example of the state of affairs is to be found in the case of Mr. Harrington's survey, in the pargana of Swarappur.[133] The Board of Revenue being dissatisfied with the returns from that *Pargana*, Harrington was appointed to survey and reassess it. He found that he had to begin by establishing a standard land measurement, for when he inquired the actual size of an Indian cubit, he received three different answers from three *kanungos*. Having, with great labour, fixed a standard, based on an old *dirra* (yardstick) bearing the stamp of the Nawab Kasim Ali Khan, Harrington discovered that not even the area of land given for the *pargana*, in the return, was remotely correct. The *pargana* was actually ten thousand acres larger than the *zamindār* had admitted, but that official's return for land actually under cultivation was no less than 17,500 acres less than the reality. Obviously, he was drawing revenue from the whole cropped area, and paying government only a part of it. Harrington examined all the returns and concluded that:

> the mass of returns by which the assets were annually checked by the Collector and his staff were, even when not fabricated, completely divorced from reality.

The significance of this sort of thing from our point of view, is as follows: on the *zamindār's* own figures for this *pargana*, the revenue was estimated at Rs. 43,521. This figure being regarded with suspicion in the first place, a preliminary check assessment was made, before that of Harrington, and a figure of Rs. 45,439 arrived at, as a reasonable expectation from the whole *pargana*, which measured 55,440 acres. The discrepancy was not, therefore, great, and it appears that the *zamindār* was willing to pay virtually the same sum from 38,000 acres, as that which was estimated reasonable by the collector if levied on 55,000 acres. Needless to say, the *zamindār* was taxing the whole *pargana* and keeping for himself the revenue from the odd 17,000 acres, which means that the soil of this district was being overtaxed to at least 30 per cent beyond its capacity. But only beyond its capacity under the bad management and in the bad state it had been reduced to under this oppressive system, for Harrington estimated that if properly managed the *pargana* could yield Rs. 66,850. The difference in the figures of actual and potential revenue are a measure of the decline of the land.

This is a single example, and one in which a proper survey was made and the real capacity of the soil and *raiyats* of a *pargana* correctly assessed and understood. The subsequent Decennial settlement, in Rangpur and elsewhere in Bengal and Bihar, was made, as Hartley points out, not after such a survey, but on the figures returned by the *zamindārs*, which were undoubtedly wildly false.

Various different systems of collecting the land revenue were tried by the British: collectors were withdrawn, reinstated, burdened with native *diwans*, again emancipated from this control. District officers wrote in from all over the empire animadverting on the miserable condition of the *raiyats* who, while the Governor-General, his Council, the Court of Directors of the Company, the Council opposition party and the Collectors wrestled with the chaos left by the decayed Mughal system, and while *kanungos* and *zamindārs* did their best to make confusion worse confounded, continued, with their long suffering soil, to go from bad to worse. Of a typical agricultural unit in Rangpur in 1789 we find, of 2600 acres fit for cultivation of which 2400 were classified as productive, only 1779 acres actually occupied and being worked by *raiyats*, the rest being derelict.[134]

Out of this sketchy account of the decline in a system of land tenure and taxation, certain things emerge. After the tribal system had decayed, the soil of India belonged to village communities of self-governing *raiyats* organized in brotherhoods on a kinship basis. In course of time each man's holding had come to be his property on condition of his continuing to cultivate it up to a certain standard of efficiency, and paying his tax to the central government, based on a reasonable settlement of the assessment, and the contract being protected by religious rules. During centuries of abuse, tax-farmers and *zamindārs* had, however, come to be regarded as the landholders, if not owners, and what had been a tax payable by the *raiyat*, turned into rent due from him, thus reducing the *raiyat* to the status of a tenant. No legal or administrative sanction whatever existed for this state of affairs; it had just come about, to the great cost of the soil, and had any attempt been made to restore the original relationship between *raiyats* and soil, it would have been right to rehabilitate the *raiyats* as land-owners, and reduce the *zamindārs* and *kanungos* to the status of tax-collectors and tax-inspectors respectively.

These facts were the more unfortunate in that the British, because of the absolute impossibility of ever getting at the real facts, were forced to make a settlement in terms of the *status quo*. If nothing else compelled them to this step, and if it be argued that they could have studied the history of the revenue and found out its origins, there was the fact of their own background and their own history in the matter of land-owning and land working. In their own country, during the past three centuries, they had been dispossessing the peasantry, enclosing common land, and creating a system of great land-owners employing paid labour to work the soil, or leasing farms to tenant farmers. And whereas it would be a labour of Hercules to come to tax agreements with every smallholder, if the *raiyats* were admitted to that status, it would be comparatively easy to collect the tax from a much smaller number of great land-owners, and allow the latter to make their own terms, within certain limits, with their "tenants".

*

Lord Cornwallis was the first Governor-General of India to be appointed, in all but name, not by the Court of Directors of the Company but by the British Government. It was his task to clear the administration of corruption, cheapen it, settle the revenue question, the commercial question and the judicial question. In the matter of the land-revenue, he was variously advised: under his predecessor, Warren Hastings, the acrimonious Sir Philip Francis, as a member of council, had maintained that the *zamindārs* were the land-owners and that therefore the government should come to an arrangement with them for the revenue. When Cornwallis was Governor-General

Francis was back in England making his influence felt in that sense, while Cornwallis was being similarly advised by John Shore, a man of great ability and experience, President of the Board of Revenue, against whose opinion that of Grant, a scholar who had gone into the history of the revenue and rightly held that the *raiyats* were the land-owners, the *zamindārs* mere officials, carried too little weight.[135] But in any case Cornwallis, a man devoted to duty and "the sense of his superiors' orders", had little choice, for before any settlement had been made, and largely due to the influence of Francis, Pitt's India Act of 1784 called for a permanent settlement by the regulation of payments due from "*rajas, zamindārs* and other land-holders". In fact, by the mere wording of this Act of Parliament, the *zamindārs* had been admitted as land-owners.

Nevertheless, under Shore and Cornwallis, the Board of Revenue did excellent work. Formerly the collectors had been paid only Rs. 1200 a month, and left to make the large fortunes with which, like Jos. Sedley in *Vanity Fair*, they played the nabob in England, by corrupt practices and illicit private trading. They were now raised to a new dignity and, by their position, given a clear interest in promoting the proper cultivation of the districts under their control. They were paid Rs. 1500 a month for their subsistence, and in addition a commission of about 1 per cent of the revenue they collected in their districts, over which they had considerable powers. The commission on revenue, and security in his post, would lead an able and conscientious officer to see that the cultivation of his district was well managed, that crops were improved, manuring properly attended to (a difficult matter in a country where deforestation led to cow-dung being used as fuel), and waste land taken up and rehabilitated.

A preliminary move towards a permanent settlement was made by the Governor-General, on the basis of making the *zamindār* the land-owner, in the Ten Year settlement; and a year later, by the decision of Pitt and Dundas, this was turned into a settlement in perpetuity. Once the decision was incorporated in an Act of Parliament, the status of the *zamindārs* as land-owners, and the dispossession of the *raiyats*, was at last legal, and an entirely alien, peculiarly western system of land ownership was imposed upon India.

This Act created for the British in India problems concerning the rights of the *raiyats* and the conservation and restoration of soil fertility which, when the Dominion was created and the country handed over to its native peoples, they were still engaged in solving, and with at least some measure of success. The *raiyats* were given leases of such length and on such terms that the relationship with the soil which had been the pride of their ancestors and the salvation of the soil in the distant past, was to some extent restored, and the *raiyats* regained that interest in their holdings which alone might save the soil from the consequences of centuries of abuse.

As for those consequences, the soil exhaustion and sheet erosion which are common, and the famines which result from them, as well as from the unreliability of rainfall where irrigation works have not been undertaken, if not wholly and solely due to the changes in a system of land tenure and taxation arising out of the decay of two great cultures and the rise of a third on Indian soil, are at least very largely due to those causes.

PART FIVE:

MAN AS A SOIL MAKER

*

CHAPTER XIII

THE SOILS OF THE WESTERN ANDES: THE INCA EMPIRE

THE peoples of America entered that Continent either by walking across the land-bridge connecting Asia to America before the last Ice Age, or across the frozen Bering Strait some time after it. In either event they were probably in pursuit of game, and were certainly at a very primitive stage of Stone Age culture. They can have brought with them from Asia but a poor equipment of tools and social customs, and can therefore, in their subsequent development, be considered as the products of their new rather than their old environment.

Those immigrants who remained near the ice showed their quality by devising the brilliantly ingenious Esquimaux culture and thus achieved the astonishing feat of establishing communities in the harshest possible environment; but since all their energy was consumed in remaining alive, they could make no progress in bettering their lot.

Other immigrants drifted south, creating communities with economies and social customs suited to the soils upon which they settled. The excessive challenge[136] of the northern tundra and ice made the response of a high culture impossible for the Esquimaux; on the other hand the great central plains of North America, teeming with game, offered an inadequate challenge: for a hunting people life in those conditions was too easy, and such congeries of tribes as the Athapascans, the Algonquins and the Iroquois had little to stimulate them into forming sedentary societies. There were no animals capable of domestication, to give rise to a pastoral economy; maize, the only cereal of the Americas really worth cultivating, had to be introduced from the south. On the other hand the great *steppe* offered these folk, while they maintained a hunting and gathering economy, fourteen species of wild esculent roots, forty-two kinds of wild fruit, twenty-five sorts of fish, twenty-two edible animals and forty varieties of game birds.[137]

As late as the nineteenth century the native Americans offered the observer the spectacle of the growth of culture from palaeolithic, through neolithic to a sort of "false" Iron Age imposed by Europeans. The Athapascans were hunters, gatherers and fishers; the Algonquins, while subsisting principally by hunting and gathering, at which they were uncommonly skilful and successful, practised an auxiliary agriculture with maize; the Iroquois confederation of tribes had settled down to sedentary agriculture, understood manuring their crops, had formed permanent territorial associations, and governed themselves as a "nation" by means of a Grand Council. Meanwhile, to complete the series without bringing European influence into consideration, the Nahuanatlaca[138] and kindred peoples had, some centuries previously, created a high civilization. (Maya—"Olmec"—Toltec—Aztec, etc.)

In the four groups above we have (i) soil members, (ii) men graduating from soil-membership to soil-parasitism, (iii) soil parasites, and (iv) soil exploiters. In the most advanced of the Mexican nations, and above all in the nations of South America we can cap the series with a people of successful soil-makers. As successful soil-making entails a social discipline of the strictest, we find in the mis-called "Peruvian", or even more miscalled "Inca" nations of the West Andes, the most perfectly symmetrical and stable political units ever achieved by man.

If the enormous plenty of game in North America prevented the human members of that soil community from settling to agriculture, excepting where game was growing scarcer, the soil conditions of the Pacific littoral of South America and in the valleys of the western Andes, as well as those of Mexico, produced a series of high cultures based on sedentary agriculture. Over a period of time impossible to determine at present, these cultures hardened into a number of nations, groups of which were, on several occasions, united into empires by military force exercised by one, or by a league of their number. A proto-empire of the people of Tiahuanaco on Lake Titicaca has been forgotten but its traces remain. An empire created by a military people with their capital at Cuzco succeeded it. These imperialists endeavoured to impose on their subject nations their own religion of sun-worship, against which the Earth-mother worshippers rose in revolt, destroying the empire. In the course of time the same aggressive tribe rose again, under the leadership of the Inca *ayllu*,[139] re-established itself in the Cuzco region, and began again, by means of armed force and persuasion, to unite the Andean Great Society into a single Universal State.

This is not the place either to enlarge the above scrappy sketch, or to deal with the origins of the Inca themselves, concerning which the interested reader will find many variations on fascinating and significant legends in the works of Sir Clements Markham, Garcilasso de la Vega Inca, Pedro Sarmiento de Gamboa, Polo de Ondegardo, Prescot and others. But one story, from the *Royal Commentaries* of Garcilasso de la Vega Inca, must be told, because it demonstrates how, from the beginning, these people were primarily concerned with good soil. When Garcilasso was a child his maternal uncle, an Inca of course, told him the story of the origins of his tribe and their greatness. In that story we learn that:

> ... Our Father the Sun placed his two children in the Lake of Titicaca ... and he said to them that they might go where they pleased, and that at every place where they stopped to eat or sleep, they were to thrust a sceptre of gold into the ground, which was half a yard long and two fingers in thickness. He gave them this staff as a sign and token that in the place where, by one blow on the earth, it should sink

and disappear, there it was the desire of our Father the Sun that they should remain and establish their court.

In short, let them settle on a deep top-soil.

Some picture of the rise of the final Universal State must be given for the benefit of those not familiar with Andean history.

The many nations of the West Andes had advanced to various levels of culture and civilization without losing the most important of their ancient tribal customs, the communal ownership and working of land. The reason for this singular and arresting conservatism will appear hereafter: it derives from the very nature of their soils. Some of these nations were primitive, others barbarous, others, especially in the north-west, polished. Technically, all were in the Stone Age, or early Bronze or rather Copper Age, for the presence of tin in their metal was fortuitous. The arts of agriculture, and of stock-raising with the only domesticable species, the *Auchenias* or llamas, were far advanced. The art of ceramics very far advanced indeed, and crafts of weaving and gold-smithing brought to a perfection of art, though not of technics, unequalled by any comparable Old World culture. None of these peoples had an alphabet, nor had they ideographical or stylized pictographical means of writing, but they were fine painters, magnificent sculptors, possessed music, and, in the *quipu*, had a mnemonic instrument enabling them to keep accounts and statistics with great exactitude, and even to record the principal events of history.

The religion of the whole Andean world from the river Maule to the river Ancasmayu was homogeneous at bottom but varied locally on the surface. Stones, lakes, animals, reptiles and birds from being, in all probability, tribal totems, had become *lares et penates*. But above these mere saints, as it were, these familiar domestic gods, were such universal deities with varying local names as *Pachamamma*, the Earth-goddess[140] and, perhaps originally her son and later her superior, *Viracocha*,[141] the creator of all things. With the ultimate secular paramountcy of the Inca *ayllu*, their tribal totem, the Sun, became the national deity, but the other great gods were neither displaced nor dishonoured.

The early Apu-Ccapac-Inca, after their clan had seized the region of Cuzco, secured their local dominion, improved their domain and began slowly to increase it by local conquest. With the exception of one or two monarchs of unusual ferocity, the Inca expanionist policy was applied in an enlightened and urbane spirit, every effort being made to bring other nations into the union by persuasion and good example before military force was used. As militarists, legalists and organizers, and also as engineers, the Inca are very reminiscent of the Romans, and they often had the same aesthetic inferiority to their victims. In due course, also, they had to fight their "Punic War", although without the disastrous consequences which afflicted the Romans: the Inca pretention to empire was disputed by the neighbouring Chanca people who mustered so formidable an army and advanced against their neighbours in so truculent a manner that the old Inca Viracocha fled to an impregnable fortress, leaving his people to fend for themselves. However, the youngest of the royal princes, Cusi, his loyal brothers who recognized his superior talents, and the two veteran generals of the nation went out against the Chanca, and in two campaigns first defeated and then routed them. Thereafter Prince Cusi became the Inca Pachacuti Yupanqui.[142] It was this monarch who began the really rapid expansion of the empire, in the late eleventh century, and his work was completed in the twelfth century by his equally able and courageous successors, Tupac Yupanqui and Huayna Ccapac. By the end of the latter's reign the Universal State of the Andes had reached its greatest extent, its bounds were decreed by the Inca himself as being the Maule in the south and the Ancasmayu in the north (2700 miles), and the empire was known as *Tahua-ntin-suyu*, the Four Combined Provinces.[143]

The Inca made no attempt to destroy the social organization of the conquered nations: the tribal pattern was simply modified to fit into the imperial system, communal land-tenure being left intact. The numbers of each tribe were so rounded off that they could be fitted into the state organization of the people in ten thousands (huana); thousands (huaranca); five hundreds (picha-pachaca); one hundreds (pachac), and tens (chunca). The words in brackets mean both the number and also the name of the officer presiding over that number, to whose title was added the word *curaça,* meaning, roughly, chief. This numbering off of the civil population into military groups, as it were, was entirely successful, and gave the government a very high degree of control over the business of the country.

Over the officers of these groups was set, as a governor of each province, a viceroy called *Michec* (=shepherd) whose business it was to collect what the chronicler calls tribute and taxes. But, as will appear, these revenues in kind were the produce of Crown lands, and all that the people had to contribute, each according to his ability, was labour, and by no means an excess of that.

The soils of the empire were divided between three classes of holders. The first was the church, which held land sufficient to maintain its temples, priests and festivals. The second and probably largest holding class was the people, through their *ayllus,* land being held in common and private property unknown. All the work of this land was done in common, but it was allotted in sections to heads of families, according to the size of the family, so that each person in the whole empire lived on the usufruct of a definite piece of land—the individual was, so to speak, endowed with the product of that land though he did not work it himself as a peasant, but worked with his fellow-tribesmen at the cultivation of all the land they held as a tribe. Finally, the Crown was a large holder, the produce of State farms supporting the Court, the Inca, the Army, the Civil Service, and also maintaining the very great stores of food, textiles and other raw materials by means of which the Inca maintained a perfectly even and unvarying standard of living among their subjects during a number of centuries, regardless of seasonal gluts or shortages.

There was an established order in which land was worked and harvests gathered. All turned out first to tend the church lands, next the common land, and finally the Crown land. When the common land was being worked, the common harvest gathered in, priority was given, by law, to the holdings of widows, the aged and the sick, and the *curaça* or overseer who ignored this law was liable to be hanged.[144] Nor were the artisans, craftsmen and soldiers outside this harmonious concert of work: each had his endowment of land at birth, and it was worked for him by his fellow citizens and its produce reserved for his use.

All adult males were liable for agricultural and military service, and children over a certain age as well as the old below a certain age were expected to perform their allotted light tasks.

In addition to their incomparable genius for government, possibly surpassing that of the Roman, the Inca and their people were magnificent engineers: their public buildings were impressive by their size rather than from any aesthetic merit, although the sculptured decoration was remarkable; but their metalled roads extending over the whole empire and crossing mountains and deserts were unequalled in the Old World, and their aqueducts and water-works generally equal to the Roman and perhaps more numerous. The construction of these great works entailed the use of labour *corvées*, but work on public utilities exempted the conscript from military service, in no way harmed his interests at home, and was carefully calculated to be well within his strength.

Famine was eliminated, for the first (and perhaps the last!) time in history. So was social strife. There were, in the twelfth century, revolts against the Inca government, but these were nationalist, irridentist, and not social: they were put down, sometimes harshly, occasionally with brutality, but as a rule in an enlightened spirit of compromise. In order to minimize such revolts the Inca introduced the policy of removing whole populations from one part of the empire, and planting them in some remote part where the natural conditions and work to be done were identical. These colonies were called *mitimaes*,[145] and they served to make the population of the whole region homogeneous by making tribal and parochial differences unreal. The colonists had in common with their neighbours only those things that were of the whole empire including the Quichua language which, by government decree, was made to replace all local languages. It is typical of the good sense of the Inca that in Quichua they did not adopt their own language, but that which was the most flexible and expressive of all the American tongues. Quichua became the "Latin" of the Andean world, and a not inconsiderable literature, despite the want of writing, came into being in that tongue.[146]

Down to the smallest detail, the ordering of the social life of the people was managed by officials: for example each member nation of the empire had not only its distinctive style of dress, but even its distinctive hair-style, with the result that when the Apu-Ccapac-Inca wished to confer an honour upon a citizen, he could effectively do so by allowing him to adopt some personal idiosyncrasy of dress or toilet, perhaps to wear the Inca ear-plugs by which the aristocracy distended the ear lobes, thus earning the Spanish sobriquet of *Orejones*.[147] From each member community of the commonwealth was expected a contribution according to its local resources and skill, whether such contribution be the dried fish of Lake Titicaca, caught by the primitive folk who inhabited its shores, or the sophisticated goldsmith's work from Quimbaya or Cuzco. The whole Great Society expressed itself in its daily life with a rhythm, an order and a grace which is entirely artificial, and which makes on the reader the impression of an immense, formal ballet.

What were the soil conditions which gave rise to so perfect a work of social and political art?

*

Of the topography of the West Andean world in which the civilization which we shall call Andean came into existence,

Cieza de Leon, one of the historians of the Andean Indians, wrote:[148]

> In this land there are three desert ranges where man can in no wise exist. One of these comprises the *montana* (forests) of the Andes, full of dense wildernesses where men cannot, nor ever have lived. The second is the mountainous region extending the whole length of the *cordillera* of the Andes, which is intensely cold and its summits are covered with eternal snows, so that in no way can people live in this region owing to the snow and the cold and also because there are no provisions, all things being destroyed by the snow and the wind, which never ceases to blow. The third range comprises the sandy deserts from Tumbez to the other side of Tarapaca, in which there is nothing to be seen but sandhills and the fierce sun which dries them up, without water, nor herb, nor tree, nor created thing, except birds which by the gift of their wings, wander wherever they list. This kingdom, being so vast, has great deserts, for the reason I have now given. The inhabited region is after this fashion. In parts of the mountains of the Andes there are ravines and dales which open out into valleys of such widths as often to form great plains between the mountains, and, although the snow falls, it all remains on the higher part. As these valleys are closed in, they are not molested by the winds, nor does the snow reach them, and the land is so fruitful that all things which are sown yield abundantly, and there are trees and many birds and animals. The land being so fertile is well peopled by the natives. They make their villages with rows of stones roofed with straw, and live healthily and in comfort. Thus the mountains of the Andes form these dales and ravines in which there are populous villages, and rivers of excellent water flow near them.

It is not possible to arrive at a complete picture of the rise of Andean civilization on the soil described above in terms of a single nation or a single locality. But archaeology and history have revealed here a part and there a part of the truth, and by putting these parts together it is possible to achieve a continuous narrative which must come near to being an account of what happened.

Of the most ancient origins of agriculture in the Andean world we can gather enough hints from all over the region to justify us in supposing them to have been much the same as in the Old World. Sir Clements Markham says that the Quichua language is particularly rich in terms of relationship; there are, for example, different words for a sister's sister and a brother's sister.[149] It has been demonstrated that this attribute of a language belongs to its phase as the tongue of an exogamous, totemistic tribal society.[150] The peoples of the Andean world were organized in *ayllus*, kinship groups reproducing the tribal pattern and tracing their descent from some animal—llama, dog, serpent, jaguar, condor; or from some sacred natural object, such as a lake or even a stone: such "ancestors" must surely have been once tribal totems.[151]

If we insist upon every culture rising in the world according to a single blue-print, we should expect these totemistic tribes to develop into agricultural communities either by way of tillage discovered by the women of the tribes, or by way of stock-raising discovered by men. Without insisting too heavily upon such consistency, there is evidence that this is, in fact what happened—for example, primitive Andean society was probably matrilinear and matriarchal. True, some authorities believe that the custom of sister-marriage in the Inca royal family was of recent origin and designed to maintain the purity of the royal blood but there is little evidence that this purity was held to be so very important, for several of the Apu-Ccapac-Inca preferred as their heirs the sons of concubines.[152] Moreover Sarmiento says that the custom was of very great antiquity[153] and its origin may be sought in the origin-myth of the Inca *ayllu*. In the Andean world, as elsewhere, its origin was surely economic, the device serving to give men property or power in a matrilinear society. We have already suggested that such societies are rooted in soil, that they derive from the economic predominance of women where women are the farmers, the principal food-getters. And in some legends of the Andean peoples the memory of this truth is preserved: the Cañari folk say that at the time of the great deluge,[154] two brothers of their nation escaped to the heights of Huacap-ñan and remained there until the waters subsided: starving, they came down into the valleys in search of food, finding herbs and roots which barely kept them alive. But two parrots entered their hut in their absence and set them a meal of cooked maize and *chicha*, an intoxicant made with maize. This continued to happen until one of the brothers captured one of the parrots, whereupon the parrot turned into a beautiful woman who gave the brothers maize seed, taught them to cultivate it and, becoming the wife of one or both brothers, thus became the ancestress of the Cañari nation. There is a *manioc* culture myth which tells how the daughter of a chief conceived immaculately: her name was *Mani*. She bore a white girl child of surpassing beauty. The child was killed and buried and an unknown plant grew upon her grave, the Mani root (Mani-oc).

In earliest times, in fact, the cultivation of maize was an exclusively feminine business,[155] as was the preparation of *chicha*, and this gave women an importance which endured in some regions and tribes until historical times. Among the Chibcha, and kindred peoples who created a culture of high aesthetic standards in what is now Columbia, the five principal nations were governed by absolute kings,[156] but their office was hereditary in the female line, the king being succeeded by his sister's son. Sister marriage was common;[157] a wife had a right to flog her husband; a dying chief wife could impose on her husband a five-year vow of chastity. A man inherited personal goods through his maternal uncle, not his father, and if his wife died in child-bed he had to pay compensation to her family. The Chibcha priesthood was hereditary in the female line, and although among the gods of these people one only seems to have been female, she was all-important, Bachue, Mother of the Human Race and Goddess of Agriculture. The proto-Columbians had no animals capable of being domesticated, excepting the dog, so that their tillage economy was stable and could not be overthrown by a rising pastoralism, or stock-raising economy.

Among modern descendants of the Ancient Andeans are still to be found myths relating to the female origins of agriculture. The Earth Mother, under the name of Nungui appeared to the ancestors of the Jibaros and taught them the cultivation of the fruits upon which they chiefly live. Offended by their ingratitude, this Indian Persephone disappeared into the interior of the earth, whence she continues, however, to ensure the growth of the crops. It seems that in pre-agricultural times plant spirits were more often male, a belief that occasionally survives the rise of female values with tillage. The Untoto, e.g., have an earth-father, Naimuéna.[158]

South America, however, did produce the antithetical pattern, that of pastoral cultures, although of a sedentary rather than a nomadic habit. An ancient pastoral economy was revealed (by Boman) among the Atacama, whose remains are found associated with much llama harness and gear. The Auracanians, who were nomadic, may have been llama-herds and were certainly patriarchal. But there is evidence of another kind.

The central and southern Andean highlands are the habitat of the animals which the Spaniards called sheep but which are really a kind of camel and which we know as the llama. But the llama proper is so completely a domestic animal that no wild llamas are found, just as there are no wild camels in the Old World. The wild species of this genus are two,[159] the huanaco (*Auchenia huanacus*), and the vicuna (*A. vicunia*). Of the huanaco there are two domesticated kinds, the llama and the alpaca, but these animals differ in so many particulars from their wild ancestor that they are distinguished from it by their own specific names, *A. glama* and *A. paco*. Furthermore, the differences are of the kind which occur when wild animals are domesticated by herdsmen, and the breeding so controlled as to emphasize those of their attributes which are of economic value: in the case of the alpaca, the fleece is much improved on that of the wild species; in the case of the llama the differences are such as to make it more valuable as a beast of burden.

Differences so great as to involve specific description and designation are only produced over great periods of time. The llama is the product of thousands of years' domestication; its remains are found associated with those of peoples living within its range back to times not long posterior to those of the giant armadillo and giant sloth hunters of the Quarternary epoch: pastoralism in the Andes is of respectable antiquity.

It is at least probable that the earliest Andean high civilization had a stock-raising economy as its foundation, and that the Andean world reproduced the familiar Old World pattern of a fertile though warlike encounter between pastoral and tillage folk. There is, first of all, a language-clue to some such encounter.

Markham says that the word *michec* in Quichua means shepherd, but is also commonly used to mean governor. The word *michisca* (from *michec*) a flock, also means *the governed*. Huayna Ccapac-Inca, when he assumed the office of Supreme Pontiff in the state religion of sun-worship, called himself *Shepherd of the Sun*. Now, the Turkish conquerors of Byzantium, a Moslem people of pastoral nomads who imposed themselves upon the Orthodox Christians of that civilization as its proprietors and governors, referred to their subjects as the *rahiyeh*, the flock or herd. Pastoral peoples, when they conquer a community of sedentary farmers so completely that no absorption of the conquered by the conquerors occurs, tend to regard their victims as domestic animals off which they live, as formerly they lived off herds of sheep, cattle, horses—or llamas. Such was the attitude of the Turks, the Bulgars, the Avars and other steppe horse-herders of Asia, to the Greek or Slav masses of their *rahiyeh*.

It is surely probable that the double meaning of *michec* and *michisca* in Quichua is the echo of some remote descent upon the valley farmers, by highland, llama-herding warriors. Just as only a people with pastoral traditions would have written *The Lord is my Shepherd*, so only a prince with similar traditions would have called himself *Shepherd of the Sun* upon assuming the Pontificate.

E. J. Payne[160] goes so far as to assert that the rise of civilization on Andean soils was entirely due to the domestication of the *Auchenias,* and there is a good deal to support this assertion. There was, at a very early date, in the neighbourhood of Lake Titicaca, a civilization "Apparented"[161] to that which was later united by the Inca. Its centre was the city of Tiahuanaco, of which the ruins remain, an immense metropolis constructed by highly skilled masons and sophisticated sculptors with an art style so distinctive (and so horrifying!) that it is impossible to mistake it wherever it appears. The size of this city, and its workmanship, make it quite certain that Tiahuanaco must have been the capital of a numerous, intelligent, industrious and successful community. But the city stands at an altitude of 12,500 feet and the climate of the soil of which it is the node is incapable of ripening maize.

On the other hand, there are vast ranges of the natural pasture of the *auchenias,* while the potato grows and matures satisfactorily. It has recently been made clear by Dr. Redcliffe N. Salaman[162] that the economy of a nation, given a very low standard of living for the peasantry and in the absence of potato blight, *can* be based upon the potato. But the cultivation of roots which are easily propagated vegetatively is so little stimulating to ingenuity and labour, that those peoples who have practised only this kind of agriculture have remained backward; and even peoples who, like the Irish of the nineteenth century, have fallen back from cericulture to root-culture, have thereafter degenerated. Root-cultivators show little energy and spirit in the face of attacks by corn- or meat-eaters: the aborigines of Haiti, at the time of the Spanish invasion, subsisted upon vast plantations of *manioc,* they were notably backward and invariably defeated by the Caribs, and according to Las Casas[163] twenty women working six hours a day for one month in the *manioc* fields produced sufficient *manioc* bread to last three hundred people for two years.

It follows that the Tiahuanacans did not make a great civilization with a mighty urban centre, out of potatoes, and the only other means of exploiting soil at that altitude which was open to them was by the domestication of the *auchenias*.

If these arguments are sound the llama was domesticated by the Colla people of the Titicaca basin, and it is a fact that these people worshipped God in the shape of a White Llama; that the descendants of these same Colla held the llama sacred, as the descendants of the Aryan cow-herds of Sind hold the cow sacred; and that the very word llama has, originally, no specific meaning but signifies simply *herded animal*.

Finally, if these civilized shepherds did descend upon the valleys and coastal strips to the west and clash and mix with the agrarian cultures, there ought to be traces of this encounter: and, in fact, the arresting Tiahuanacan art style intrudes into the native styles over a considerable tract of the coast, and in many of the coastal valleys (e.g., Truxilo) quite unmistakably.[164] From all of which it would appear that the soil-exploitation pattern of the rising Andean civilization resembles closely the patterns with which we are familiar in the Old World.

*

From beginnings such as have been sketched above there arose in the neighbourhood of Lake Titicaca a proto-civilization to which, although at some remove in time, the Inca civilization was affiliated. Apart from the *auchenias,* the makers of this soil-exploiting civilization had the potato.

It seems that the histories of maize and the potato are linked in an interesting manner, and the early history of the former has been established by Messrs. Manglesdorf and Reeves[165] who say that the primal plant was a pod-corn growing somewhere in what is now Paraguay, that it was first cultivated east of the Andes, that it was brought across the mountains into the west

Andean valleys, and there cultivated; and that a mutation produced the prototype of the corn which we now grow. Meanwhile, those immigrants who settled on the Titicaca plateau instead of going farther west, found that their corn would not ripen at that altitude, and seeking a substitute among the local wild plants, lit upon the potato. Subsequently, the valley people received the potato from the plateau people, and from the latter the Maya learnt of maize, the cultivation of which passed north by their means, to become the staple of all the Americans, and the support of societies varying in their advancement from primitive agrarian tribalism to high urban civilizations.

But while maize was, as it were, being prepared for this high destiny, the potato was enabling the people of the Collao to exploit their austere soil and make a beginning in the arts of civilization—the potato and, as we believe, the llama.

Although Dr. Salaman might probably not agree with Payne in the importance given by that author to the llama in the exploitation of Andean soils, he does point out that *charqui*, dried llama meat, was probably invented by the same people and at the same time as *chuno*. *Chuno* and *charqui*, stored and accumulated, became that surplus wealth out of which civilization is made: it would seem that the austere conditions of life at twelve or thirteen thousand feet offered a challenge to the Tiahuanacans to which they responded aggressively, and thus advanced more rapidly in the arts of civilization than their cousins farther west, cossetted by the easy circumstances of their alluvial valleys.

As we have seen, root cultivation generally appears to be debilitating to the people who practise it to the exclusion of cericulture. But it seems probable that the Tiahuanacans did not choose to live off potatoes, and that they had a past based on the pod-corn variety of maize. By the time their resources enabled them to descend aggressively into the valleys, the valley people would have developed the cultivation of the new maize, product of a happy mutation, and the highlanders would have seized upon this superior instrument of soil-exploitation while, at the same time, bringing the potato to the valley people as an auxiliary crop. *Oca* and *ulluca*, two other tuberous roots of the highlands, as well as the hardy bean *quinoa*, also helped the Tiahuanaco folk to develop their soil.

The disadvantages under which American man laboured are such as to make the rise of the Andean and Central American civilizations all the more creditable. The want of milch animals deprived them of that food by means of which human children can be quickly weaned, and it therefore checked the rate at which populations could grow. The presence of the potato and the *manioc* tempted the Americans, as the Africans were tempted by the *yam* (but as primitive European and Asiatic men were probably never tempted), to rely upon an easy, insipid and unstimulating means of subsistence. For the most part they resisted the temptation and went forward to the domestication and cultivation of the most magnificent and beautiful of all the cereals, maize.

By a happy coincidence maize is the one cereal which can be cultivated on a scale sufficiently vast to support a high civilization without the aid of the plough or any other tool for producing a surface area of tilth: the reason is the relatively enormous size of the plant. From the insignificant pod-corn varieties the Andean women produced, in the course of much time, cultivated varieties between six and eighteen feet in height, the ears between four and ten inches long, the grains themselves as large as a pea, and the ears on a single plant very numerous.[166] Such a plant can be cultivated singly, and does not require a ploughed and harrowed field. On park-land and forest soils the ancient Andeans began the cultivation of maize by the pernicious method of burning off the jungle and dibbing-in the seed in holes, thereafter hoeing round each plant as it grew, and continuing to crop the same site until the yield fell disastrously: the first crop of maize on virgin soil may yield as high as four-hundred-fold; the second one-hundred-fold, the third about thirty-fold. The exhaustion of the soil was perhaps delayed by the practice of interplanting with the maize a legume, a bean which was trained up the growing maize stalks. But even so, such shifting tillage cannot become the basis of a civilization; for that, permanent settlement is necessary.

As we should expect from the history of agricultural societies in the Old World, sedentary tillage developed in the New World on the alluvial and flood soils of the Andean valleys:

> It is, however, in the valleys of the rainless tracts that nature points the way most clearly to permanent cultivation. Here the periodical overflow of the rivers leaves the alluvial lands on their banks in the condition of a natural seed-bed, available for the cultivator's use with little or no labour. . . . The process is clearly marked in the rainless valleys on the Pacific side of America.[167]

In most of the Andean highlands occur valleys of alluvial deposits and the plateaux through which the rivers flow are rich pasture for the llama. Thus both tillage and stock-raising could be practised together, and it was also in the valley alluvia that the Andeans first made a continuous surface tilth, using the digging stick, the *taccla*, in lieu of the plough, and working in teams to the rhythm of song or music, the diggers being followed by cultivators who broke up the sod into a tilth. On the soils created by the mountain streams they could do this indefinitely without manuring, for those soils were naturally renewed: the streams were laden, at flood-time, with the products of mountain rain-erosion, the detritus of volcanic rock which they deposited on the soil whenever they overflowed their banks. Volcanic detritus is particularly suitable for the recreation of soils carrying maize crops, replacing exactly those nutrients which are being consumed.

But although the valley soils of the West Andes watershed resembled, in their cultivation-promoting attributes, those of the Nile, the Euphrates-Tigris, the Indus and the Hwang-ho, they were narrow and local, the product of scores of small streams, not of great river systems. Had the Andean people been content to remain parasites on their alluvial soils, they could certainly never have advanced to make the great civil and military empires of Tiahuanaco, Cuzco and of the Inca. The exiguous surfaces and inconsiderable number of naturally exploitable soils forced them to become soil-makers, to create the soils on to which they might expand their numbers, and by so doing to bring into existence the conditions in which civilization could rise.

As the good and settled living in the Andean valleys began to cause increase in the population, and as the application and industry demanded by maize culture challenged the ingenuity of the cultivators, while its profits conferred on them the surplus wealth which makes specialization of labour and therefore progress in the arts possible, the people became numerous and improved their techniques. Both necessity and self-confidence would urge them to increase the area of cultivable land. If they were to expand over soils which did not receive flood waters, they must discover the principles of manuring: they appear to have made this discovery by the accident of frequently tilling plots of land which had formerly been the sites of dwellings and on which, therefore, had accumulated much organic refuse which had subsequently rotted. They must have connected the fine quality of the crops on such plots with the organic material left there, and so gone forward to the idea of deliberate soil regeneration. Even so, in their narrow and mountainous tract, they lacked not merely fertile soil, but level surfaces of any soil at all. It was necessary to expand on to the mountain slopes, and to do this they must check the erosion of the sloping soils and build surfaces level enough to be worked even without the plough. They must turn to the rainless coastal strips of apparent desert, and to the desert areas inland. The alternative to doing all these things was to remain at a relatively low level of culture, which the Andeans did not choose to do, or which their increasing numbers did not permit them to do: the rich alluvia of the valleys and their success with the *auchenias* had produced populations so great that they were confronted with a malthusian problem.

The native American peoples seem to have been singularly aware of the very precious, and indeed sacred, quality of fertile soil. From their earliest times they were less guilty of crimes against the soil than other peoples, and even when they had become, in certain centres, sophisticated by the progress of their culture, they never lost touch with the soil; their attitude to it became intelligent without ever ceasing to be "natural", and they continued to allow themselves to be guided, in their relationship with the living soil, by their senses and instincts and even by their traditions, rather than by their not inconsiderable agricultural science.

That this was so is not to be attributed to any superior genius or sensibility, but to the nature of the soil itself: it was natural that they should understand and respect what they had had to make with their hands. But, more important, the fact that they were forced, in the Andes, in Central America and in Mexico, to create their soils in order to expand, meant that they were forced to retain, what other peoples have always rejected at a certain stage of development, the ancient structure of society, at least in so far as it relates to systems of land-tenure and land-working. In the absence of machinery or of an advanced slave-owning economy, large works of terracing, or reclamation and of irrigation can only be carried out by communal efforts and common labour. The organization of communal labour entails the development of the faculty for co-operation, and also a respectable central authority: in primitive communities it also entails establishment of that authority by religious sanctions. The religion of a people who rise by agriculture will be fundamentally an agricultural religion; for all the American peoples the soil itself was sacred, the Earth was the Mother-goddess of all things from the beginning; there is nothing peculiar in that, but what *is* peculiar is that She remained enthroned into civilized times and when finally dethroned by Christ, the soils of America fell upon evil days.

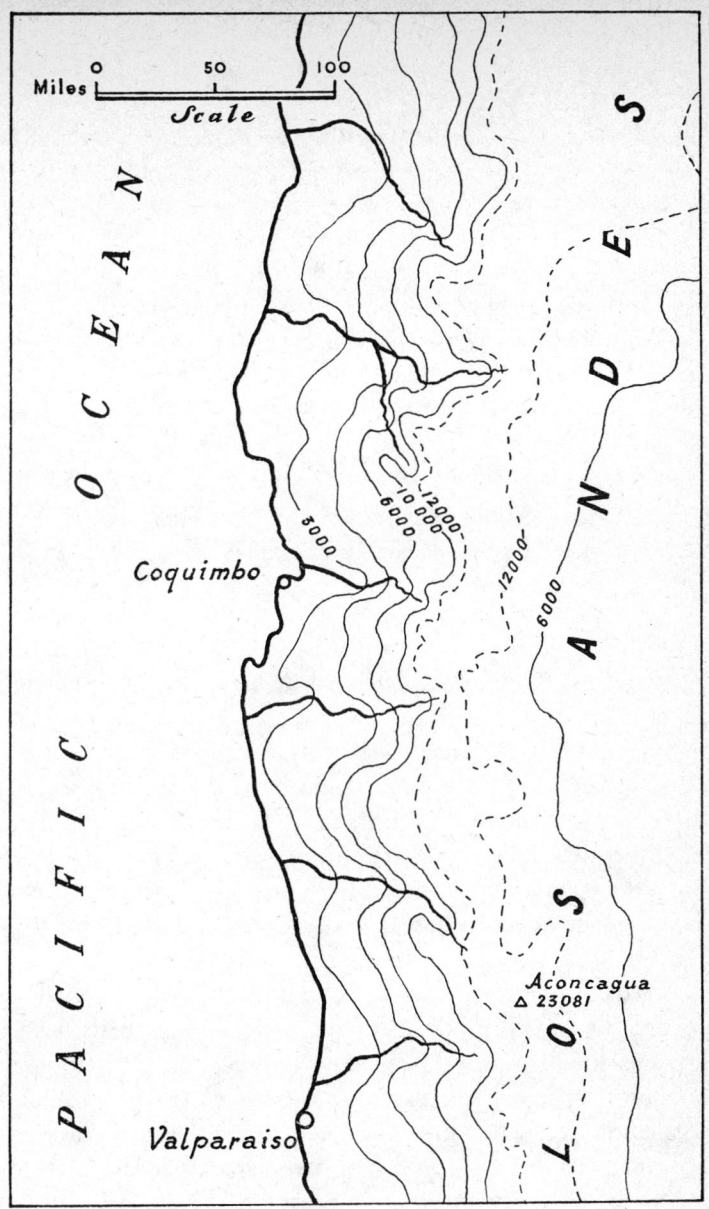

5. THE INCA EMPIRE

Short, steep river valleys provided the alluvial soils upon which the Andean natives built their culture

The Colla of Titicaca prayed to their soil:

> Mother of all things,
> Let me too be thy child.

The women of Cuzco, domain of the Inca *ayllu*, offered maize and *chicha* to the soil at planting time. The rise of the Inca did later entail the predominance of their tribal deity, the Sun, and the imposition of his worship as the State religion, but among the people the worship of Earth remained the popular cult, of *Bachue* among the Chibcha, of *Pachamamma* among the Inca.

Probably the first manurial technique discovered by the Andeans was that arising from the "Law of Return". At first this law was obeyed in a very imperfect manner, for all parts of the crop-plant not consumed as food were burnt and the ashes returned to the soil. Subsequently it became usual to bury this vegetable carrion, so that nothing was lost. Irrigation was, perhaps, originally a manurial device, designed to carry not so much water, as silt to new soils, for the valleys were not rainless. Human excrement was early used as manure.

The Andeans of the coastal nations were the first to discover the manurial value of dead fish, today an important fertilizer. The fishermen took great quantities of sardines in their nets, which they worked from *balsa* rafts. The bodies of the fish were eaten, but the heads were sent to the farmers, who planted the maize by dibbing a hole, dropping in a fish-head and two or three seeds. And these coastal people had an even more valuable manure: the islands off the Peruvian and Chilian coasts were, and are, the haunts of large numbers of sea-birds, whose droppings during the course of thousands of years had accumulated in great white hills of *guano*, perhaps the most effective of all manures. From very early times there existed by custom, or perhaps by treaty after military disputes, a system whereby certain coastal nations had exclusive rights in the *guano* of certain islands. How the manurial value of *guano* came to be discovered is not clear, but it is certain that the coastal nations attached great importance to their rights in it, and that after the unification of the Andean world by the Inca, to kill a sea-bird was a capital offence.

By the carefully regulated and controlled use of these manures the Andean peoples built up the fertility of their natural soils, converted natural soil communities into rich and stable artificial ones. That done, however, they were still faced by the want of land, until, by the following methods they enormously increased the area of tillage, as well as its fertility.

*

All the civilized American peoples were adept at making new soils. The Aztecs of Mexico turned their lakes into a lacustrine paradise by constructing "floating" gardens, first anchoring mud by means of osier reinforcements, then planting the mud with trees which, by the great extension of their roots fixed the new islands in the lake bottom. To this nucleus more mud accrued, until a considerable surface was available for planting. Beautiful though they were, these islands were created for economic and not aesthetic reasons.[168]

The Andean peoples had three ways of increasing their soil area. Of the first method, Sarmiento says in his History:

> ... Pachacuti Inca Yupanqui,[169] considering the small extent of land round Cuzco suited for cultivation, supplied by art what was wanting in nature. Along the skirts of the hills near villages, and also in other parts, he constructed very long terraces of 200 paces more or less and 20 to 30 wide, faced with masonry and filled with *earth*, much of it brought from a distance. We call these terraces *andenes*, the native name being *sucres*. He ordered that they should be sown, and in this way he made a vast increase in the cultivated land, and in provision for sustaining the companies and garrisons.[170]

Sarmiento here seems to attribute the invention of terracing to this Inca, but in fact it was of much greater antiquity, and was continuously increased over a great part of the Andean world during hundreds and perhaps thousands of years. The method of terracing was to build long parallel walls of undressed stone which followed the contours of the mountain. Each wall inclined inward, and the space between it and the hillside was filled with earth. The result was a series of horizontal surfaces like a flight of gigantic stairs, decreasing in depth as the mountain was ascended. These terraces were carried to great heights, as much as 1500 feet and decreasing in width until, whereas the lowest might be as much as 100 yards or more wide, the highest would be as little as two feet. Since the climate became cooler as the mountain was ascended, the crops varied in nature from bottom to top, and a single mountain-side would display a whole range of garden flora from such tropical crops as cotton and *coca*[171] at the base, through tobacco, tomatoes, fruit trees and vegetables, maize on the middle terraces, to such hardy crops as *quinoa* beans and potatoes at the summit. Such terracing is not, of course, peculiar to South America, but in no other country and by no other people has it ever been practised on such a scale. The increase of terraces was regulated by the increase in population, so that once the technique was perfected the Andeans had the means to solve their malthusian problem by cultivating the whole eastern face of the Andes foothills.

Terracing was, moreover, used as a means of increasing the Crown revenues without taking land at the expense of the people: whenever a new territory was incorporated into the empire, or new expense incurred in the business of government, the level fields were left in tribal tenure as before, while terraces were built or increased on the hill-sides in order to provide the land from the produce of which the exchequer could be filled. By the same means, the quantity of goods held in store could be constantly increased as the size of the empire increased, the danger of famine, or even shortages due to crop-failures, eliminated, and the obligation of the state towards the widow, the orphan and the sick readily met.

As to the antiquity of the terraces, Sarmiento was so far wrong in his attribution of the device to the Sapa-Inca Pachacuti Yupanqui, that in many provinces the aborigines knew nothing of their origin, and believed the terraces to be part of the original creation of the earth: Viracocha, they said, had brought the terraces into existence by a creative word, on the steep sides of ravines, and had caused the walls to rise and sustain them.

Wherever terracing could be used to increase the area of soil, it was so used, but there were regions, and those the most populous, where the topography of the country made this impossible. In the fertile coastal valleys, therefore, no building was ever done upon soil which might bear a crop,[172] houses being confined to such sites as were naked rock. Beyond these fertile but narrow tracts lay the desert, but the Andean people supposed that these barren places had been created by the winds, which had deposited sand upon what must once have been fertile soil. They therefore undertook to remove the sands of the desert and reclaim these areas, at least in part: they dug out great pits in the sands, some as large as an acre in area, and as deep as was necessary to uncover the soil, even as much as twenty feet. When soil was reached, it was tilled and planted,[173] and the sides of the pits providing shelter against the wind, such crops as were grown on these plots would no doubt have been early and of prime quality.

The origins of irrigation in the Andean world are, like those of terracing, lost in antiquity, although its invention was also attributed to a monarch: Sarmiento says that the Inca Rocca, "discovered the waters of Hurin-chacan and Hanan-chacan[174] and led them in conduits, so that to this day they irrigate fields; and his sons and descendants have benefited by them to this day". But irrigation was certainly a practice much older than the Inca empire. The people of the *ayllu* of Copara, living in the mountains above Lima, said that the God Paria-cacca fell in love with a girl of their tribe whom he found weeping because her maize crop was perishing for want of water. He therefore diverted a stream high in the mountains, carrying it to her plot by means of an irrigation channel which he built. At the girl's own request, he changed her into a stone at the head of this channel, and this stone became an object of worship.[175]

In other parts it was said that Viracocha had created the irrigation channels at the same time as the world, by the creative act of hurling a hollow cane; or that he had set certain animals, notably the fox, to work on their construction. It seems most probable that the earliest irrigation channels were constructed by men of the pre-Inca "Apparented" civilization of Tiahuanaco, and that all memory of this had been lost during the chaos and *Völkerwanderung* which separated the two great ordered societies in time. The Inca, however, knew how to value these works, and successive governments added to them. Huayna Ccapac Inca, in the course of his visitation of the empire from Quito to Chile, caused new irrigation works to be built in the Collao, and Pachacuti Yupanqui Inca appointed official visitors, one of whose tasks was the extension of irrigation systems. And, indeed, most accounts of the royal progresses include references to such works.

The most remarkable achievement in the making of soils by means of irrigation was that of turning the absolutely barren and arid coastal strip into a luxuriant garden of fruits, corn and herbs. The Yunca people of the north-west littoral inhabited a rainless soil but they had, by means of irrigation, created a culture superior to that of their Inca conquerors. The water of many mountain streams was tapped at source, led into vast reservoirs of masonry, and thence by way of aqueducts to the coast, where it was distributed by an elaborate system of channels. The system employed by the Yunca must have been much the same as that examined by Markham in the Nasca Valley, and of which he says:[176]

> In 1853 I examined the irrigation system of this valley very carefully. All that nature has supplied in the way of water is

a small water-course which is frequently dry for six years together; and at best only a little streamlet trickles down during the month of February. The engineering skill displayed by the Incas[177] in remedying this defect is astonishing. Deep trenches were cut along the whole length of the valley and so far into the mountains that the present inhabitants have no knowledge of the place where they commence. High up in the valley the main trenches or *puquios* are some four feet in height, with floor, roof, and sides lined with stones. Lower down they are separated into smaller *puquios* which ramify in every direction over the valley and supply all the estates with delicious water throughout the year, feeding the little streams which irrigate the fields. The larger *puquios* are several feet below the surface and at intervals of 200 yards there are manholes, *ojos*, by which workmen can get down into the channels and clear away any obstruction.

An earlier historian than Markham, Garcilasso de la Vega Inca, describes a similar system constructed under the orders of the Sapa-Inca Viracocha, of which the main *puquios* were twelve feet deep and wide, and traversed a distance of 450 miles. The great length of this and other aqueducts is accounted for by the fact that the Andean builders, like the Greeks, did not know the principle of the arch, were therefore unable to throw their aqueducts across ravines, and were forced to go miles out of the straight way in order to pass round the origins of such an obstruction. The aqueducts were fitted with sluices at the junctions of subsidiary *puquios* and irrigation channels, so that the distribution of water could be exactly regulated. Each land-holder was allowed the flow of water during a time predetermined by experience of what was necessary, and if he failed to make proper use of it he was liable to be flogged.

The supply of water alone could not account for the inexhaustible fertility of the made soils of the coast, nor, perhaps, could the careful systems of manuring employed. But it was the opinion of Liebig[178] that all these irrigation waters were muddy with the volcanic detritus of mountain provenance, and that consequently the soils were continually supplied with all that maize and other crops took from them.

*

Enough has been said concerning manuring, terracing, pit-digging and irrigation in the Andean world, and of the antiquity of these practices, to establish that the soils upon which rose the great ordered state of the Inca were artificial; and that the Andeans, unlike the civilized peoples of the Old World, not only did not exhaust their soils by parasitism, but on the contrary greatly increased both their fertility and extent.

This achievement was the prerequisite condition upon which a great and prosperous empire *could* be created on western South American soils, but if it be true that the Inca will-to-power was responsible for the ordering and unification of the most stable and perfect artificial soil community in man's history, it is equally and conversely true that the pre-Inca foundation of the soil community was not only the perfect basis for the building of the Inca theocratic bureaucracy, but indeed demanded some such social and political system. Andean soils, Andean artificial soils, and the uniquely successful system of Imperial Communism which arose on them out of the ancient agrarian and pastoral communisms, were so closely interdependent that while it is true to say that the want of sufficient natural soils and the consequent making of artificial ones determined the way in which the Andean social and political system would develop, it is also a fact that the nature of that development made sure that the soil-policy, the soil-relationship of these peoples, would continue along the same lines.

There has probably never been, unless under European Feudalism, a system in which agricultural practice and social organization were so locked together in a perfect artifact of the mind and spirit. And nothing makes this clearer than the results which followed the imposition of the European system and religion on the Andeans. The soil was not directly attacked, for the Spaniards were at first interested only in gold, but the social organism was destroyed and at once the soil itself began to die. Those wiser men of the Council of the Indies, by far the most enlightened body of colonial administrators until the twentieth century, men who might have tried to maintain the social organism intact by substituting for its heart, its priest-king, the Apu-Ccapac-Inca, Philip II in the person of his Viceroy, came too late to check the ignorant and wanton destruction wrought by such ruffians as Pizarro and Almagro.

With their beautifully symmetrical and delicately balanced social system in ruins, the Indians fell into a kind of desperate and surly state of passive resistance. Neglect of the irrigation systems soon entailed the ruin, by drought, of the coastal gardens and farms. Nor did matters improve, from the Indians' point of view, with time; no conceivable system could have been more contrary to their traditions and instincts than that of capitalism: property in land or in anything else for that matter was contrary to their religion and their history, and some of the actions committed under the sanction of the doctrine of *laissez-faire laissez-passer*, such as the selling overseas of vast quantities of *guano* in exchange for the raw materials of an alien, incomprehensible and oppressive culture, must have seemed to the natives as criminally blasphemous as they were, in scientific fact, ecologically wicked.

CHAPTER XIV

ATLANTIC EUROPE: THE PERFECT ARTIFICIAL SOIL

A SOIL consultant of international reputation told a branch meeting of the British National Farmers' Union: "Whenever I get back to Britain it is a relief to handle English soil." He was making a very favourable comparison between the texture, and therefore the fertility and stability of English soils, and those of other parts of the world. He added that there were one or two other places in Europe similarly endowed. These fertile and stable soils are, with rare exceptions, confined to Atlantic Europe. Their nature is a product of their past, and they have been slowly transformed from forest soil communities into artificial soil communities; transformed and maintained.

It is probable that an observer from another planet who understood human values would judge the achievements of Western Christian man, in religion, philosophy, science and the arts to be of a higher order than those of any other men in the world. It is true that these achievements have resulted in the building-up, in the soul of Western Christian men, of an overweening, blind pride which now becomes his *hubris*. It is, ironically, in an alien, classical tradition that out of *hubris* rises the *atê*, whereby the sinner against the earth shall be chastised: Western Christian man appears to be about to destroy himself by means of his powers over nature, and if he is spared after all it will perhaps be because there is one great sin against earth which he has *not*, at least on his native heath, committed. As a peasant, a farmer, he has shown a remarkable and almost singular sense of responsibility, a respect for valuable traditions, and a sure and subtle tact in making use of new devices and techniques with intelligent moderation. Atlantic European soils are not only *not* exhausted by seven or eight thousand years' association with man; they are probably more fertile and stable today than they have ever been. The crop per acre taken annually from North-west European soils is much in excess of the world's average, and equal or superior to that taken, in classical times, from the richest soils available to Hellenic man, for example, the volcanic soils of Sicily.

This greatest of the many great achievements of European man has, moreover, been accomplished not, as in South America, by a unified culture under a theocratic communist dictatorship; nor with the enormous advantage of a soil-worshipping religion enduring from primitive to highly civilized times. European man has kept himself tolerably free, and as for his religion, though anciently the Europeans worshipped their soil, during the last three thousand years of their history they have adored gods and goddesses with less and less interest in or association with agriculture; and during two thousand years they have worshipped a group of Mediterranean deities whose own creative background was singularly inappropriate to Atlantic European conditions. These handicaps are very real, very grave: God and soil are so immediately connected that unless an alien God can be acclimatized, modified in his nature to flourish in the soil he is colonizing, the people who worship him or her on that soil will suffer serious psychic and psychological wounds. Recall the sound religious instinct of Naaman, who, in order to worship Jehovah for cleansing him of the leprosy, carried Palestinian soil back with him to Syria.

An account of the relationship between Atlantic European soils and men must be broken into several sections and must include some times and places not strictly within its limits of reference.

*

As the ice of the last Ice Age retreated, it left Atlantic Europe a tundra, a cold *steppe* community of grasses and graminivorous animals, bison, reindeer, horse and mammoth; and of carnivorous men, the men of the Old Stone Age. These hunting Europeans enjoyed, in the vast herds of game which teemed on their soils, so plentiful a supply of food that they had little need to change their economy for one of agriculture or stock-raising. For where meat is ample men will not readily eat plants. In parts of the region under discussion, towards the south where the climate was doubtless rather less harsh, these men of the Pleistocene epoch were by no means mere brutes. Their communal hunting, like the pack-hunting of wolves, probably made them communistic in their economy, without permanent chiefs, and with no more law than custom and expediency entailed. They cultivated the arts, however, and brought painting to a pitch of perfection so high that, considering craft, skill, and ignoring the question of content, they have never been surpassed. Whatever its significance, its idea, their painting itself, as such, is sophisticated, far more so, for example, than that of a Giotto, or a Fra Angelico.

The Magdalenian painters were as sensitive to life, and as apt in expressing what they perceived, as El Greco, or Picasso. The latter artists have had to be preoccupied with the problems created for man by man; the former might have given their attention to problems created for man by the gods. The great thinkers of Egypt or Hellas were as advanced and sophisticated in the power of mind and spirit as Newton, Einstein or Russell. Tools, and psychological techniques have become more ingenious; nothing else has changed.

But each culture has its own terms of expression and these are predetermined for it by the nature of the physical problems with which it has to deal. Since man ceased to be a soil-member a colossal amount of energy has been diverted to the work of trying to restore his ancient leisure, his ancient liberty, his ancient freedom from the endless labour of forcing the soil to support him, instead of allowing it to do so; of defying, in short, the primaeval curse . . .

cursed is the ground for thy sake; in sorrow shalt thou eat of it all the days of thy life. Thorns also; and thistles shall it bring forth to thee; and thou shalt eat the herb of the field. In the sweat of thy face shalt thou eat bread, till thou return unto the ground; for out of it wast thou taken: for dust thou art, and unto dust shalt thou return.[179]

But had the necessity for this diversion of energy never arisen, had the Palaeolithic way of life in the more favoured regions continued to support man in return for very little effort, and had man not proliferated so as to become a disease-organism of the life-complex of earth, it is at least possible that he would have responded with all his genius to the challenge of the universe as a whole, and not merely to that of the parish; have understood better with his aesthetic sensibility than he has done with his philosophical intelligence.

The method used to turn us out of the Eden of the tundra, to turn us from soil-members to soil-exploiters, was that of altering the climate. Higher temperatures and rainfall brought in the trees, the great herds of the tundra species vanished, and with them the Pleistocene communities of hunters and artists. In place of grass, grew trees, in place of the great herbivores the shy, small creatures of the forests, in place of great hunting communities of men the smaller, poorer, less polished if not less ingenious Mesolithic groups, devising an economy of forest food-gathering, and independent hunting.[180]

The history of the advance of trees in Atlantic Europe has been reconstructed by palaeobotanists. Pollen grains preserved in such material as peat moss tell the story.[181] The advance-guard of the trees was composed of birches and willows, then came conifers, notably pines, later hazel, elm, lime, oak and beech. Doubtless the order varied from locality to locality.

The dominance of Atlantic Europe by trees, meant a falling back by man: Mesolithic communities were relatively poor and ill-equipped, yet their members devised techniques and tools suitable to their environment, and which, passed on to their successors and neighbours, enabled the latter to begin the attack upon trees which the ambition of man as a species made necessary.

*

Neither the tundra mammoth hunters, nor the forest folk who came after them were ever farmers, and during their tenancy of our soils these were left to grow fat undisturbed. The agricultural idea, tools and techniques were brought to Atlantic Europe from the south-east by immigrant peoples. The crafts of tillage do not, in Europe, slowly develop before the eyes of the archaeologist, as in the Fayum or in Mesopotamia. The Neolithic farmers appear abruptly, as it were, in a world hitherto inhabited only by soil-members in good standing.

This primal infection of Atlantic European soils by man as a parasite was mild and harmless at first, and for many centuries. The typical primal agrarian civilization is the Danube I Culture, so labelled by archaeologists from the area of its principal habitat. Whence these Danubian people came, and where their crafts were invented, it is not here our business to inquire. In any case, north-west European agricultural society did not derive from that source: the three great centres of agrarian civilization were, as we have seen, the Nile, the Tigris–Euphrates, and the Indus. From them the soil-exploiting tools and techniques spread like ink on blotting paper, intense at the point of origin, and growing fainter and fainter towards the ever-widening periphery. At that periphery were the peoples in the process of being turned from Eden conditions into farm labourers.

The direction from which the agricultural crafts spread into Atlantic Europe, not only by contact of people with people, but by the immigration of advanced societies, was that of Anatolia and the Balkans.

The first European soil-exploiters, although they may have been relatively advanced by aboriginal standards, practised agriculture in the simplest way. They were nomadic, they kept to the light *loess* soils, and in Britain to the chalk and limestone and gravel terraces. They shifted their cultivated sites as frequently as the exhaustion of the few inches of soil within reach of their tools made necessary; they were assisted by an ample rainfall. They used the hoe as the principal tool, and no doubt their women were the cultivators, for among all of them the cult of the Earth Mother was honoured, the usual steatopygous female figurines being many from their settlements. Settlements, perhaps, is a misleading term, for they were not permanent: the peasant who noticed that the fertility of a plot was declining, went and cleared a new one, began its cultivation, then shifted his dwelling to the new site, and finally quite abandoned the old one.

The crops cultivated by these early European farmers were fairly numerous—barley, *einkorn*, wheat, beans, peas, lentils and flax. By the time all these plants are found in cultivation, hunting, as an economic recourse, has been abandoned, at least among the Danubians who, in addition to their domesticated plants, raised small numbers of oxen, sheep and pigs. Farther west, on our own soils, the emphasis was different and less likely to begin the erosion of the soil—cattle were enormously more important than plants, and the area under cultivation relatively inconsiderable.

To invoke a picture of the primitive European "farm" is not easy. There would be no hedged or regularly walled fields, and all round the periphery of the cultivated plots there would be a sort of no-man's land, neither jungle nor sown, where the hoe and the advancing wild plants held each other in balance. Perhaps we can best visualize such plots by thinking of places which, during the war, were ploughed as allotments in common land, and which received only a bare minimum of attention. The huts of the farmers would be squalid and roughly made. The lairs and precincts of carnivorous or omnivorous animals, such as men, are always unseemly. We do not know at what stage of social development the first farmers had arrived, but probably the family unit was still in process of emerging from the tribal one. By analogue with Africans of our own time, we might guess that the first European farmers had not yet thought of the idea of land as property, that it was worked in common by women, with suitable religious rites, that the crop was communally distributed and that chieftainship was ephemeral and confined to war conditions. Socially, in the first ages of this agriculture, the women, the mothers, would have been dominant.

Probably the tilth achieved by these people would have appeared to us extremely untidy. The beautiful surfaces and textures of worked soil which afford one of the most agreeable visual experiences in a modern countryside, are the consequences of plough and harrow cultivation of one sort or another. True, as soon as the spade had been invented, some kind of pleasingly ordered surface could be achieved. The author has produced quite a seemly tilled surface with a digging stick and a great deal of sweat. The ancient Peruvians produced a beautiful tilth with the *taccla,* and so do the twentieth-century Irish with the almost identical *loy.* No doubt even a stone hoe in skilled hands, would produce an even and regular tilth. There is no reason to suppose that the Neolithic men and women found any less satisfaction in making a pleasant pattern of their worked soil than the modern gardener with a spade, or the farmer with a tractor plough. But the levelling of humpy surfaces is another matter, the Neolithic farm must have been relatively disorderly and only the fact that barley and wheat were grown makes it probable that some sort of continuous surface tilth must have been produced.[182] The Europeans, having no giant cereal like maize, could not make do in the Peruvian manner.

Shifting agriculture was practised in Europe for the usual reasons, but the Atlantic European cultivators had an enormous advantage over their tropical brothers in this respect: they could not do serious damage to the soils they cultivated since they had no means of deep cultivation and all but two or three inches of their soil was out of their reach. The fertility capital of a temperate soil is not working in a teeming vegetation, but locked up in the soil itself, in the slowly accumulated humus of centuries of decay. And if the primitive farmers could exploit the fertility of the loess and other light soils, the major part of Atlantic European soil fertility lay waiting for the axe and the plough to make it available.

The social and economic pattern of the earliest farming in our region was not everywhere identical, any more than it is today. But it was nearly so, and probably the crops were much the same everywhere. Those peoples who found themselves on the fringes of forest and park-land soils, continued to hunt for the pot as much as they tilled. But there is no universal progress from hunting and gathering, through shifting tillage, to sedentary agriculture and nomadic stock-raising, and the story is confused by the relative backwardness of some folk and forwardness of others. Neolithic civilization is not identical in, say, Britain and Flanders or Switzerland. Soil itself imposed differences in the manner and style of the agrarian civilizations which arose, and although, for example, agriculture was introduced to Britain by immigrants with set ways and a well-formed culture, the colonized soils imposed terms and conditions in which that culture could be expressed, and to suit which it must be modified.[183]

*

The second phase of agrarian culture is marked by the reoccupation of the abandoned sites of the first nomadic cultivators by people who made larger settlements and among whom stock-raising was of greater importance; a fact which, if they made use of manure, would have enabled them to occupy the same site for a longer period. There is also increased resort to hunting, perhaps a retrograde step but one which would have rested the soil; on the other hand, a warrior class appears among people formerly—by the absence of weapon relics from their sites—pacific. War is bad for soil. This change-over suggests a shift of values from feminine to masculine. Population increased, and at about the same time bronze began to come into use and a little less reliance was placed on stone.[184] The change from stone to metal tools was a very slow one, and for long after metallurgy was widely diffused, stone continued to be used and preferred for some purposes. The influence of the shapes assumed by stone tools at their most evolved and polished, endures today: our axe-head is identical in all but material with that of the Neolithic woodman, and the iron knife of the modern Chinese peasant, in appearance resembling a butcher's cleaver, is precisely the same as the so-called "rectangular" knife of the Chinese Stone Age. Stone tools not only have a very long life as an idea, but in physical fact, and the author uses today a well-knapped flint scraper, picked up on his holding and knapped for cleaning hides perhaps four or five thousand years ago, to clear his steel spade when digging in heavy clay.

In the later phases of the "Danube" type of economy no great change took place in the relationship between men and soil, but pressure on soil grew and men became numerous, and by the end of this period the malthusian problem had become grave, a fact which would have helped to turn the attention of natives and immigrants alike to the forest soils. The accumulated wealth of *loess* and alluvial agriculture, and of advancing stock-raising, the numbers and prosperity of the farmers in plain and river valleys, made possible the release of men from general to specialized labour, a condition pre-requisite to the development of metallurgy. Bronze Age, and then Iron Age axes made a serious assault upon the trees possible at last.

Forest trees grow densely only on strong soils and wherever they grow they create a rich mould of enduring fertility and give the soil that granular structure which results from the flocculation of clay by very thorough mixing with organic particles. Moreover, the trees "cultivate" the soil to a great depth.

Horticultural and agricultural writers have tended to give the impression that life is confined to the top-soil skin of the planet, and indeed it is in that thin and precarious integument that the basis of all life is to be found. But a far greater depth of soil is of more importance than is generally realized; of a wheat plant or an apple tree, less than one third of the total substance of the plant is above ground. We ourselves have traced the roots of one small perennial, which seldom grows more than a foot tall, *Tussilago farfara,* the common coltsfoot, to a depth of fourteen feet in apparently barren clay. Tree roots are found more than forty feet down in the subsoil, and some of them are apparently capable, by means of the secretions in their feeding roots, of breaking down the fundamental rocks themselves, that is of making soil. It is not doubt true that these deep roots are primarily of mechanical importance, but they do an important work of top-soil creation. Rainfall leaches nutrients out of top-soil into subsoil, nitrates particularly being easily lost in solution. Moreover an inexhaustible supply of new mineral nutrients is available in newly broken-down rocks deep in the subsoil. The deep roots of forest trees tap supplies of nutrient solutions at great depths, the trees convert them into foliage, which is dropped in autumn to enrich the top-soil. And even the timber itself, though it pass through an avatar as a manufactured article, the handle of a hoe, or a Chippendale chair, will ultimately return whence it came, as ash or by rotting. The whole of Atlantic Europe, with the exception of the chalk and some few exposed or arid sites, was, by the end of the first farming phases, a forest soil.

Typical of human forest-soil members were the Maglemosian people, living on small game, on wild-fowl and on fish which they took with a small spear, hooks or nets. These were the people who devised tree felling tools, first heavy core axes of stone, later flake axe heads with a wide cutting edge. These, and like peoples, if in themselves they succumbed to the changed conditions and fell off from the level of Palaeolithic cultures, at least contributed, for use by their successors, some of the tools by means of which:

> Man began to escape his complete subservience to nature, assert his will and make her work for him.[185]

... or, in our terms, to step outside the good order of a balanced natural soil community, create his own prosperity at the expense of order and the cost of soil debility, and so confront himself with the task of making an artificial soil balance.

*

In a work as brief, in relation to the subject, as the present, fine distinctions would be out of place. We pass rapidly over the intervening stages to the first Atlantic European age of settled farming. There is a temptation to linger, to build up, for we are aware of approaching one of the Great Ages of the region under review.

Children used to be taught that north-west Europe was barbarous until the Romans carried civilization over the Alps. What actually happened was that the Romans carried an already declining civilization over the Alps and imposed it upon a young and growing one, with fatal consequences. The Romans brought a sophisticated military, legal and economic system and thrust it by force on peoples with aesthetic gifts and sensibilities greatly superior to those of the conquerors.

The development of early Celtic crafts is economically associated with the turnover, in metallurgy, from Bronze to Iron, and thereafter with the Iron Age. Iron came into use in the ancient civilizations of the east Mediterranean about 1000 B.C., reached mid-Europe by about 800 B.C., and Atlantic Europe by about 450 B.C. Celtic iron culture began with Hallstatt and culminated with the glories of La Tene. This, unfortunately, is not the place to dwell in praise on the work of the La Tene smiths and enamellers, and it will have to be sufficient to refer the reader to the relevant objects in the British and other museums, and to express the opinion that, as regards workmanship and taste, nothing finer has since been made in Europe, or anywhere else.

Our own short inquiry must be into the nature of the soil-exploitation which supported this high culture.

*

From the customs and laws of the various Celtic nations at the earliest times of which any record survives, and from the vestigial maintenance of such customs and laws in remote Celtic enclaves today, it is possible to guess that the Celtic peoples were originally organized on a matrilinear, exogamous tribal pattern, and that therefore they began their career of soil-exploitation as tillers, rather than as stock-raisers.

By the time of their Great Age in pre-Roman Atlantic Europe, however, the Celts, although practising plant husbandry, were primarily stock-farmers. So much so that when they first conquered their new soils some of the land under cultivation may have been allowed to go back to pasture, tillage may have been reduced under their aegis, to increase gradually as the Celtic peoples settled down until, with the Belgic Celts, tillage began to be as important as grazing.

Since animal husbandry was dominant in Celtic economy,[186] we should expect the Celts to be, socially, patriarchal. They were, in fact, organized in agnatic groups—that is groups of persons connected as kin on the paternal side. Such groups, tracing descent from a common male ancestor, are exactly reminiscent of the pre-Mughal Indian communities. And, indeed, the parallel is close, for, like the Indians, the Celtic villagers were equal and self-governing within the sept or clan to which each belonged. The villagers either dwelt in hamlets of households, each house sheltering an adult male and his immediate family; or in great farmsteads, the whole clan together; or in isolated farms. The soil, and not social custom, dictated these differences, the isolated farmer was a shepherd or cowman, whose isolation was due to the location of pasture, and he was none the less a member of the clan, and working as such. Where pasture lay close to the arable, the integrity of the clan could express itself in the huddling together of its members in physical proximity.[187]

The primary importance of animal husbandry among the people who dominated pre-Roman Atlantic Europe was one more gain to the soil, for the maintenance of grass cover during another long age, and the enrichment of stubble fields with the dung of grazing cattle, continued to build up fertility for Europe's future wealth. The best part of cow and sheep manure may have been lost by the practice of seeking distant summer pastures, but from the point of view of the present, this is not important, for soils subsequently to be ploughed received it. Pigs, moreover, were important in Celtic economy, and their dung might have been available during at least part of the year.

There was no property in land among the Celts. As among all peoples in an Heroic stage of society private property in personal goods was like gentry and aristocracy, class pride and distinction, important: in spirit the Celts were not egalitarian, but in the important particular of land-holding, the holder was the clan. Pastures belonging to a clan were the exclusive right of that clan (though even this does not imply the idea of ownership as we know it), and the limits of the pastures were marked, maintained and defended at need. But not even the greatest man of a clan could properly say "this is *my* land"; at most he could say, "this is *our* land".[188]

It is comparatively simple for a community to own and work pasture in common—in fact it is difficult to do otherwise with any regard for equity, but arable is another matter, for the governing factor in successful tillage is quality of labour, and goodwill. The tilled land of the Celtic septs was held in common but worked in severalty, each head of a household being allotted land from the common holding, in strips, so that there should be a fair distribution of good, bad and indifferent soils. These strips were redistributed at intervals, and no man ever "owned" one, but simply had a right to it for the subsistence of his family and the maintenance of his social position as a free and equal member of the clan. His sons inherited, but what they inherited was not property, but rights —the same rights as their father's. If population declined, each man's share increased proportionately, until population rose; then the shares declined again, and continued to decline until the level of subsistence was endangered by want of land, when either a colony was thrown off, or the metropolitan holding was increased by "assartage"—that is by clearing the waste land.[189]

All this applies to Celtic free tribesmen in good standing. The aboriginal inhabitants, descendants of the earlier farmers, had no such status. In some cases (see below) they were enslaved, at least enserfed. But on the whole they existed in their own communities, holding their own land, and paying tribute to the Celts but not otherwise troubled by them. There was no question of these natives being made working slaves of the Celtic freemen, to labour on the freeman's land. Whatever the natives may have suffered as men, by becoming a tributary state within the dominant Celtic state, the soil was spared the ill effects of slave exploitation, and the Celtic overmen were not tempted to forget their responsibility to the soil, nor spared the constant lessons deriving from close manual contact with it.

Celtic good sense in soil management saved the soil from another ill effect which might have been expected to arise from their system of dividing the land equally among the heirs of the tribesmen, at the latter's death.[190] Such an arrangement tends, as we have seen elsewhere, to a progressive reduction of the size of the holdings, to pulverization as it is called, until the smallness of the holding which must support a household is such that the abuse of the soil becomes a condition of survival. The Celts got over this by making their attributions of allotments ideal, not real; a piece of land continued to be worked as an integer, if its nature demanded it, and although rights in its working might be held by several and even by numerous tribesmen, no attempt was made to divide it physically. Moreover, the tendency, as population increased, was not to resort to intensive farming, as in Italy, but to clear virgin soil. It was realized that share-holding in the right of a strip might not suit all temperaments, and such share-holding was therefore voluntary; no man was forced to accept such an arrangement, to "hold in joint tenancy", if he did not want to. That, in practice, such joint tenancy was common argues a fine sense of unity in the clan, and of responsibility towards the community and the soil.

The Celtic agrarian communities, then, were villages of joint and equal tenant farmers, the "landlord" being the community itself, and with a gentry distinguished by birth, and also by wealth in anything but land, until the system began to degenerate and land-owning was introduced. Meanwhile, during the course of many centuries, the Celts kept the soils of Atlantic Europe in growing heart.

*

With their armies, municipal organizations and law courts, the Romans brought with them an advanced agriculture, an agriculture which had enabled them to exploit their southern soils for all the wealth they were worth, and to ruin them in the process. The ingenuity of the Roman farmers was admirable, but its consequences, in the long run, shocking. Roman agriculture was not, unmodified, suited to the Atlantic European soils. These soils were by no means cleared of trees, forests still dominated. The late arrival of iron in the north-west once again favoured the soils we are discussing, for deforestation could not proceed at a pace liable to do much damage to climate.

Roman agricultural methods were, to a large extent, adapted to "dry farming", since most Mediterranean soils were relatively, and are increasingly, arid. Such methods, although they cannot be avoided on such soils if crops are to be raised, are destructive of soil fertility and structure, and result in the long run in the total loss of top-soil. The farmers on arid soils are almost bound to ruin the source of their own livelihood, unless they take to stock-raising as a primary technique of soil exploitation. But in the Mediterranean region stock-raising land is relatively scarce, and summer drought forces shepherd and herdsman to seek mountain pastures, whereby dung is lost to their valley arable.[191] The Mediterranean soils were under-manured and over-tilled.

In order to preserve winter-rain moisture Roman farmers ploughed and cross ploughed their land with a light plough and a straight share to produce what is now called a "dust-mulch". Dust mulching, by breaking up and pulverizing the soil, alters that structure which enables water to move upwards by capillary action.[192] The water is thus held in the soil at about the point where it is available to the roots of crop plants. In modern practice this tilth is achieved by means of disk-harrowing; anciently it was done by repeated ploughing. The method, in arid climates, results in soil erosion, by wind and water. Not only was such water-conservation unnecessary on Atlantic European soils; had it been practised, it would have done less harm. True, it would damage soil structure, one of the best assets of the farmer; but the soil would not actually be quite lost.

Thus the soils of our region were protected by their own nature against Roman malpractices; today, whereas Atlantic Europe has no soil erosion problem, the soils of the Mediterranean shores are gravely diseased.

In typical Roman farming conditions it was necessary to thin cereal crops for fear of over-cropping the land. This was done by grazing cattle on the springing corn. In southern, light soils this might be effective by many plants being pulled out by the roots. But on a strong holding soil, on the soils of Atlantic Europe, the same method exactly is used to thicken the crop, not thin it. This has long been the practice, but for how long we cannot determine.[193] And forest soils under a 25 to 50 inch mean annual rainfall can stand this thickening very well, can support a crop three times as heavy as arid soils:

> The ancient farmer (says Stevens) had accumulated, in centuries of practice a large body of doctrine upon the relations of crop and soil; and perhaps because agricultural technique was the possession rather of the conservative and practically-minded peasant, than of the scientific thinker, the doctrine tended to develop rather on this line than in the direction of sacrificing the perfection of soil suitability to the advantages of a varying rotation. Ancient authors are casual and unsympathetic in their treatment of it, and most of them seem to have regarded the change of crop on land as an exception justified either by the soil or the climate. On low-lying volcanic soil, well-watered and rich, liberties could be taken. In Campania for instance the land was cropped all the year round with *Panicum*, with millet and with a green crop. This looks dangerously like overworking the soil, and it may be no accident that this is a district which reveals evidence of derelict land in the fifth century. More commonly

rotation was practised because fortunate climatic conditions permitted it; a wet summer, for instance, might allow a spring-grown green crop or even a spring wheat or barley to be slipped into the ordinary crop-fallow rotation, and it is significant that the authorities assign to the Alps and the Po valley—regions where more than the normal summer moisture is to be expected—the principal developments of such a practice.[194]

In short, in arid "Roman" conditions, the "rotation" was crop-fallow—no rotation at all. The fallow was supposed to restore the land to heart: by keeping it clean of weeds, in fact, the fallow had a chance to build up supplies of available nitrates for the following season. But this would restore its sinews rather than its heart, and unless it were heavily manured, each fallow season would simply see a further exhaustion of nitrogenous material. In Atlantic Europe a true rotation, with the green crop sometimes ploughed in, could be used, so that the heart of land could not only be maintained, but made slowly more heroic, as it were, and the soils could grow great-hearted.

In the matter of arboriculture too the north-west soils and the practices on them, offered conditions favourable to their own improvement. The Mediterranean farmers were forced to plant vines and figs and other fruit trees on eroded soils which would grow nothing else. But the culture of the vine was so enormously profitable that it was always spreading on to the better soils. While viticulture was, for the individual planter, certainly the most profitable way of exploiting soil, it was, for the community, a mistake, and the Roman government was frequently forced to legislate against the spread of the vineyards on to soils needed for bread crops. But in the south even viti-culture entailed elaborate special techniques for the conservation of water and the protection of the ripening fruit against excessive sunshine, with the interesting result, incidentally, that early north-west European treatises on viticulture are full of advice, lifted from the classical treatises, and entirely unsuitable for Atlantic conditions. In Atlantic Europe, the community was protected against the spread of the vineyards by the fact that strong, forest soils are unsuitable for viticulture, which however can be very successful on steep hillsides and bluffs of poor soil, unsuitable for other crops, but yielding a wine much superior to that grown on rich soils, or in too much sunshine. The vineyards at the northern limits of the zone in which grapes will grow and ripen (traditionally, but not accurately, 51° N. lat.) have always yielded the finest and most delicate wines.[195]

C. E. Stevens estimates the Roman mean wheat yield as about nine bushels per acre. In Britain today it is nearer, and often surpasses, twenty cwt. The yield on the arid American soils under dry-farming conditions is about eight cwt., obtained only with fertilizers, and at the cost of losing top-soil bodily at a catastrophic rate.

Farming in Atlantic Europe under the Romans would have approximated to general Roman practice, but must have been very much modified to suit the soils, and by Celtic practice. The Romans did not by any means find a virgin soil, nor cultivators confining themselves feebly to the light and treeless soils. The Belgae, both on the Continent and later in Britain, had made progress in attacking the trees and cultivating the forest loams and the lighter clays. On such soils dust mulching and pulverization with the light Roman plough would have been inappropriate, whereas deep ploughing with the massive Celtic plough, drawn by a team of eight oxen, and provided with something like a mould board, was necessary. Such a plough, according to Pliny, in a passage said to be corrupt, originated in Gaul or Rhaetia, that is among the Celts.

That system of land tenure and soil exploitation which became typical of the Middle Ages was already emerging towards the end of the Roman Imperial era, and was to some extent a creation of the soil itself, of the physical conditions in which farming was carried on. The land was either worked by the inmates of separate and isolated farmsteads and hamlets; or by a community composing groups of farms, that is by villages or country "townships". Land-holding was of two types; the common, unenclosed field; and the enclosed holding which was the holder's property.[196] Not by any means all such enclosed holdings were the result of seizure of common land, and there are very ancient traditions for enclosed farms existing side by side with the common-field holding. However, the common-field and strip cultivation, the size of the strips being a product of the heavy Celtic plough and the length of distance the team could draw it without resting, were commonplace in late Roman times.

We have already seen that the very nature of the soils of Atlantic Europe, and the difficulty of clearing them, as well as the climate, protected them against debilitation by exploitation. What is more the application, in the north, of certain southern practices, would have tended to build up soil. The use of manure on an arid soil scale, would, for example, enrich the soil to a greater depth in conditions of high rainfall. Moreover, with ample pasture available, not in distant mountains but in the near neighbourhood of the arable, land which would later be ploughed, as the arable expanded, was manured. Nevertheless, had the empire continued prosperous, had population continued to grow and cities to be built, exploitation of the still relatively new and unstable north-west soils would have tended to become excessive in Atlantic Europe, as in Italy itself. Fortunately for the soil, the Roman Empire was falling to pieces, rotting from within and battered from without. Clearance of virgin soil ceased, in the third century on the Continent and in the fourth in Britain. Population fell, cities declined, the wild species, plant and animal, crept back to reconvert the artificial into natural soil communities, and during the *Sturm und Drang* of the Teutonic *Völkerwanderung* the land rested, and man, potentially a disease organism of his living soils, was severely checked.[197]

*

The new Teutonic tenants of Atlantic Europe, combining with the ancient peasantry when they did not exterminate it, inherited from Rome more than the pattern of a settlement system. They brought their own ideas of the values of men, but they did not despise the techniques which had been taught to the Celtic natives by the Roman farmers. They also inherited abuses, which had their consequences in the shape and style of the new communities. The system of later Roman land taxation,[198] if it was to yield adequate revenue "depended upon the most intimate connection between the labourer and the land (and) would hardly be practicable unless the connection were stabilized. By enactments, notably A.D. 332, cultivators were fixed permanently to the soil."[199] It is at least possible that in this practice is one of the origins of a serfdom which marred the Feudal system, although, indeed, it was mitigated by the great body of rights which protected the manor serfs. Such serfdom is, however, more ancient than the Roman fiscal law would make it, for Caesar characterized the people of Gaul as "little better than slaves", and, in fact, the Celtic conquerors of Atlantic Europe had reduced the aboriginals, as we have seen, to tributaries. Caesar's remark, however, seems to us to indicate a misunderstanding: as a typical tycoon in a system which had degraded a rule of freedom to one of irresponsibility in the service of individual private wealth, he would be capable of nothing but contempt for a way of life based upon service to the community, rather than profit. He was surely condemning the Celtic system of communal responsibility in much the same spirit as nineteenth-century historians condemned the state socialism of the Incas. Personal freedom to abuse soil and other commodities in order to get a fortune, a state of affairs which is typical of the moral and social anarchy of declining civilizations, is not compatible with service to the community, or to any other social idea.

In practical matters, the Atlantic European provinces inherited from Rome the practices of sub-soiling, drainage, frequent and clean cultivation, and the use of such fodder crops as vetch, lucerne, fenugreek, chick-pea,[200] of some stall feeding by means of these crops, and of the conservation of manure.

For the most part, however, what the Teutonic peoples introduced into Atlantic European lands was new, and derived from their respect for the ideas of equality: this attribute was most powerful among the Norsemen, least powerful among the Franks. The Anglo-Saxons fall between the two: the Norsemen would with difficulty recognize any high chief at all, the Saxons made kingdoms but had difficulty in maintaining them, the Franks were able to produce a centralized empire. Britain, as we know her, was a product of Norse and Saxon qualities, modified in the eleventh century by a new Norman governing idea, Norse in origin, Frank and Latin in what it had learnt. To this fact, as much as to any other, can be attributed the British political genius, which succeeded in creating a working democracy.

The Teuton hordes which seized Atlantic Europe from the senile hands of Rome were not simply armies of soldiers, but migrations of whole nations. Bede says that the original home of the Angles and Saxons was left empty after the seizure of Britain, and doubtless the same was true of the Frankish homeland. However, the immigrants did not utterly destroy or dispossess the Romano-Celtic inhabitants of their new countries. These people were treated much as their ancestors had treated the aboriginal Britons. Within their own communities they were left with land and laws, constituting a tributary state within a state; subsequently they were absorbed into the new English —and on the Continent Gothic, Frankish, Thuringian, Lombard, etc., system—as it was necessary that they should be, since even among the Norse people central authority was stronger than among the Celts. That the natives were left free in essentials is clear from the fact that Celtic, or Romano-Celtic natives were entitled to *wergeld*.[201] It is equally clear that the Celtic citizen did not enjoy the same status as his Teutonic social equivalent, since his *wergeld* was fixed, at least in England, at half the figure to which the Saxon was entitled. It was thus half as expensive to cut the throat of a Briton or a Gaul, as to cut the throat of an Englishman or a Frank, but this does not mean that the Romano-Celt was a chattel slave.

Like the Celts, the Teutonic peoples settled their soils in village communities and cultivated the land in common, and these communities, however soon the fact was lost sight of, were agnatic kindred groups at first. These groups, however, were given a head, a lord[202] responsible for them to the King. This lord, although possessed of great powers and in some sense a land-owner, was not a land-owner in our sense of the word. He could not sell the land, he was not a freeholder, he owed service in return for his holding. He was a sort of king's agent for the management of the land of his estate, but he could not manage it according to his will, but only according to custom and with the agreement of the tenants in council. He was in very much the position of the managing director of a joint-stock company, responsible to the shareholders, the latter being the tenants. It amounts to this: that among the Teutonic peoples all land whatsoever belonged to the people, in the person of the king; the Crown was the symbol of the commonwealth, the commonwealth that idea which expressed the equality and the will of the people. The land was managed by the people who worked it, their immediate executive for enforcing their will was the lord, and their national executive the king. This was a system as sound, as sensible and as noble as any ever contrived for the management of soil, and of men: it suggests in the people who contrived it an incomparable political tact. In England, where it was at its best, it endured for a thousand years.

The soldier lord settled by the king in the management of an estate was not merely responsible for order and taxes, but for the proper cultivation of the soil. If tenants were wanting he had to find them, and he had to see that custom was not departed from and that the soil was efficiently exploited; if he failed in this, he was guilty of a specific and punishable offence.[203] However, the lord was not free to initiate agricultural novelties; he must see to the good management of the soil, but it must be within the limits of custom, and subject to the criticism and agreement of the tenant shareholders in council. This was true whether the tenants were freely settling Teutonic peasant-soldiers, or half-servile natives. In both cases, according to Vinogradoff:

> the customary arrangements are made and enforced by the community, probably with more or less pressure from stewards and powerful people, but in the main on communal lines: so communal indeed that even the strips[204] on the lord's shares were in many cases intermingled with the rest, and he was bound to submit to the plan of management and the rules laid down by the common consent of the meetings of the shareholders.

The freely settling Teutonic peasant communities were originally, as we have said, kindred groups[205] but they seem soon to have lost the kindred tie, substituting economic and social ones.

Within the holding of the community, i.e. later the lord's "property", rights in land to cultivate for subsistence were distributed and called "family land". This right was inherited by the heirs of a man's body, among whom it was subject to division. But—to emphasize—that which was thus divisible was not the physical land as property, but a share in the right to certain uses of the land. Even so such division would have resulted in the reduction of holdings to sizes inconveniently small, if each had to be worked by the individual householder to whom it was allotted. This was not the case, division of right did not entail physical division, and a man's heirs continued to work his strips as a united household of cultivators.[206]

Communal responsibility for soil management, governed by custom, and symmetrical arrangement of mutual service from top to bottom, the whole resting on the open-field system of cultivation of soil—such was the state of Atlantic Europe from about A.D. 500 to about 1500—throughout which time the gradual substitution of a cash economy for a subsistence economy was breaking down the system, and bringing in that of private property which succeeded it. In certain places the system broke down—where, for example, the pasturing of vast flocks of sheep was produced by the demand for wool. But, on the whole, the system was stable, and its treatment of soil, although by no means ideal, was such that when the agrarian revolution brought in high farming, the soil with which the new men had to work was, on the whole, in good heart.

*

The amount of tree felling and land clearance carried out in Europe during the Roman epoch was more or less in proportion to the intensity of Roman civilization at any given point. Caesar, in his *Gallic War* describes the country east and north of the Rhine as all forest for hundreds of miles. It was, moreover, forest still primaeval, unknown, and Caesar appears to believe the tales of some excessively queer animals said to inhabit it: as to the methods of hunting them, he would seem to have been taken in by a leg-pull. The point is, trees still dominated and it was the Teutonic farmers who first moved on to the heavy soils, a move which entailed a heroic work of pioneering. The Saxons in England, in particular, by making the heaviest soils available to agriculture, were responsible for a major agrarian advance. They exploited their new soils by means of the open-field system and a three-course rotation.

The open-field system of soil management entailed the following arrangements: to each township belonged a given area of land, the greater part of which was unreclaimed waste and not divided according to the share system, being common to all villagers. Part of this untilled land was composed of meadows, and each householder had his turn at grazing stock or cutting grass in these valuable pastures.

Arable strips were scattered all over the village holding, on the most suitable soils and sites, and a householder's share consisted of a number of such strips, distributed fairly, so that he would have some good soil, some indifferent and some poor. There were cases in which the villagers were shuffled round at intervals, moving to a new holding, in order that equity might be even more rigorously observed. In any case the householder's absolute right over his share endured only during the season of cultivation, to lapse after harvest, when his strips reverted into the common field, and to be resumed in the following ploughing time. Moreover, even during the season of cultivation, his right was limited by custom and the decision of the tenants in council as to what should be sown, when, how cultivated and when the harvest should be carried. Thus, the rotation of the crops on all the arable land of the village was managed as one piece, and each shareholder grew the same crop in a given season. The rule was wheat, followed by beans or oats, followed by fallow.

Manuring consisted in driving the cattle belonging to all the villagers on to the stubble after harvest.

This system would not have done much to improve soil, but nor would it have consumed it, or only very slowly. Generally speaking, the men and soil of the whole medieval period held each other in balance, and there is not much evidence that the weight and quality of crops were any less at the end than at the beginning of the period. It seems probable, however, that there was a very slow consumption of soil fertility, and that the stability of the manorial land-tenure practice, its very long endurance, was in itself mildly pernicious.

In England, for example, notably in Oxfordshire, on a typical Manor,[207] the average yield between 1277 and 1285 was eight and three-quarter bushels of wheat per acre, but between 1350 and 1353 it was only six and a quarter. A hundred years earlier yields were of the order of twelve bushels.[208] It is at least possible that exasperation due to declining fertility may have been as much the cause of the numerous *jaqueries*, as more reasonable grievances. On several occasions, it is true, the soil was rested by the interference of other species which sharply checked the increase in human population, in any case slow. The bacillus of bubonic plague did excellent work in this respect, and doubtless there were other micro-organic species which helped. On the whole, despite these allies, fertility was slowly being lost to soil, but the happy fortune which had protected Atlantic soils for so long again intervened, the preliminary changes preceding the agrarian revolution arrived before the damage became at all serious, and much degenerate land went back under grass.

The amount of land "belonging" to each township was very extensive, so that men sat thinly on soil and could therefore infest it only mildly. The limits of the land of one Manor might be marked to separate them from the lands of its neighbours, but this was not always the case. Certainly, in the beginnings, there was plenty of waste land for everyone and no need to quarrel over boundaries, for only about 10 per cent of a manor holding was arable. The rest, pasture, woodland, marsh, moor and hill, was common, and where it was ample for the population of the manor few restrictions were placed on the use of it, although the lord might and often did regulate the hunting of the community on the waste, in order to retain the best of it for himself, and sometimes even the sole rights. Where necessary, in the waste as well as the arable, ditches, canals and dikes were made by the community or, where "inter-commoning" occurred, that is where no boundary was fixed between the common lands used by several neighbouring manors, then all the interested communities contributed labour to this common work.

Such inter-commoning, however, gave rise to disputes and the necessity to fix boundaries, out of which seems to have arisen the idea of land as "belonging" to a village, and in this we might look for one of the origins of the notion of land as a chattel. Vinogradoff says:[209]

> In some cases the waste not appropriated by a single township may have been considered as appertaining to the Hundred, and many disputes concerning it may have been decided in the Hundred court. But there are also instances of the jurisdiction of the shire in such trials; and if we examine the concrete examples of intercommoning which have come

down to us, we see that in most cases it arose between two or three contiguous villages by reason of their natural position on the border of a large moor or waste thicket. This fact has a certain importance as illustrating the original vagueness of all legal distinctions in this respect. They start from a gradual appropriation of the soil, and proceed step by step to clearly defined and limited rights.

Rights, that is, of the manorial community as an integer, not of individual farmers. But the idea is there, boundary suggests inclosure first by the village, and subsequently, by way of the marking off of one man's holding from his neighbour's, by individuals.

As population increased and "stinting" of common rights had to be resorted to, the manor courts laid down rules for the management of the common as well as the arable land.

The use of common pasture was also regulated, each peasant having rights to so much pasture for a certain time, his "stint".[210] Certain kinds of pasture were allotted to horned cattle, other grass to sheep, and the poorest to goats, and the specific needs of these various animals had been studied and understood before the allotments were made.

A social system which is tightly interlocked with its soil system seems to imply, in its rigidity, a static population, for clearly changes in population would entail a flexibility in the system of land tenure and soil management which neither the Feudal system, nor the Incarial system seem to possess. While, indeed, there was so much waste land that extension of arable, and of the cattle population, could always be met by going farther afield and clearing virgin soil, the population of a manor could rise without straining the system of soil management. But when this was no longer the case, when making of new arable or pasture meant the stinting of the waste not merely to individuals, but to the whole village, then two "rights" came into conflict—although both of them belonged to the same farmers and it was up to them to decide whether it was more important to have more arable or retain the waste. But the more difficult case was that in which the right of an individual, an enterprising peasant willing to inclose and improve waste, came into conflict with the general right of his village in that waste.

The problem of reconciling freedom, equity and order, while maintaining the progress of improvement, is so difficult that it has never been solved. The Incarial system was perfectly orderly, very equitable, and progressive in making soil; but this was achieved at the expense of freedom, an indulgence which the ancient South Americans did without. The United States society has enjoyed unexampled freedom of the individual, but this, its greatest glory, has been enjoyed at the cost of frightful damage to the community's heritage in soil, and at the cost of order and equity. The creators of the British Welfare State are finding themselves in great difficulties over this same problem, and in some danger of favouring ordered equity at the expense of freedom, and if the English, with their unique political tact, cannot solve the problem, it seems likely that it will never be solved.

In Feudal Atlantic Europe the lord of the manor had at first the right to approve cases of "assartage", or inclosure undertaken by enterprising individuals, including himself. In making their decision whether or not to approve, the lords had to balance the value, to the community, of the new arable, against the loss of part of the common waste. Whether the lords abused their right of approval in their own interest, or whether some other cause operated, a restraint upon this arbitrary power was set up, and in due course it became the practice to permit the lords this right of approval only upon condition of the tenants being satisfied that the inclosure of part of the waste would not reduce the common land below an amount which left "sufficient" pasture for the cattle of the free tenants:

> Now this right of tenants to "sufficient pasture" is highly characteristic. . . . The sufficiency had to be tested by the custom of the village in regard to the kind and number of beasts allowed to take advantage of the common.[211]

... and it seems that this all-powerful custom even governed decisions made in the King's Court, when a tenant had recourse to them in an action against his lord.

As to the rise of private property in land it is far too tremendous a subject to be dealt with here. Two prime causes for this change can be mentioned: the emancipation of serf-tenants who owed service to the lord for their holding, by the introduction of a money economy and the payment of service as rent in cash, led to the rise of a class of tenant, "copy holding" farmers; and the inclosure of the land of free tenants as permanent, individual farmsteads produced the yeoman farmer, the working of the lord's land by paid labour the gentleman farmer. Meanwhile, during a thousand years, the manorial system had protected the soil against excessive exploitation for profit, and had fed the population more or less adequately. It had maintained a nice balance between plant and animal husbandry, between agricultural and pastoral pursuits.

*

If the manorial and common-field system conserved soil, it did little to improve it, and while it was equitable, it was necessarily unenterprising. Governed by custom its people were highly conservative, and although there are cases of Manor Courts adopting new crops and new methods, they are exceptional. Agricultural improvers were not, however, wanting throughout this period, and especially towards the end. In the south, where the Romans had advanced in their farming to the limit of what the soil would stand, nothing new could be done; but in the north, and even in the north of Italy, where the soil conditions were favourably humid, it was possible to advance to and beyond the limits of Roman practice. Stevens says that at the end of the thirteenth century Pietro dei Crescenzi[212] was urging the use of green manuring, and in the sixteenth, Torello[213] "systematically inculcated a rotation in which fodder crops should replace fallow".

It was, indeed, in Northern Italy that a new social system

was being tried out; the rise of Italian city-states which were to be the model for the new democratic nationalism brought to its logical conclusion in the much larger states of the north might be expected to be accompanied by innovation in all the arts which support the community. By the same token, we should expect the Netherlands, where the new political idea was carried a stage farther, to produce agricultural novelties, and, in fact, during the two centuries, interregnum between the failure of feudalism and the rise of the new nationalism, either as absolute monarchy or as parliamentary oligarchy, the Dutch took the lead in agricultural improvement. They were planting clovers, turnips and other crops more or less new to the field, devising new and lighter ploughs, and breeding improved livestock while the rest of Atlantic Europe was still trying, uneasily, to make the open-field system work, and sticking to the old three-course husbandry. But the Dutch example was quickly followed, and in England improvers were importing Dutch stock bulls and Dutch ideas from as early as the fourteenth century.

In order that the English might follow Dutch progressiveness, it was necessary that there should be great economic and social changes. These changes were forced upon them by the state of their soil, as much as by any other cause. We have already seen that the yields of the open field were falling, and meanwhile the profit from wool was rising. The obvious thing was to put the land into pasture. This, to the great advantage of English soils, had been done on a vast scale, and both great landlords and small farmers had made fortunes out of wool, while the poor cotter had suffered and the land of whole counties was depopulated of men in favour of sheep.[214] But as it was not feasible to do quite without arable, for there must be bread, the Manor tenants tended to come to agreements among themselves, divide the open field up into permanent farmstead holdings, inclose them, and stand each on his own feet as freehold or copyhold farmer. Such individual farmers could, of course, more easily try new ways.

It is convenient to trace the agricultural advances of the interregnum period, very briefly, in English rather than Continental terms, and by way of the sort of books which were being published during that time. These were numerous, but a few of the best will serve the purpose.

The only two books written in England, but not in English, before 1523, on the subject of husbandry, were those of Walter of Henly and of Grostête. In 1523 came Fitzherbert's *Boke of Husbandrie and Surveying.*[215] The theme of this author's farming advice may be expressed in two short quotations from the work: "An housband," he says, "cannot well thrive by his corne without he have other cattell, or by his cattel without corne." This was the essence of the mediaeval system, in which pastoral and agricultural practices had been nicely balanced, at least in theory. But Fitzherbert explains the superiority of the new over the old system, in his advocacy of inclosure, by implying that the relationship between corn and cattle can be best exploited in the enclosed field, "by reason of the compostyng and dungyng of the cattell that shall go and lie upon it both day and night".

Thomas Tusser[216] (1557) advocated inclosure and a four-course rotation instead of a three-course. He was in agreement with the other improvers of the time—begin by inclosing. Mascall, in his *The Government of Cattell* had moved so far in spirit from the mediaeval idea, that we find him drawing upon Mago the Carthaginian. Among the arguments which the improvers could use in favour of inclosures was the very strong one that inclosed land, being unquestionably more productive under the new methods, was worth at least 25 per cent more than uninclosed.

For some thousands of years seed, excepting in the maize-growing countries, had been broadcast by the sower, and still is so broadcast in some places and by some smallholders. In 1594 Sir Hugh Platt published his *Newe and Admirable Arte of Setting Corne,* which described a method of dibbing in seed through holes drilled in boards laid on the tilth. This might be considered the forerunner of drilling seed in rows, with the same saving in seed corn, and the same open cultivation, excepting that Tull had yet to be born and to convince farmers that clean cultivation was important.

The seventeenth century saw an immense increase in the flow of farming books in French, Dutch, Latin, Italian and English. Among the latter were the very numerous and repetitive ones of Gervase Markham, and in the middle of the century came Weston's very important *A Discourse of Husbandrie used in Brabant and Flanders,* whereby the English were introduced to the improvements which had been adopted on other Atlantic European soils, and which were to be the basis of their own great advances. The books, pamphlets and news letters of the following half century clearly show what was happening: inclosure, improvement, for those who could afford these blessings: eviction, urbanization, proletarianization for the small peasantry, who could not. For every book instructing the man of substance how to cultivate his farms, build up his soil, make his garden and orchards and vineyards, there was a pamphlet crying out that there is a new class of rural poor in misery and want, and that the new trend must be reversed. Here and there it was so reversed, by force. But on the whole it made progress, because it was, apparently, only too true that with the perfectly good social case of the old-fashioned apologists, went a very bad technical one—they seemed to think that restoration of the common absolutely *must* entail restoration of the three-course rotation and the old crop succession. There was no reason why this should have been the case: it would have been possible to keep the communal land tenure and adapt it to the new crops and methods; but the power of the ancient association between a social and an agricultural system was too strong, and since the new ways of inclosure and private property in land were clearly more productive because they could and did entail the adoption of new techniques, it was not possible to abandon them, immoral though, from the social point of view, they certainly were.

Nevertheless, resistance to novelty was strong and the diffusion of new crops and ways very slow. Potatoes took well over a hundred years to establish themselves as a field crop, though their value had been well understood quite early.[217] The old way had concentrated on subsistence crops, the old farmers wanted to see food, not cash-equivalents such as hemp or flax, standing in their barns.

With the various European movements for a new system of land-tenure and the cultivation of new crops, began, tentatively, the invention of new machinery and tools. Sir Hugh Platt's rather elementary and laborious method of *setting corne* was at least practicable, but Wortledge's seed-drill, a drawing of which was published in his *Systema Agriculturae*, failed to work. On the other hand, the new ploughs were perfectly practicable: responsible for these was Walter Blith, who studied the ploughs in use in many parts of England and the Low Countries and out of them all produced his own improved model.

From the point of view of the soil's health, what was the significance of these novelties? More numerous crops meant that the net draft on fertility was smaller: the planting of fodder crops of legumes would not only be good for soil, but would permit the maintenance of larger and better herds of cattle, and produce more plentiful supplies of manure. Far above these advantages of inclosure methods, was that of reducing the population living on the land. It was far better for the soil, though far worse for the men, that fewer people should be engaged in growing the food for everyone, since there is a very definite limit to the rule that small subsistence husbandry is better for soil than large-scale soil exploitation: the new methods did not mean such exploitation; they meant, in time, an optimum soil-man relationship. The common-field system might mean that 600 acres supported 30 families of four persons each; the common-field crops were poor and thin, the cattle small and sickly, the herds reduced, every winter, to a mere handful by necessary slaughtering in the absence of winter feed. The six hundred acres would make about eight enclosed farms of seven persons each, and the crops would be better, the cattle healthier and growing larger.[218] After ten centuries man as a strip cultivator at 25 to the 100-acre plot was becoming a disease of the soil. But men suffered for the salvation of the soil, and a great part of the rural population, poor but self-respecting small peasants, was pauperized.

In the seventeenth century no improver seems to have been in any doubt, however, that this was necessary and Walter Blith, who pioneered land drainage, fen reclamation, new manuring techniques, new clovers, as well as inventing ploughs, thought the open-field farmer an ass not to change his ways.

> he will toyle all his days himself and his family for nothing, in and upon his common arable fielde land; up early and downe late, drudge and moyle and ware out himself and family; rather than he will cast how he may improve his lands by impasturing, and enclosing of it.

In England inclosure proceeded so fast, both by agreement and by force and fraud, that by the time, in the middle of the eighteenth century, it was made subject to Act of Parliament, about half the country seems to have been already inclosed. In France, where the free tenancy system had broken down and given way to absolutism on the manor estates as well as in the nation at large, the distribution of land to freeholder peasants had to wait for the Revolution. It was particularly in England, in the north of Europe, and in the Low Countries that, by the beginning of the eighteenth century, the agricultural stage was set for the entrance of a folk-hero, an innovator who would show how to bring order out of social chaos, how to make a new social-agrarian system out of the beginnings made during the preceding two centuries. The social change would look after itself if the technical means could be found to express it. Jethro Tull was cast for the part, and with him worked a fine supporting cast of his own countrymen.

Tull, a barrister of means, began his inquiry into agriculture in 1699 on his own land in Berkshire and Oxfordshire, and like other innovators started with the question, how do plants get their food? He discovered that root systems were far more extensive than was supposed, from which he correctly concluded that plants ought to be more widely spaced in the soil, and that the soil should be kept well worked, the latter correct conclusion being based upon an entirely erroneous deduction from the results of some experiments, that plants actually absorbed, for their nourishment, minute particles of earth. Tull might have done a great deal of harm, had it not been for the saving conservatism of farmers, for he believed animal manure to be useless where tillage was adequate, and wrote that such nasty stuff merely tainted the plants growing in it. As it was, he devised and tried, with remarkable results, drilling seed in widely spaced rows, and keeping the soil rather deeply cultivated throughout the growing life of the plants. To do this he had to invent two machines, the seed-drill, and the horse-hoe, which he did, perfectly successfully. He held clean, open cultivation to be sovereign in agriculture, and proved his point. His example was not followed, or only followed very slowly. The anonymous author of the Preface to the second edition of his *Horse-houghing Husbandry* indignantly asks: "How it has heppened that a Method of Culture, which proposes such advantages to those who shall duly prosecute it, hath been so long neglected in this country." He attributes this wanton disregard for their own interest to the "Characters of the men on whom the practice thereof depends. . . . For it is certain that very few of them can be prevailed on to alter their usual Methods upon any Consideration; though they are convinced that their continuing therein disables them from paying their rents, and maintaining their families".

About a hundred years were required[219] before Tull's discoveries were generally applied, and in the meantime the farmers having refused to give up dunging their land, and other improvers having discovered that animal manures were, as had always been supposed, useful in creating fertility, Tull's wrong conclusions did no harm, his right ones a great deal of good.

The improvement, rather than the mere maintenance of fertility, by manuring, was another product of the eighteenth century, but of that anon. Blith, in the seventeenth, had advocated not only marling and liming, but also the use of a very long list of all kinds of organic refuse, which would delight the heart of a modern compost enthusiast. The principal source of manures being cattle, if manuring was to be stepped up to high-farming levels, it was necessary that cattle should be improved and herds enlarged, and for this end it was first necessary that winter feeding should be possible on a large scale. Hay had long been used for that purpose, but in the open-field system there had never been enough of it. The use of turnips, carrots and potatoes as winter feed was a seventeenth-century, or even a sixteenth-century notion. But the field cultivation of turnips, and later of swedes, depended upon the devising of a method of clean, deep cultivation. The work of "Turnip" Townsend was, therefore, only made possible by that of Tull.

It was a pleasant and useful singularity of the eighteenth-century noblemen that they were often only very moderately attached to and corrupted by their political power, perhaps because it was accepted as a birthright. Charles, Viscount Townsend, having quarrelled with Walpole, his chief in the government, retired to his estates at Rainham in Norfolk and turned his attention to farming. His land was light and poor— his wife described the similar land of their neighbour, Coke, as "nothing but one blade of grass with two rabbits fighting for it". Townsend applied Tull's principles to the cultivation of turnips as a field crop, building up his soil by marling and other manuring, and cultivating deep and clean. Defoe had long before remarked upon the enrichment of certain East Anglian farmers by the feeding of turnips to cattle. But by substituting turnips for fallow in a new rotation, by growing clovers, by Tull's methods of hoeing, Townsend demonstrated, on a sufficiently large scale, that cattle need not be slaughtered for the winter, that they could be fed on clamped turnips, and that fallowing could be dropped out of the rotation with advantage to soil structure. The turnips at Rainham were fed off by folded sheep, they were succeeded by barley and oats, then clover, then wheat. In a few seasons these methods, combined with very heavy marling, transformed the soil of the estate farms.

The names of Tull, Townsend, Coke and Arthur Young have been allowed to obscure those of dozens of other successful improvers, and must again do so here, for these men, although not alone, were representative. Coke transformed a large tract of light and erodable Norfolk soil, formerly poor pasture infested with rabbits, into a rich farmland. This again was done by marling, by muck, product of the new breeds of cattle which Coke brought in from the West Country, by the increase of flocks of sheep, by a new and fallowless rotation and by the cultivation of drilled swedes. Moreover Coke persuaded his tenants to let him enrich them, and they followed his example with remarkable results. The annual gatherings for the Clippings, at Holkham, became forerunners of the County Agricultural Shows: all visitors were welcome as guests of the house, and at the last, the forty-second of these meetings of farmers and improvers from all over Atlantic Europe, there were seven thousand such guests. They carried to their homes the tale of the agricultural miracle of soil-transformation which they had seen, which had been explained to them; and their new knowledge enabled them to go and do likewise.

In addition to turnips and swedes and even cabbages for winter feed, if stock was to be improved then better summer pasture would be necessary. Improvers not only developed an already established technique of making leys, with sainfoin and lucerne, with vetches pioneered by the French, but with grasses selected from the innumerable wild species by the careful collection of seed.

The breeders of new livestock were working simultaneously with the men who were solving the problems of winter feed and new pasture, and they had to work largely with unimproved pastures; but still, by the time the results of their work were ready for general application, the better pastures were beginning to be available.

The story of the breeding of new strains of cattle and sheep, improved almost out of recognition on the old ones, is long and involved and only a sketch of it can be given here. The work was started, probably before the beginning of the seventeenth century, by farmers in France and Flanders, and the flocks and herds of these men had been studied by Robert Bakewell of Dishley during his Continental tours. Bakewell was a Leicestershire farmer, large, hearty, slightly dishonest, who ruined himself by indiscriminate and ostentatious hospitality to those who came to observe his methods and results.[220] He was no Coke, but he was a very remarkable breeder. His methods entailed the abandonment of the established rule that one went for new blood outside the breed with which one was working; Bakewell inbred cattle and sheep for the qualities he wanted in the offspring, intensifying their good points by this means in very few generations. His success with Longhorn cattle was ephemeral, largely because the breed itself was awkward and unpopular; his success with sheep, however, was so complete that the qualities of the sheep which now teem in three continents are largely due to him. A similar service was rendered, with Shorthorn cattle, by the Colling brothers, using Bakewell's methods.

And so it went on among both the tillers and the stock-raisers, the improvement of plants and animals, the diffusion of local attributes, parochial qualities, all over the Atlantic European region; the crossing of plants and of animals to produce superior strains and special attributes. The men who did this work had never heard of genetics, had usually to feed their beasts off wild pasture, were in no sense "scientists". They used their brains, certainly, but above all they used their *tact* as countrymen, as fellow-members of soil with the creatures upon whose bodies they worked. Not only cattle and sheep, but pigs and horses were prepared for the new era of soil-making;

pigs, largely by the crossing of local breeds to produce a compromise of qualities, and by the introduction of Chinese and, later, Indian blood. Horses by selection and crossing among the animals which, for some centuries had been used to pull carts, or as pack animals, but for very little else about the farm. We, in our generation, are inclined to see the passing of the horse and the establishment of the tractor as the end of a long age of service in the harness of the plough. In point of fact it is the end of a brief incident. The horse did not begin to take the place of oxen, in most parts of Europe including most parts of Britain, until the beginning of the nineteenth century. The passing of oxen was indeed the end of a very long age of service to man and soil, but horses have not played an important part in Atlantic European agriculture.

By the end of the second decade of the nineteenth century the agrarian revolution was complete. A new social system had given rise to a new system of mixed, high farming. What were the consequences for the soil? They were wholly good. For the very basis of the new farming entailed larger and better herds of cattle, and flocks of sheep, the constant enrichment of the soil with organic material in enormous quantities, the maintenance of a balance between "corne and cattell" on every farm, the cultivation of a very much more numerous range of crops, the use of soil-making legumes, drainage with the newly invented tile drainage pipes, hedging and ditching and the planting of shelter belts of trees. Perhaps never was soil so coddled. True, the weight of crops, whether vegetable or animal, was greatly increased, but the soil could stand these drafts on what was no longer capital fertility, but a considerable and rising annual increment of fertility.

*

It has been pointed out several times that the temporary ruin of an agricultural community may be and often is the salvation of their soil. The constant check put upon the Russian peasants by the Tartar horse-herds long saved the Black Earth from exploitation. The misery of the mediaeval cotter, dispossessed of his arable for the extension of sheep runs, meant that diseased soils were regenerated by going back under grass. The European soils resisted the Napoleonic wars to admiration, but had the colossal new population of the industrial towns which arose with the industrial revolution been fed off their native soils, strong though these had now grown, they could not have withstood the plague of men which infested them. In the first decades of the new industrialism, surely the most dreadful disaster which has ever befallen mankind, the proliferating and sickly masses of the horrible agglomerations of factories and slums which sprang up everywhere in the service of the ingenious entrepreneur's profit, were fed off native soils, to the great enrichment of the farmers and their landlords. While those landlords ruled, the system was maintained but as soon as the new industrial bourgeoisie was able to wrest power from the landed interest, the system was destroyed. It had, even in the name of humanity, to be destroyed. Not that humanity had much to do with it: the industrialists of north-west Europe, and notably of England, used the children of their fellow-citizens for mining work which, among the Greeks and Romans, had been thought suitable punishment for convicts and prisoners of war. But even these men could see that it would not serve their purpose if the entire working-class starved to death, and that the operatives could not afford even bread at the prices demanded by high-farming, and by the rents which high-farmers had to pay. Happily for them, the farmer's monopoly could be broken, for the Americans were beginning on that career of mining soil fertility by means of wheat and other corns, which was to reduce seven states of the union to semi-desolation in one century. Imported corn poured into Britain, and later into the other north-west European countries. Imported meat also. Throughout the nineteenth century the process was a cumulative one, and, to take England as an example, between 1875 and 1885, the English wheat land fell by a million acres, which went back under grass. Nor could this grass be profitably fed off to raise meat, for while the North

Americans were buying European culture with soil fertility mined by means of cereals, the South Americans were beginning to do likewise by means of vast herds of cattle, improved by the import of British bulls. The middle west of North America, and the south-west, were also overstocked with beasts for the rising trade of meat packing, the centre of which was Chicago, a city of mass slaughtering revolting to contemplate. English and many other European farmers were left with dairying and market-gardening.

There can be no doubt that greed and humanity together, or rather the habit which incorporates both, would have led European farmers to ruin their magnificent soils by feeding the urban masses off those soils, had it been possible to persuade the financiers and industrialists that a policy of high wages was a good one. They were, at the cost of their own impoverishment, saved from impoverishing their soils. European industrial man, trebling his numbers within four generations,[221] became a serious, and in places fatal disease of soil; but by reason of the Liberal "cheap food and a high birthrate and devil take the hindmost" policy, associated with the Manchester School of Economics, whereby production for its own sake is considered more important than the people you are producing for, these men were a pest *not* of their native soils, but of alien ones.

In feeding these enormous masses the American soil-miners, and the European farmers who still tried to compete with them, were assisted by chemistry. For centuries, indeed for thousands of years, men had been trying to discover how plants got their food, for if they could do that, then farmers could "fatten" vegetable crops as they could fatten animal crops. During the second half of the nineteenth century Baron Justus von Liebig's *Chemistry Applied to Agriculture and Physiology*, later his *Natural Laws of Husbandry* were published in numerous editions and several languages. Liebig, and other chemists, had made the fundamental discovery that plants feed on mineral salts in solution. They knew only of the three principal nutrients, had not yet heard of trace-element nutrients, knew nothing of photo-synthesis. But they did confirm the importance of nitrates, which had been discovered but not realized in the seventeenth century, and discover that of potash, and of phosphates. They did make it possible for farmers to replace in the soil some of the mineral elements which plants removed from it; they also made it possible for crops to be grown in total disregard for the "life" of the soil, by means of a kind of "hydroponics" in which plants stand in the soil but are no longer part of its life. As a result, they made possible the killing of soil without the warning fall of crop yields which had formerly signalled to farmers the moment to grass down the soil and move to a new plot; the Dust Bowl was to be one result of Liebig's discoveries.

Liebig himself, although a great chemist, was not that monster of deformity, a specialist; he was one of the last "complete" men among the great Europeans. He understood perfectly well man's place in the soil community: Dr. Blyth, his English editor, wrote in the preface to *The Natural Laws of Husbandry*:

> The excrements of man contain all the mineral matter, not only of corn but also of the cattle sold from the land. Could we restore these excrements to the soil, a perfect circulation of the conditions of life for plants and animals would be established, and our fields would be retained in a permanent state of fertility.

J. B. Lawes, the founder of the Rothamsted Research Station, and J. H. Gilbert, who together had already established a factory for manufacturing superphosphates, launched a test of the new fertilizers which has been going on ever since, a test of wheat grown with fertilizers against wheat grown with dressings of dung. It has demonstrated that from the point of view of the crop, the one is equal to the other.[222]

But whereas fertilizers are simply mineral salts, dung and other organic refuse, containing the same salts, also add to the soil material which maintains and builds up its structure as a complex of organic functions. The spectacular American demonstration of the dangers of chemical fertilizers, and of an industrial attitude towards soil, came just in time to save European soils from a like fate when, economic conditions having changed and European farming being again profitable, it might have paid European farmers to follow the American example. European farmers used fertilizers, of course, and even took advantage of them to practise monoculture on a small scale. But on the whole they were prevented, by the land tenure system obtaining in Europe, by the smallness of holdings, by their own traditions, by the fact that they had inherited a valid rural way of life, from abandoning the old high farming, the older mediaeval farming rule of balancing stock against corn, pasture against arable, and so maintaining both in good heart.

Moreover, the same American disaster, followed by similar ones in Australia and in South Africa, gave rise to new agricultural thinking, to the work of men like Sir Albert Howard, who demonstrated that composts of animal and vegetable refuse not only improve soil structure, but provide all the mineral elements required by crops. As a result of the work of organic husbandry, sneered at by brash journalists as "compost mysticism", it would appear that crops grown in such composts are free from many of the ills, many of the pests which infest crops grown with chemical fertilizers. Certainly the crops seem to be healthier, sturdier, and there can be no doubt at all as to the state of the soil; it is altogether more lively, more flexible than soil which receives no compost. As a result of the work of the compost men and women, there should be no danger that any European farmer will make the mistake of supposing that the existence of chemical fertilizers emancipates him from responsibility towards the soil as a living organism in union with which he, and his customers, live. Economic accident, and the incomparable soil sense of Atlantic European man, has once again saved Atlantic European soils from man as a plague organism.

CHAPTER XV

TOOLS, TECHNIQUES, AND STATES OF MIND AND SPIRIT

THERE is no peculiar merit in ancient things, but there is merit in integrity, and integrity entails the keeping together of the parts of any whole, and if those parts are scattered throughout time, then the maintenance of integrity entails a knowledge, a memory, of ancient things. The community of men is kept whole and healthy by some valid idea, some inspiring feeling, the components of which are scattered throughout time and space. Until very recently men have tended to act as though the past were done with, and to concentrate upon present and future, but in our own time some progress has been made by mathematicians towards understanding the nature of time, which has come to be considered as one of the four dimensions in which we live. The integrity of idea and feeling which hold the community of men together must therefore transcend not only space, but time, for no dimension of space, and nothing which is contained in space, has reality excepting in so far as it persists. *Present* is a relative term, it is a point in time and as such has temporal position but no temporal magnitude. To think, feel or act as though the past is done with, is equivalent to believing that a railway station through which our train has just passed, only existed for as long as our train was in it. A community which ignores or repudiates its origins, in its present acts, is no more whole and healthy than a man who has lost his memory. One of the conditions for the achievement of full human status by man is that he should "remember" every detail of his past; and this is the importance of all the arts and sciences which recreate the past in our consciousness.

In the foregoing chapters I have tried to consider men as members of a community living on soil, or as parasites on a soil, or as creators of an artificial soil community. Everything that man has ever done in his relationship with soil is significant for what he now does, and agricultural man can no more safely ignore his past than architectural man can ignore the Gothic cathedrals or the Baroque palaces, or a mathematician afford to know nothing of Newton. Man, being an organism living on organisms, his works have organic attributes, and the work man does grows out of the work he has done in the past.

When men do work upon matter they employ tools which are of two kinds: physical tools of wood, bone, stone, metal; and psychological tools which are expressed in methods, and which become formalized as techniques. Philosophically, there is no difference between these two classes of tools: the plan a man makes concerning the way in which he will move a boulder, is just as much a tool as the lever he uses to carry out his plan. The psychological tools can be divided into two subclasses, the intellectual and the spiritual; the intellectual tools are concerned with method and collected in sets as sciences; the spiritual tools are concerned with relationships with the rest of the universe, and are collected together in mythologies and religions. A man using all three kinds of tool to turn a piece of waste land into a farm, uses the spiritual tool to invoke the help of the God whose writ runs in that parish, and thereby puts himself into an effectively wilful and purposeful state of mind; he uses the intellectual tools to decide how to set about the work; and the physical tools to cut down trees and plough the virgin soil.

Man devises these tools for himself, but he cannot do so until he is provoked or stimulated by the challenge of the work to be done, and consequently the nature of the tools depends upon the nature of the matter upon which they will be used.

If that matter remains unchanged, the tools, once perfected, will do likewise, for their form has been subtly shaped so that it is effective in bringing man's muscles and brain into creative contact with his material. The radius of the curve of a sickle is not arbitrary: it has been fixed by the way in which grass reacts to the blow of a knife edge, and the way in which a man's arm can move. The form of tools is as persistent as the nature of the work to be done with them. The nature of the work which man does on soil is the same today as it was in early Neolithic times: he makes a tilth, plants it with seeds or trees, hoes them, and reaps or gathers the harvest of grain or fruits.

Of course, there is change, but it is chiefly of one kind—the more efficient application of power to ancient tools. Even this calls for creative thinking and feeling—feeling as well as thinking because the soil community is a complex of organisms.

An early problem which man had to solve was that of tree felling, and in course of time he evolved a perfect axe head. This tool was as good as it could be by late Neolithic times, and it remains unchanged in form; only the material of which it is made has changed—stone, bronze, iron, steel. But the axe was only the physical tool which ancient man used to cut down trees, and the intellectual tool enabled him to devise the most effective way to swing his axe, to see where the tree should be cut in order that it should fall in a certain way. But what of the spiritual tool? It is this member of the trinity of tools which enables men to control and check their actions by reference to the "feeling" which they possess for the consequences of the changes they make in their environment. Man was anciently aware of the whole world as alive, and finding himself animated by spirit very properly supposed all other living creatures —and for him life was manifest even in stones—to be similarly animated. If it be true that primitive men were prevented from cutting down many trees by their inconsiderable numbers and poor tools, it can also be said that even without these handicaps, their tree felling would have been closely and sharply controlled by their state of mind and spirit on the subject of trees.

For men believed that trees had souls and were worshipful; and they associated certain gods with certain trees. Osiris with acacia, Apollo with oak and apple. The temples of many primitive peoples were groves, and in some, for example that of Upsala, men were sacrificed to the spirits which inhabited trees. This point of view is not one which we could adopt today, but it should be recognized that it was immensely valuable to the soil community and therefore, in the long run, to man. It meant that no trees would be wantonly felled, but only when it was absolutely necessary, and then to the accompaniment of propitiatory rites which, if they did nothing else, served constantly to remind tree fellers that they were doing dangerous and important work, and to foster their sense of responsibility towards the other species of the soil community. As an example of the effectiveness of such a state of spirit, in many places, when clearings were being made, the lesser trees were cut down, but the finest were left standing, to provide homes for the spirits ejected from the fallen trees. No Agricultural Executive Committee, no Soil Conservation regulation could have been more effective. We use today the axe-head made by the earliest tree fellers, but not the spiritual tools of which they made use to regulate their tree felling. What have we put in their place?

The persistence of form in tools is very usual: like the axe, the spade and the sickle are much what they ever were, and even when these tools are power driven, the primaeval form persists in the actual working parts, because the work to be done shaped them, and the work is the same. Out of the digging stick developed the spade and the plough, and it is probable that the plough took two distinct lines of development, one from the straight digging stick, the other from the mattock-like digging tool which appears to have been one of the earliest agricultural tools used in Egypt.

The straight digging stick underwent its first great change by becoming some sort of a foot plough, such as the Scottish *caschcrom,* the Irish *loy* or the Peruvian *taccla,* at least two of which are still in use. The blade or share of such tools is driven under the sod with a thrust of the foot, and the worker then bears back on the long lever or handle, to raise the turf. Later, the foot plough acquired a handle at right angles to the main shaft, by which the worker could give it a twist, thus moving the sod aside and turning it over.

The use of such a tool, however, still means a series of separate muscular motions for each sod turned, and the next step must have been to make the forward motion of the tool continuous. In cultivation of the kind which merely entailed pulverization of the soil, this would not be difficult: the fixing of a digging stick in a chassis, at an angle to the horizontal, and later the mounting of the chassis on a wheel, or wheels, would have enabled it to be dragged forward so that it tore out a furrow. The Roman plough, however elaborated and refined, was hardly more than this. In very early times the shape of the plough—beam and share in one piece—was not worked in the timber, but obtained by choosing a "plough-tree" which had grown into the convenient shape. Hesiod, in *Works and Days*, gives useful advice as to the kind of tree most suitable.

In the digging stick, loy, straight plough line of development, the principle was forward motion. Another way to break up soil is to swing the tool towards you—the pick-axe principle. Tools of this type were the origin of the Egyptian plough, or seem to have been so. The handle becomes extended into harness, first for a man or woman, later for a draft animal: the blade becomes the share.

Neither of these types of plough will turn over sod, to make a furrow and a ridge. The use of a coulter, for cutting a guiding line for the share, and a mould board to thrust the cut sod aside, are first definitely known in the Saxon plough, but it is possible that the northern soils had called for some such device before Saxon inventiveness began the cultivation of really heavy soils, and that the huge Celtic plough, drawn by a team of eight oxen, was so provided. Celtic or Teuton, this type of plough was a northern invention, and it was completed by what is, to my mind, as a feat of applied observation, one of the most beautiful of man's works, the plough-share which, by means of its shape, almost moulded by the soil itself and the work to be done in ploughing, lifts, shifts and turns the turf, combining in its forward motion all the effects formerly obtained by the flexibility of man's arm and a number of muscular movements in several directions. Once this share was perfected, the only change which could usefully be made was the application of power to its traction.

All the tools which are basic to the farmer's work remain much what they were when the men who used them were also making use of certain psychological tools described hereafter, but if we seek for persistence of form in these, the story is very different, and in that difference may be found the beginnings of our fatal tendency to exploit soil as if it were mineral wealth. But before we come to the nature of man's ancient spiritual tools, it will be as well to make clear what is meant by persistence of form in psychological devices.

When we consider in what manner the past persists in ideas and feelings which influence our present actions, it is futile to seek instances in traditional habits which happen to survive, but which are no longer significant. One who is not a Christian can make no effective use of the sign of the Cross. The cottage in which I live was built in the sixteenth century, but this demonstrates merely the survival of an artifact, not of an idea in building. The beams in my cottage are joined by a certain type of mortice; I see that this mortice is being used in the construction of some new council houses in the village. This demonstrates the persistence of an idea in building. Gothic buildings were being erected in Britain as late as 1925,[223] but the fundamental form of such buildings no longer derived from the structural needs and principles of the Gothic; new structural frameworks were simply covered with a Gothic skin, and the buildings were self-conscious archaisms, not demonstrating the persistence of a valid and useful style, but the existence of social and artistic debility.

Similarly, the fact that a backward farmer in a remote valley sows his seed on certain days which an antiquary can identify as traditionally favourable moon-phases deriving from Earth-Mother worship, mean not that the farmer is still using a magical or religious formula to help him to a good harvest, but only that his habits of work, like my house, have happened never to encounter the kind of shock which would have destroyed them.

Traditional behaviour only represents the persistence of valid ideas and feelings when it still serves a social purpose.

But it need not serve that social purpose in a way identical with its origin. Ritual can persist longer than its first object and still serve the original purpose, by the substitution of a new object, but one having the old function—the substitution, say, of the Virgin Mary for Demeter or *Pachamamma*. Naval men when they board H.M. ships, salute the Quarter Deck, and this ritual is a survival of the salute formerly offered to the Virgin Mary and her altar in the poop, and before that to the pagan patronesses of sailors. The fact that no such image is now carried, and that the men do not believe in the Goddess today, does not invalidate the ritual, for the idea which *now*, equally effectively, serves their purpose, is that of the spirit of community in service, which is what they are really saluting as they cross the gangway and set foot on deck.

There is almost no trace of a similar persistence of ritual in agriculture. Here and there fields are blessed; Harvest Festival is celebrated in churches; rain is sometimes prayed for. In some backward areas these celebrations may still have significance, but in the typical, representative modern farming community either the celebrations are wanting, or they survive, like the Gothic style in architecture, as self-conscious archaisms, like Morris dancing and bell-ringing. They are no more socially meaningful than ancient stones, and the modern farmer must be rare indeed who would be seriously uneasy over next year's harvest because he had failed to attend Harvest Festival thanksgiving. The reason is obvious: the needs of the soil and the antiquity of the mental and physical motions which the farmer makes may, on the most ancient of the artificial soils, have preserved the peasant from adopting an industrial attitude towards his soil, but the dominant spirit of the times is urban and industrial, and the use of spiritual, as well as intellectual and physical tools, is no more felt necessary to a good harvest and the continued fertility of the soil, than propitiation of Vulcan is felt necessary by the Steel Board for the production of an adequate quantity of sheet steel. Our thought and feeling in these matters represents the antithesis of those of the Neolithic flint-miners: *they* set up an image of the fertility goddess to help them to a "crop" of flint in a barren seam, because the dominant spirit of their times was agricultural: we fail to propitiate the goddess in trying to maintain the fertility of our soil, because the dominant spirit of our time is industrial.

What were the ancient spiritual tools of the cultivator? With great and fascinating local variants, the pattern into which these devices arrange themselves is universal. Frazer, in the *Golden Bough*, says:

> ... in antiquity the civilized nations of Western Asia and Egypt pictured to themselves the changes of the seasons, and particularly the annual growth and decay of vegetation, as episodes in the life of the Gods, whose mournful death and happy resurrection they celebrated with dramatic rites of alternate lamentation and rejoicing. But if the celebration was in form dramatic, it was in substance magical; that is to say, it was intended, on the principles of sympathetic magic, to ensure the vernal regeneration of plants and the multiplication of animals, which had seemed to be menaced by the inroads of winter.

This pattern of behaviour is found everywhere, as Frazer and his disciples have demonstrated. And since the Greeks were paramount at expressing, aesthetically, such creative magic, if we examine the Greek section of the pattern, we can see it at its best and clearest. While doing so, however, it is possible to generalize.

There are two principal myths.

A god is born to a goddess, generally identifiable with the Earth-Mother, Astarte, Demeter, Cybele, Ishtar, Maia, Mary. Before the time of agricultural societies, this god is the natural vegetation of the spring; thereafter, the fruitful tree or vine, for arboriculture is probably earlier than cericulture; thereafter, he is the springing corn. The young god has a brief reign of every kind of sensual pleasure. Dionysos, the Greek version of this deity, coming from Thrace and beyond as a vine spirit, later associated with all fruitful trees, later with corn, was drunken and lecherous, and his early rites were orgies. Not wanton orgies, however, for drunkenness, within certain limits, was the origin of his lechery, and his lechery was worshipful, since it was generative, and the promotion of generation was his purpose. At the end of the young god's reign of creative pleasure, he was sacrificed, and either buried or eaten by his worshippers. Followed a period of mourning, and then resurrection. The cycle is that of vegetation.

Dionysos was first depicted as a vine or a tree, and subsequently represented and addressed as a bull or a goat, and it was in one of his animal incarnations that he was sacrificed, torn to pieces alive by his frantic worshippers, and the flesh eaten raw. In many barbarous societies as late as the nineteenth century, and in civilized ones, such as the Aztecs, as late as the sixteenth, the rôle of the god was played not by a beast, but a man, who was likewise torn in pieces and eaten by his fellow citizens. Perhaps, in his earliest manifestations, Dionysos had no father, and his mother, the Earth herself, was his only parent. Later, when the function of the male in generation had been understood, he acquired a father, of whom more hereafter; probably at the same time his status as a representative of the spring vegetation was enlarged, he became the actual generator, and his worship was associated with the symbol of the phallus. It may have been then that the practice of eating the god yielded to that of burying him, for he was the seed.

Such a change would have entailed the recognition that the

death of the god was an illusion, a sleep, and his resurrection an awakening. At all events, when he acquired a father, his status changed, he became not primary, but secondary, a scapegoat. He was begotten on the goddess by the sky god, by Zeus; or, in the magical-dramatic rites, he was the princely son of the priest-king. It was the function of the god to die for the people, as a sacrifice to the continued fertility of their soil. Only the goddess was conceived of as enduring for ever. But if the annual death of the god, the annual onset of winter with its consequence of death to vegetation, were understood rather as a sham-death, then the god must endure. Moreover, there would, with the rise of masculine values, have been obvious social objections to the killing of the god, the king. But a death there must be. The son of the god, or the king, was the scapegoat: at the time of his importance, in the spring, his father seemed to retire into obscurity, the stage was held by the son, he went through the reign of pleasure, he was sacrificed, and the resurrection was represented by the re-emergence of his father, rejuvenated perhaps, into his former splendour:

> Dionysos (says Proclus), was the last king of the Gods appointed by Zeus. For his father set him on the kingly throne, and made him King of all the Gods of the world.

But this, according to Frazer, was preliminary to sacrificing him instead of his father.

The resurrection is by no means always managed by the reappearance of the father in his former office. Diodorus Siculus says that Dionysos was the son of Zeus and Demeter, and owed his resurrection to his mother who, after he had been rent in pieces by his worshippers, reassembled his mangled remains and made him whole again. In other accounts, after the remains of the god had been buried, he rose from the dead and went to heaven; in others again, Zeus swallowed his son's heart, and begat him again on Semele; or the heart itself, pounded up, is seminal when eaten by Semele.

If, in many of the Dionysos and similar myths, the mother

of the god is Demeter, or Persephone, who tend to become indistinguishable from each other in certain stories, these two goddesses have a myth of fertility to themselves, without any male interference. This myth, the Greek version, is less widely diffused than the Dionysos myth, yet it is found beyond the Hellenic world also.

In the Greek version the worship of the Earth-Mother took shape in Eleusis, a small country of flat corn-lands marching with Attica. The Eleusinian Mysteries were of very ancient origin, but the Demeter-Persephone story as we have it in the Homeric Hymn of the seventh century B.C. seems to be relatively sophisticated and refined. The rites, no doubt, were less so.

Persephone was the daughter of Demeter. One day she was gathering flowers in a meadow when the earth gaped and Pluto, god of the underworld and the dead, appeared and carried her off. Her mother, stricken with grief, and with her yellow hair veiled in black, failed to find Persephone, and learning from the sun her daughter's fate, retired in sorrow and anger to Eleusis, where she mourned beside the well where the girls came to fill their water pitchers:

> In her wrath at her bereavement the goddess suffered not the seed to grow in the earth but kept it hidden under ground, and she vowed that never would she set foot on Olympus and never would she let the corn sprout till her lost daughter should be restored to her.

Thus Frazer. The men and oxen ploughed in vain, famine would have extinguished mankind, the Olympian gods would have perished for want of sacrifice, had not Zeus forced Pluto to give up his unwilling bride, but not until the husband had made sure of her return to him "by giving her the seed of a pomegranate to eat". Zeus commanded that henceforth the young goddess must spend two-thirds of the year with her mother in the upper world, one-third with Pluto in the underworld. Demeter, consoled and rejoicing, caused the corn to sprout again, the flowers to blossom, and the fruit to swell.

This resurrection she showed to the princes of Eleusis, and revealed to them her rites and mysteries.

The poet who composed this story was imposing a sophisticated and charming explanation of the origin of the Eleusinian Mysteries. These mysteries seem to have entailed obscene rites, and certainly the "use of scurrilous language and the breaking of ribald jests". The rites were, in all probability, a fertility ballet. But perhaps the poet's story was acted in the rites. In this simplified version of the tale, however, it is obvious that the sweet form of art has been imposed upon the chaos of myth. In the innumerable stories concerning Demeter and Persephone, the matter is not so clear, the goddesses are sometimes the same, sometimes different. Demeter may be herself the Earth-Mother, or she may be the spirit of the corn, or only the spirit of the ripe corn, while Persephone is the spirit of the green corn. One might be seed corn, the other food corn. There is no need to go into these variants, which have their equivalents in a score of other cultures and in every part of the world.

That the Eleusinian rites should have been obscene is understandable; it is again a question of the generative virtue of lechery.

The Greek farmers not only invoked Demeter's help in every farming operation, but some of them, for example the corn-growing Boeotians named the month of sowing the winter wheat, Damatrius. The Latin name of the goddess was Ceres, and we use her name today when we write of cereals, though whether she would have approved of patent breakfast foods is another matter.

The Harvest Home and Festival, at which Demeter was offered part of the crop and the gratitude of the peasants, took place not in May when, according to Hesiod, the corn harvest was carried—for the poet tells the farmer to reap his corn at "the morning rising of the Pleiades", in his century, by our reckoning, May 11th—but in October, at the same time as the vintage. Whether this was in order to associate the two festivals, or whether it was to remind the goddess of her duties at the time of ploughing, and sowing a new crop, when her help would be most useful, we do not know. Probably the latter reason was the more important.[224]

For the ancient farmers, and even for those not so far from us in time, every plant and animal and stone and the very Earth herself were alive and animated by spirit. And since, from self-knowledge, man knew that mind and matter, soul and body must be in harmony, in order that the whole should function, he also knew that in manipulating the body of the living world, he must be at one with the spirit animating it.

That spirit was, in the earliest agrarian societies, female, as the social life of the society was dominated by female values. That dominance must have derived from the fact that women, in bearing children, did the most important creative act, for man's part in generation was not suspected. It was apparent that the earth, like one's wife and mother, brought forth life: it followed that the earth was female. We have already seen that in societies which earned their living by tillage, a female device, the adoration of the Earth-Mother endured; and where the tradition of peasantry was ancient and never broken, this worship has been interrupted only by repeated changes in the name of the goddess, never in her nature. In some remote and backward societies not even the name changed: in Eleusis Demeter was worshipped by nominally Christian villagers until the nineteenth century.

The conflict between science and religion which occupied so many men's attention in the nineteenth century, is as ancient as man. Observation of nature and deduction of laws from such observation is the basis of science. By some such observation, entailing a sharp break with conservative tradition, men discovered that the pleasures of a somewhat brutal love, for only poetry and manners have made it otherwise, issued in the responsibilities of paternity. The kudos of the creative act was transferred to the male. In primitive societies, the active role must always be given more importance than the passive. When, like human babies, the god acquired a father, the importance of the male deity began to rise and that of the Earth-Mother to decline.

In earlier chapters it has been shown that where masculine economic values dominated, that is in those societies where the male business of hunting had given rise to the male business of stock-raising, and in due course to nomadic pastoralism, the importance of women declined with the declining importance of tillage. The gods of the primarily pastoral Hebrews, Danaans, Aryas, were male. The great goddess, in such societies, became the consort of the sky-god, generally a tribal war god, Zeus, Jahveh, the atrocious Huitzilopochtli. Her importance might at first be but little diminished by this marriage: it is perhaps not too much to suggest that as the kings, and even the fathers, in formerly matrilinear societies, derived their title by virtue of their marriage to the eternal heiress, so the war gods derived their title from their marriage with the Great Mother. I have no authority for the idea, and do not insist upon it. But as war became increasingly important as a social activity, the importance of the great goddess would be certain to diminish among the warrior class, the leaders, while their allies, the priests, would favour this revolution against the divine candidate of their female rivals. But such displacement was never easy and never complete. At Delphi, the Oracle, the god, was Apollo; but the interpreter was a Pythoness. It is a female gypsy who tells our fortune, not a male. And among the peasants, the goddess never seems to have lost her predominance: they might, under pressure, concede an outward homage to the sky-god, yet in their rites they continued to give honour where honour was due; nor did the most arrogantly male governments dare interfere with the Eleusinian Mysteries. The struggle between male and female gods has gone on until very recent times, and the ruthless ferocity with which the Christian churches, especially the ultra-masculine Protestant churches, urged on the persecutors of witches, miserable survivors of the goddess's servants, gives some idea of the plane of savagery upon which this fight was conducted.

And when pastoral nomads with their male gods, the Israelites, the Danaans, the Aryas, came into warlike but fecund contact with such peasant peoples as the Canaanites, the Pelasgoi, the Dasyu, they conquered, imposed male values, and male gods. But there was no absolute imposition, their own beliefs, like their social practices, were modified by the more ancient ones: the great goddess, and the arts of tillage, endured.

Christianity came to peoples who were either barbarous, worshipping war-gods, or super-sophisticated, tolerating all gods and believing, perhaps, in none. The notion of a god who was a scapegoat, and died for the people, of respectable antiquity, found acceptance; subtle Greek metaphysicians worked on the story to make it acceptable by the sophisticated. But for the peasantry, in due course, it entailed nothing but the substitution of the name Mary for some other name—Cybele, Astarte, Demeter, Persephone, Pachamamma, Maia. If, among the people of the nations which took the creative lead in the world, agriculture had remained in the hands of true peasants, the most ancient psychological and spiritual tools of the farmer would have continued in use. It so happened that our world, the modern world, was made by the English, a people who used a thorough-going industrial-commercial device to meet the challenge of their condition, and who destroyed their peasantry in carrying the spirit of industry and commerce into their countryside.

It is not suggested that the failure of this psychological and spiritual device to persist like the form of physical tools, could or even should have been avoided. There occurred, as humanity moved from soil exploiting towards soil making, a tactfully managed evolution, following each sudden high religious revelation, from the ancient myths into the high religious beliefs. Christianity, for example, took over ancient rituals, ancient moon-phases for the Christian festivals, while the Christian gods and saints took over the functions of their pagan predecessors. They performed, no doubt, also higher functions; it is not suggested that there is no difference between the concept of Christ and that of Dionysos, but the similarities are very obvious, and the Mass is a god-eating ritual. At all events, for the ordinary peasant and for the soil, there were no great differences: he still felt that he was responsible to Divine providence for his soil, and must be grateful to that same Spirit for his harvest.

While this state of spirit endures the behaviour of the ordinary man continues to be governed not only by a certain humility, but by a sense of unity and order to which expression is given in an art that, in such periods, has an integrity and a power to move, both lost when men emancipate themselves from such beliefs. It is not necessary to think of the phenomena of magic and of religion in terms which give them objective reality; in any case, to do so would be impossible for a typical modern man. But these things have had and in some places still have subjective reality, and that which is in the mind of a man makes his behaviour. There is absolutely no point at all in discussing whether magical and religious phenomena are *true*. We know nothing about truth, we have not a single clue; since Palaeolithic times our consciousness of the universe has widened, we know more facts, we have discovered how some small parts of the mechanism works, but there is no reason to suppose that we are any nearer than the Magdalenian cave artists to understanding the nature of the universe, which remains a complete and, if dwelt upon, terrifying mystery. What is important, in our context here, is whether a faith in sympathetic magic and in the gods was effective. That it certainly was, for it made for man's ease in the world, it gave him a working method, a unity with the whole community of species, and it also made for the conservation of the soil upon which he lived.

However, Dionysos has died for us, died never to be resurrected. Men are his heirs, they now possess some of his powers, and these have enabled them, by means of several very badly integrated sciences, to increase their numbers tenfold at the expense of the fertility of vast areas of soil. The damage is great and it is continuing, and we may, on our present course, reach a point in time when the corn, quite literally, will not spring again. That point is far distant but none the less real. Nor is this the only disaster which is in the future; not only soil, but men were kept whole by virtue of the belief that man had a definite place in the community of things and species composing the world, and the loss of that belief has been debilitating and nerve-racking. Man, in his god-like rôle, behaves like a neurotic.

Is this a necessary consequence of the failure of the ancient states of mind and spirit to persist? I do not believe that it is: man has repudiated magic as practised by the priests, but there remains magic as practised by the poets, the artists, the oldest priests of all. If men have a thwarted religious instinct, they have also aesthetic sensibilities which need not be thwarted, because the values upon which these rest have never been repudiated, and art is still admitted to be a means of revelation, a means of uniting men, by enlightment, with the world.

When religion as magic fails, religion as an ethical code comes into its own, and man tries to behave well not for fear of the consequences, if he does ill, but by seeking the source of good within himself. This is the basis of the more austere kinds of protestantism which are the results of reformatory movements at a certain stage in the history of the higher religions. In the West, however, the very process of intelligent virtue, entailing the development of great intellectual skill, created, in that skill, the tool which could be used to destroy the whole basis of magical beliefs. Men thought that they could reason their way into an understanding of God and his law, only to find that they had reasoned both entirely out of existence, and were confronted with the need to put something in their place. Neither intelligent religion, nor philosophy, nor science can confer on their disciples that mysterious power of super-normal co-operation with the motion of life, the power to be one with some essence felt, but not known, as the spirit which makes all life a single phenomenon. When the beautiful and symmetrical principles reasoned out by the most powerful minds are put into any sort of practice, their hopelessly inadequate artificiality is at once revealed: they are, in some odd way, extraordinarily thin, and foolish, and unreal. They have the same failing as intellectually produced revolutionary political constitutions: they are inorganic. Any one of the poets whom Plato distrusted, could have felt his way to a better method of governing men than the absurd system devised by that powerful thinker, and which the Emperor Marcus Aurelius tried to apply with such a shocking aftermath.

But no sophisticated society can reject its intellectualism and return to mysticism, can throw away science and return to myth; unless, indeed, it was done in the manner described in Robert Graves' *Seven Days in New Crete*! Once the power of religious belief has been lost, societies must do the best they can with their brains. But they still possess aesthetic sensibility.

In the beginnings of rationalism the various sciences and arts are felt to be manifestations of a single superior state of mind and spirit, and poets are philosophers, painters, mechanics, sculptors, chemists or physicists. In the early days of the Royal Society, scientists and artists were allies, almost indistinguishable, and serving one discipline. With specialization, necessary consequence of the rapidly growing bodies of the sciences, this unity was lost. The specialist is by himself, he has no body of philosophy, no grand general idea to which his work subscribes. When ordinary men are led by a creative minority in a state of spiritual and intellectual anarchy, then they no longer sense or know the world as a unity of which they are a part, the principal motive for action becomes a brutal self-interest; and even in his dealings with his fellow-men, man's "nature", his feeling tends to vanish away, and he acts at best intelligently, at worst "bestially", and almost never feelingly. If the prospect before us were one of the continued fragmentation of art and science into special techniques, then our industrialism, our divorce from the soil community, could have no issue but the most frightful disaster.

There is, however, an alternative, and it has been suggested by the need, in America, to rehabilitate soils: for this purpose, various sciences become the servants of a kind of aesthetic insight, and in that service they are reunited. The process is likely to be assisted by the fact that, in any case, the actual advance of certain sciences is bringing about the overlapping of one special field by another which gives rise to such bastard sciences as bio-chemistry, and even bio-physics. The chemist, the biologist, the botanist, the crystallographer, the electrician are finding that their work is converging; when the poet and the musician and the painter and sculptor begin to be drawn in by the same unifying force, then a new integrity for man will have been made, a relationship with the universe as valid as that expressed in the ancient myths will become possible.

The ecologists of America, and the practical men working to their plans, have found that they can restore dead soils to life by recreating upon them a "natural" and balanced soil community. They begin by introducing some undemanding weed which will colonize the most exhausted soils, they gradually introduce nobler vegetable species; they have to work with great care and great insight, balancing species against species, making sure that the trees they plant, when that becomes possible, will find themselves able to establish a mode of life with the ground plants. In the course of time species intrude of their own accord, and the ecologist has to decide whether these intruders shall or shall not be allowed to stay. Some of the artificially introduced species may grow too prosperous at the expense of others, and must be checked; others, too meek, encouraged. In time animal species are introduced, some living off the vegetation, and others, predatory on the former, to hold them in balance. The work must be like building a house of cards, excepting that when every single feat of delicate balance has been successfully accomplished, then the equilibrium of the finished artifact will be massive, not precarious. Now this creative ecology, if that will do as a name for it, is unquestionably an art: aesthetic insight, right feeling for the grain of life is what must animate it. Yet its servants are the sciences. And its end product is a fertile soil which, in time to come, can be safely cleared and ploughed and sown, and will yield harvests.

If man can also think of himself as one of the materials of this new art, as well as the artist, he may yet learn from his ancient contact with soil how to live nobly and at peace.

NOTES

1. *Treatise on the Gods.*
2. By the interesting and suggestive Comparative History device of Oswald Spengler, his period is equivalent to our eighteenth century.
3. According to a research carried out by the John Innes Institute, earthworms, except as soil aerators, are of no importance.
4. But there are wild species of forest-dwelling cattle, e.g. the *sedang* of the East Indies, and presumably *Bos sylvestris*. On the whole, however, the genus favours park-land.
5. Where water is excessive, *loess* soils tend to become not forest but marsh. Thus, although the buffalo may be a marsh animal, it still belongs to the *loess*. According to Professor Gordon Childe (*What Happened in History*) the domesticated buffalo was introduced into Greece in Hellenic times.
6. See *Gestalt und Wirklichkeit*, Oswald Spengler.
7. It is held by some that the order in which plants were domesticated is: fruit trees—edible roots—cereals.
8. Among the things unearthed by the excavators of the Indus Valley culture are typical objects of Earth-Mother cults, such as figurines of the Goddess, and sacramental Phalli.
9. For the purpose of our demonstration there can be no harm in sticking to the account of the descent of the Aryas upon the Dasas, of this suggestive encounter between Energy and Form, as we have it in the *Rigveda*. It should be said, however, that whereas scholars had deduced from this account the presence, in the Indus Valley, of an aboriginal, "Australoid" type of primitive farmers, in the Neolithic phase, excavation at Mohenjo-daro and Harappa, as well as numerous other sites in the region, has, since 1921, revealed a very different state of affairs, which suggests either that the *Rigveda* is exceptionally unreliable as a source of information, or that it is wrongly dated or that the immigration of the Aryas into India is wrongly dated (c. 1500 B.C.). From R. E. M. Wheeler's *Five Thousand Years of Pakistan*, it is clear that if the Aryas came down into India about 1500 B.C. they must have encountered an olive-skinned, comely, "Mediterranean" type of people, in a rather late phase of a high civilization of the Euphrates-Tigris type, living in town-planned cities. This "Mohenjodaro" civilization appears to have extended over a vast territory, up into and beyond Baluchistan, and resembled hardly at all the picture evoked by the *Rigveda* hymns. Moreover, the civilization appears to have been in the phase called by Professor Arnold Toynbee, the Universal State, a phase which would have been identified by Spengler as one well on the way to a final decline. In short, the civilization was probably a thousand years old. Despite all this, however, the *Rigveda* hymns express a valuable poetic truth, and Professor Stuart Piggott makes no difficulty over the discrepancies (see

his *Prehistoric India*). Nevertheless it is odd that the *Rigveda* is clear enough on the subject of the *anasa,* the noseless, that is the Australoid part of the population, which, according to archaeological evidence, was in a minority, and never even mentions the "Mediterranean" majority. Perhaps the latter were the overlords, and sent the conquered aboriginals to do their fighting for them against the predatory Aryas?

10. See, e.g., Pushkin's *The Captain's Daughter*.
11. Roman legionaries received unground corn as their rations and ate it as frumentum (cf. the Elizabethan dish *frumity*).
12. J. and C. Hawkes, *Prehistoric Britain*.
13. See below.
14. One school of anthropology reverses cause and effect in this argument. E.g. "The fact that most garden plants are regarded as feminine (e.g. among the S. American Indians) also explains woman's prominent part in agriculture in primitive societies, etc. etc."—Rafael Karsten, *The Civilization of the S. American Indians*. This argument implies that plant spirits were not feminine because women were the first cultivators, but that women were the first cultivators because plant spirits were feminine. The effect upon female prestige would have been much the same in either case. But the theory does not tell us *why* garden plants are feminine.
15. cf., in particular, George Thomson's *Studies in Ancient Greek Society*. Thomson, however, believes that matrilinear systems antedate all forms of production, and are maintained by tillage, abolished under pastoralism. Thus "Reviewing the evidence as a whole, we find that matrilineal descent preponderates slightly in the hunting grades, but then declines, rapidly in the pastoral grades, much more slowly in the agricultural."
16. But by no means identical.
17. As well as the known and obvious cases in this connection see Robert Briffault's *Les Troubadours* for a most stimulating theory of Arab influence on Western literature.
18. See G. Thomson, op. cit.
19. Emil Ludwig, *The Nile*.
20. Impossibility of finding reliable relative dates makes this statement highly speculative.
21. If this figure seems incredible, it must be remembered that the delta did not appear above sea level until 14,000 years ago. This piece of land contains, allowing a mean altitude of 55 feet, a volume of about 25×10^{10} cubic yards of soil, the whole deposited by the Nile in 140 centuries. And as silting must have been far greater since deforestation of the highlands, most of this huge quantity has been laid down in the last seven thousand years.
22. Relatively earlier are such folk as the Taixans, Badanians and others whose sites have been excavated on Egyptian soils.
23. But see, against this, Dr. Henri Frankfort; see also, in *The Civilization of the S. American Indians*, Dr. Rafael Karsten's argument that totemism originates in the primitive theory of the transmigration of souls and that the attribution of ancestorship to totem animals and objects can be explained by reference to primitive theories of generation and conception.

NOTES

24. *History of Egypt.* New York, 1910. See also 225.
25. *Social Life in Ancient Egypt.*
26. op. cit. Thomson is a vigorous Marxist-Morganist.
27. See A. M. Negrul, *The Genetical Basis of Grape Breeding.* Commonwealth Bureaux of Agric. Plant Breeding Abstracts.
28. Near Hit are the bitumen lakes which provided the Sumerians with a natural cement and with water-proofing for their bricks.
29. See Chapter VII.
30. The *Anabasis.*
31. This is not a term used by prehistorians, who call the phenomenon in question The Harappa Culture. Indus empire is a phrase coined by the author for convenience. The country and state will have no name until the pictographic writing of its people can be read, and even then, since there is little of it, it may not give us a name for their country.
32. Royal India and Pakistan Society.
33. Pelican Special.
34. Jacks and Whyte, *The Rape of the Earth.*
35. See, e.g., Piggott, op. cit.
36. ibid.
37. R. Zon, *Forests and Water.*
38. e.g. by Dr. Paul Schrieber, and see also Collis, *The Triumph of the Tree.*
39. *Natural History of Selborne.*
40. In short, they practised shifting agriculture.
41. The translation is Jowett's.
42. *The Wanderings of Plants and Animals.*
43. *Maria Chapdelaine.*
44. The Roman smallholding, *after* 393 B.C., was 7 *jugera* (4$\frac{2}{3}$ acres).
45. *An Economic History of Rome.*
46. *De Re Rustica.*
47. op. cit.
48. op. cit.
49. Livy, II, xxxiv.
50. Livy, V, xii.
51. ibid.
52. op. cit.
53. Turkey, of the Young Turks and Ataturk, is the analogous case in our own civilization.
54. An exception might be made in favour of our dam building, e.g. Assouan, Dniepr and T.V.A.
55. i.e. the movement away from smallholding, to plantation slavery.
56. My italics. E. H.
57. These were lands, as e.g. in the Po valley, which had gone over to Hannibal. Thus they were not "liberated", but ferociously punished.
58. *Bevölkerung.*
59. All these figures are, of course, approximate. They stand for a truth, but are not the exact truth.
60. The Peruvian coastal soils, depending on irrigation, are the exception.

61. See *The Formation of the State of Oklahoma*, Roy Gittinger.
62. ibid.
63. The annual report of the U.S. Secretary of the Interior gives the figure as 60,000 by the November of 1889.
64. The Cherokees sold, on this occasion, 6,000,000 acres for 8,500,000 dollars.
65. "European" culture, here and throughout, means Western European Catholic-Protestant civilization, and is distinguished from its parent and predecessor, the Hellenic Culture. The beginnings of the true "Western Civilization" can be placed *c.* A.D. 1000.
66. op. cit.
67. The following is by G. V. Jacks, quoted from *The Rape of the Earth*: "When a large open area has been consistently mismanaged and its fertility reduced below the safety point, wind erosion can produce chaos within a few days. The wind lifts the pulverized soil bodily from the surface, the atmosphere is choked with sand and dust, men and animals are suffocated, standing crops are torn up in one place and buried in another, leaving the countryside as though a hurricane had passed. The great dust storms which have swept the American prairies in recent years, and darkened the sky over the Atlantic cities and far out to sea, were not freaks of nature. Fifty years ago, stronger winds than accompanied these dust storms would have blown over the grass-grown prairies and left no trace of their passage."
68. Jacks and Whyte, op. cit.
69. *Geography of the Soils of China*. Nanking, 1936.
70. *My Country and My People*.
71. The term is used for the people who lived in what is now China; the Chinese, properly so called, are of later origin.
72. *Children of the Yellow Earth*. London, 1934.
73. The Yellow River is comparatively new. Dr. Andersson (op. cit.) was able to show that the river has come into being since the deposition of the *loess* plains. Elsewhere in this book we refer, on good authority, to N. China loess "2000 feet deep". Andersson says that this estimate is due to confusion between real *loess*, the *Huang-tu* or Yellow Earth, with the *loess*-like *Hipparion* clay, and that *Huang-tu* is probably nowhere more than 100 metres deep.
74. Teilhard and Licent.
75. "The Neolithic Age in Northern China," *Antiquity*, 1933.
76. Bishop, ibid.
77. Schneider, *Muschelgeldstudien*. A friend of the present writer saw cowrie-shells being used as small change in the State of Orissa in 1940.
78. *Shells as Evidence of the Migration of Early Culture*. 1917. See also Schneider, op. cit. and Steran, *Ethno-Conchology: A Study of Primitive Money*.
79. *Histoire Naturelle du Senegal* (*c.* 1760) ". . . Concha venerea sic dicta foemineam quodam modo repraesentat externe quidem per labiorum fissuram, interne vero propter cavitatem uterum mentientem—Sunto igitur dictae Porcellanae (id est Venereae) ob aliquam cum pudendo muliebri similitudinem."

Porcellanae: Cowrie from Greek, a little pig. Latin for this shell is "porculi". On the other hand there is an obvious phonetic derivation from the Urdu *kauri*. The Latin and Greek words suggest a naming from the look of the shell. The two possible derivations do not necessarily clash, but this is not the place to discuss this.

80. J. C. Melville's monograph on the *Cypraea*.
81. Harley Glessner Creel, *The Birth of China*.
82. Bishop, op. cit.
83. Creel, op. cit.
84. Creel, Andersson, op. cit., and others.
85. Creel, op. cit. (our italics).
86. See 88.
87. The bush was evidently fired by the beaters.
88. *The She King: The Book of Poetry.* Trs. James Legge, London, 1865.
89. Chestnut-soil. The soil between the black earth steppe and the arid *steppe*. Fertile, but unstable when ploughed. The passage is from Jacks and Whyte, op. cit.
90. B. Keller, "Distribution of Vegetation in the Plains of European Russia," *J. of Ecology*, 1927.
91. D. S. Mirsky. *Russia: A Social History*. London, 1942.
92. ibid.
93. See Part V.
94. Reindeer herding, indeed, is between pastoralism and hunting . . . a link between the two economies.
95. See Part V.
96. Brovka, *Scythian Art*. Berlin, 1928.
97. *c.* A.D. 955. The Russian prince in question was Swatoslaus, of whom Gibbon says: "By an embassy from Nicephorus, the Greek Emperor, he was moved to undertake the conquest of Bulgaria, and a gift of 1500 pounds of gold was laid at his feet to defray the expense, or reward the toils of the expedition. An army of sixty thousand men was assembled and embarked, they sailed from the Borysthenes to the Danube, their landing was effected on the Moesian shore and after a sharp encounter, the swords of the Russians prevailed against the arrows of the Bulgarian horse."
98. See Mirsky on the origin of this name. Gibbon says: "The name of Russians was first divulged in the ninth century by an Embassy of Theophilus, Emperor of the East, to the Emperor of the West, Lewis, the son of Charlemagne." The Greeks applied the name $\varrho\omega\varsigma$ to the Crimeans. The popular derivation from an eponymous hero, Ruric, seems to be fanciful, yet it has the kind of truth which commonly goes with folk-derivations, in that certainly the Swedish adventurers gave nationhood to the Slavs.
99. Niederle, *Manuel de l'Antiquité Slave*. Paris, 1922.
100. cf. the Carthaginians, and the modern Americans.
101. See Mirsky, op. cit. All these *steppe* peoples were Mongols. Tartar means "subject of the house of Jenghizkhan".
102. Marco Polo, *Travels*.
103. I must confess that I had allowed my ideas of the Tartars to be much

influenced by the common meaning of the word *Horde*. This mistaken idea has been corrected by Mirsky (op. cit.). *Horde* seems to be a bad translation of the original, which is *Orda*, and from which, nevertheless, horde is derived. *Orda*, Russian, comes from *Ordu*, Turki, meaning both corps or division of an army, and its H.Q. Thus, *Golden Horde* can mean either Golden Army Corps, or Golden G.H.Q., but not simply a rout of mounted men. The "Golden", in the context, comes from the gold leaf or paint top of the principal pavilion of the camp of the western Tartars. In modern Turkish, *ordu* actually means an army corps. Hence, also, by derivation, *Urdu*, meaning "camp language", "military jargon", etc. Mirsky uses *Golden Orda*; I shall stick to the more familiar term.

104. Sarai on the volga.
105. Harold Lamb, *Tamerlane*. London, 1929.
106. Mirsky, op. cit.
107. cf. Qazaqs. A federation of tribes which had seceded from a former federation.
108. See also James Mavor, *An Economic History of Russia*.
109. Treaty of Nerchinsk, 1689.
110. See Mavor, op. cit. The novel referred to in this passage is, of course, *Dead Souls*.
111. Mirsky, op. cit.
112. See Chapter 14.
113. Professor E. Washburn Hopkins, "Family Life and Social Customs as They Appear in the Sutras," *Cambridge History of India*.
114. Mrs. C. A. F. Rhys Davids, "Economic Conditions According to Early Buddhist Literature," *Cambridge History of India*.
115. Rhys Davids, op cit.
116. W. H. Moreland, *Cambridge History of India*.
117. Rhys Davids, op cit.
118. Professor E. Washburn Hopkins, op. cit.
119. O. Spengler, *Gestalt und Wirklichkeit. Der Untergang des Abendlandes*.
120. W. H. Moreland, op. cit.
121. A term now used for all peasants.
122. *Not*, be it noted, of the *profit*. The taxation of the profit is a device only possible in an advanced capitalist society engaged primarily in cash-cropping. The raiyats were, primarily, subsistence farmers.
123. Moreland, op. cit.
124. See Moreland, op. cit. "When orders for assignment could not be met in full, the figures in the valuation were arbitrarily raised so that orders could be carried out on paper, but the assignee would, in fact, be unable to realize the income to which he was entitled, etc. etc."
125. The Minister responsible for this reform was Raja Todar Mal.
126. Moreland, op. cit.
127. *Zamin* = Persian for "land".
128. *Diwan* = State Secretary, Minister. Hence *Diwani*, an Administration.
129. Apart from the principal authorities, notably those of the *Cambridge History of India*, on which I have drawn for the following brief study, I

have had the very great advantage of the personal advice of Mr. Arthur Hartley, I.C.S., O.B.E., one time settlement officer in the Rangpur Survey and Settlement operations (1931-38) and author of the Report of those operations. His work entailed a detailed study of the revenue system of Bengal, historical and actual. The Report was published (1940) by the Bengal Government Press.

130. See E. I. Company Revenue Board proceedings for 15 December, 1772, and subsequent Proceedings. See also Philip Francis, *Original Minutes of the Governor General and Council of Fort William on the Settlement and Collection of the Revenues of Bengal.* 1782.
131. ibid.
132. Letter from Edmund Baber quoted by Ramsbottom.
133. A. C. Hartley, op. cit.
134. Hartley, op. cit.
135. See, for this period, J. T. Gwynn, I.C.S. (Retd.), "The Madras District System and Land Revenue to 1818." *Cambridge History of India.* That the *zamindārs* did not even feel themselves, or behave as, land-owners is strikingly obvious from, for example, a report of a Mr. Goodlad, Collector, quoted, op. cit., by Hartley.
136. *vide* Toynbee, *A Study of History.*
137. *Allouez*, quoted by E. J. Payne.
138. Some writers have Nahua and others Nahuatl; it seems the latter is an adjectival form and its use as a name a solecism.
139. Clan, but without any of the conventional anthropological implications of the word.
140. *Pachamamma* was also, significantly, the patron deity of pregnant women. Santillán, *Tres relaciones de antigüedades Peruanas.*
141. For Garcilasso de la Vega Inca, *Huira-cocha* is a "modern God" and the Creator is called *Pachacamac.*
142. Sarmiento's account.
143. In the west, *Cunti-suyu*, from the Apurimac to the maritime cordillera and the coast. In the north, *Chinchay-suyu*, the coast valleys, Huamanca, the Jauja valley, Huanuco, Caxamarca as far as Quito. In the south the *Colla-suyu*, being the Titicaca basin, Charcas, Tucuman, Chile, and the Arequipa, Moqegua and Tacna valleys. In the east, the almost unknown forests penetrated by Inca armies were *Anti-suyu.* See Markham's *History of the Incas.*
In his *Royal Commentaries*, Garcilasso de la Vega Inca also calls the Empire *Yncap Runam*—the Inca's Vassals or the Inca's Men.
144. Garcilasso de la Vega Inca.
145. G. de la V. in op. cit. has *mitmac.*
146. Markham. See his translation of the Ollontay drama; this appears as an appendix to his *History of the Incas* in which he also discusses other works of literature. See also G. de la V. in op. cit. Book II, Chapter XXVII.
147. G. de la V., op. cit.
148. Translation by Markham (Hakluyt Society).

149. And for all other terms of relationship see G. de la V., op. cit., Book IV, Chapter XI.
150. See, e.g. among others, George Thomson in op. cit.
151. Markham, *The Incas of Peru*; Saavedra, *El Ayllu*; Cunow, *Organization of the Empire of the Incas. Investigation into their Ancient Agrarian Communism.* See, concerning the maintenance of the tribal pattern in imperial times, Belamunde, *El Peru antiguo y los modernos sociologos*.
152. e.g., Viracoha, and his son Urco. And it was another such preference which gave rise to the Civil War which put the empire at Pizarros' mercy.
153. *History of the Incas.*
154. The New World, like the Old, has a universal flood legend.
155. The actual process of change is implied in G. de la V's. statement (op. cit.) that in the Inca provinces men and women cultivated the soil, in the barbarous provinces, chiefly women.
156. The nations were: Guaneuta, Tundama, Sogamoso, Tunja, and Bogata. See Joyce, *South American Archaeology*.
157. See, concerning also sister-marriage among the Inca, G. de la V., op. cit. Chapter XXV.
158. Koch-Grunberg, *Zwei Jahren unter den Indianern*.
159. *Auchenia glama* and the other *auchenias* are, like the camels, *C. dromedarius* and *C. bactrianus*, of the family Camelidae.
160. op. cit.
161. *vide* Toynbee, op. cit.
162. *History and Social Influence of the Potato.*
163. *Apologetica Historia.*
164. We do not refer here to the influence of T. A. Joyce's Tiahuanaco I and Tiahuanaco II cultures on the ceramic styles of Proto-Chimu and Proto-Lasca, but to an earlier, megalithic Tiahuanaco. Markham finds the masonry and sculpture styles of megalithic Tiahuanaco occurring in Cuzco, at Ollontay-tamper, Couchaca, and in such relics as the Chavin Stone. See *The Incas of Peru*.
165. Bulletin No. 574, Texas Agricultural Experimental Station.
166. As usual, regarded among all American Indians as animated by a female spirit—a corn-maiden, the *Chicomecoatl* of the Mexicans, the *Hag* of the Cherokees.
167. Payne, op. cit.
168. George Vaillant, *The Aztecs of Mexico*.
169. Regnabat, *c.* 1090-1190 according to Sarmiento. The Inca seem always to have lived to ages exceeding one hundred, but we have not been able to discover whether this was really so. It is possible, but improbable. The ages and reigns given by G. de la. V. in op. cit., are more normal.
170. Translation by Sir Clements Markham.
171. This narcotic was one of the most valued crops, was used in religious rites, and was exclusive to the Inca. Its use outside the Inca aristocracy was rigorously controlled by the government.
172. In Britain today farming land is being lost to the builder at the rate of about 50,000 acres per annum.

173. Squiers, *Peru.*
174. The Upper and the Lower waters, i.e. Cuzco. But Hurin—and Hanan—seem to have a significance other than one of place. The division of communities into two groups thus designated evidently had some social significance. It may possibly be of great antiquity, perhaps a vestigial remainder of tribal division into *Phatries*? G. de la V. in op. cit. says *Hanan* refers to the Sapa Inca's party, *Hurin* to that of the *Ccoya,* the queen, and that *Hanan* families took a sort of elder-brotherly precedence over *Hurin* families.
175. Markham: *Rites and Laws of the Incas.* The Inca had an attractive myth concerning rainfall. *Pachacamac* caused a maiden to stand in heaven with a pitcher and water the earth when necessary. She had a naughty brother and he sometimes broke her pitcher, when the consequences, on earth, were thunder and lightning. The story occurs in a set of verses, which we print for the benefit of those interested in the musical possibility and simple metre of Quichua poetry. We are not sure of the stresses in this language, but the metre appears to be that of *Hiawatha*: it may have been one common throughout the American Indian cultures, and perhaps Longfellow borrowed from an Indian source. Our translation attempts to retain this metre, and the exact sense; we make no other claim for it. It is made not from the Quichua, with which we are not familiar, but from a Latin line-for-line translation by Father Blas Valera.

	Line-for-line	*Not line-for-line*
Sumac nusta	Pulchra nympha	Lovely maiden
Turallayqui	Frater tuum	See—thy brother
Puynuyquita	Urnam tuum	Shatters now thine
Paquin cayan	Nunc infingit	Urn of water
Hina mantara	Cujus ictus	Hence this lightning
Cunununan	Tonat fulget	Thunderbolts and
Yllapantac	Fulminatque	Thunder, yet we
Camri nusta	Sed tu, nympha	Know, royal maiden,
Unuy quita	Tuum lympham	Thy clear waters
Paramunquic	Fundens pluis	Still will rain, and
May nunpiri	Interdumque	Sometimes also
Chichimunquic	Grandinem, sue	Fall as hail, or
Ritimunquic	Nivem mittis	Fall as snowflakes.
Pacha rurac	Mundi factor	Earth's Creator,
Pachacamac*	Pachacamac	Pachacamac,
Viracocha*	Viracocha	Viracocha
Cay hinapac	Ad hoc munus	For this service
Churasunqui	Te sufficit	Thee appointed,
Camasunqui	Ac praefecit	Thee created

*Both names for the supreme God. Pachacamac means, literally, "teacher of all things". We can find no literal meaning for Viracocha, which is perhaps simply a name, or is in some proto-language, and the meaning lost.

176. In a note to his edition of Cieza de Leon. The Nasca Valley is in the north-west coastal region.

177. Markham uses the word Incas to mean peoples of the Andean civilization.
178. See Chapter XIV.
179. Genesis iii. 17-19.
180. See V. Gordon Childe's *Dawn of European Civilization*.
181. Clark, G., *The Mesolithic Settlement of North Europe*.
182. But perhaps not certain. Something of the sort seems always to be assumed by archaeologists, who are perhaps not aware that in certain parts of Canada where bitter experience has made farmers afraid to plough soils which ought never to have been ploughed in the first place, wheat is successfully grown on a large scale by simply scattering seed among the stubble of the last harvest, without any ploughing or cultivating. The seed germinates in the autumn rains and roots itself by main force.
183. J. and C. Hawkes, *Prehistoric Britain*.
184. For a vivid evocation of this time of change, see Kipling's "The Knife and the Naked Chalk" in *Rewards and Fairies*. Significantly the hero of this tale, a stone-armed shepherd, goes to the forest folk for his metal knife, paying with the sight of one eye and by having an unwanted greatness thrust upon him.
185. J. and C. Hawkes, op. cit.
186. Caesar, *De Bello Gallico*.
187. Vinogradoff, *The Growth of the Manor*; Hubert, *The Greatness and Decline of the Celts*.
188. cf. North-west China, Great City Shang, c. 1400 B.C. [See Chapter XI.]
189. cf. Greek city state practice during the seventh and sixth centuries B.C.
190. cf. the Kentish system of *gavelkind*.
191. C. E. Stevens, "Agricultural Life in the Later Roman Empire," *Cambridge Economic History of Europe*.
192. But see Norman Carew, *Ploughmans Wisdom*. The author's experiments are very far from convincing, but they give rise to some doubts. What actually happens seems to be uncertain, and in some conditions dust mulching promotes capillary action.
193. See Liebig, *Natural Laws of Husbandry*.
194. op. cit.
195. Edward Hyams, *The Grape-Vine in England*.
196. Stevens, op. cit.
197. In India (Chapter XII) when a similar cause might have had a similar effect, the British stepping into Mughal shoes and maintaining order, prevented immediate human suffering, but at the expense of soil, and of future suffering.
198. See Stevens, op. cit.
199. ibid., cf. the Mughal attempt (Chapter XIII) to bind peasants to soil for fiscal reasons.
200. And *farrago*, a mixed crop of barley and green legumes.
201. *Wergeld*, a compensatory fine payable to the family or tribe of a murdered man by the family or tribe of the murderer. The amount which any given victim was worth depended upon his social position, logically enough, since a high social status obviously entailed more expensive living. The

irrational modern system of hanging a murderer instead of making him compensate the family of his victim is of oriental, not European origin.
202. Saxon *Thane* or *Earl*.
203. Vinogradoff, who derives these facts from the laws of Ine. These are specifically Saxon, but the pattern was similar though not identical all over Atlantic Europe.
204. See below.
205. In the case of England these were called *maegths,* as were the territories they occupied. Many *maegth* names survive—e.g., Woking, Tooting. See Kemble, *Saxons in England.*
206. cf. the ancient Kentish tenure of *gavelkind.*
207. Downton. (See Ballard.)
208. *Anonymous Husbandry.*
209. *The Growth of the Manor.*
210. This was still the case in our own time in Ireland. According to Mr. Maurice Healy, K.C., 50 per cent of the law-suits in Kerry in the early twentieth century were disputes over stinting.
211. Vinogradoff, op. cit.
212. op. cit.; but this *Liber ruralisa comodorum* was apparently not published until 1471 (see Fussell), at Augsburg.
213. *Ricordo d'Agricoltura.*
214. Eileen Power.
215. For an admirable bibliography of English farming books see *The Old English Farming Books* and *More Old English Farming Books,* by G. E. Fussell, F.R.Hist.Soc.
216. *A Hundredth Good Pointes of Husbandrie* and subsequent books.
217. John Forster's *England's Happiness Increased; or a sure and easie remedie against all succeeding dear years by a plantation of the roots called potatoes* was published in 1664.
218. Fussell, op. cit.
219. *Horse-houghing Husbandry* was translated into French shortly after its appearance in English, yet in Flaubert's *Bouvard et Pecuchet* (1880) we find an improving Norman landlord using Tull's work as a manual.
220. Robert Trow-Smith, *English Husbandry.* But see, for some interesting doubts on these questions, Mr. H. J. Massingham's *Faith of a Fieldsman.*
221. In Britain, at least.
222. R. Trow-Smith, op. cit.
223. e.g., Bristol University.
224. In 1802, an English traveller named Dodwell carried off the statue of Demeter from the middle of the threshing-floor in the ruined temple of her cult at Eleusis. By his own account in *A Classical and Topographical Tour through Greece*: "In my first journey to Greece this protecting deity was in its full glory ... the villagers were persuaded that their rich harvests were the effect of her bounty, and since her removal, their abundance, as they assured me had disappeared."

225. Professor Henri Frankfort has raised a number of points casting doubt on this and subsequent arguments. He doubts whether women were the sole property owners; he does not derive the animal gods from totems; he points out that a rule of primogeniture could be deduced from Pyramid texts, and that the whole Horus story is based upon such a rule. Is it possible that the whole thing is a matter of dates? It is not argued that matrilinear practice endured, but only vestiges of it as the primal economic and social device.

INDEX

Note: Only significant references are indexed

Achaeans, immig. into Greece, 96; as meat-eaters, 103
Aegospotami, battle of, 106
Africa, soil destroyed, 83
ager Romanus, 123, 136
agrarian revolution, 253
Akbar, Mughal emperor, 191
Akkad, ancient civil. of, origins, 59
Alani, 170
Alban Hills, vineyards planted, 124
Albert, Lake, 43
Alcibiades, 106
Algonquins, 201, 202
alpaca, *see* llama (212)
Altyn-Khan Tartars, 179
alluvium, as origin of agrarian cultures, 40
Amanita muscaria, 19
America, S., *steppe* ecology of, 88
Ananyino, prehis. agrarianism, Russia, 171
Anatolia, diffusion of agricultural crafts, 234
Ancasmayu, river, 234
Andean Great Society, 203
andenes, Peruvian agricul. terraces, 223
Andersson, Gunnar, 153
animal husbandry, invention of, 36
Anyang, China, 156
Aphrodite, 159
Apollo, 286
Apu-Ccapac-Inca, 205, 208, 210

arable farming, invention by women, 38
Arapahoe tribe, 146
Araxes, river, of Xenophon, *see* Khabur, 58
Aristophanes, 111
Armenia, ancient ecology of, 56
Arpachiya, site of ancient agrarian society, 62
artificial soil community, 116
assartage, 242; right of barons to approve, 257
Assignments (India), 189
Assyrian State, *see Homo militaris* (58)
Astarte, 281
Astrakhan, Chazar capital, 171, 179
Atacama, ancient S. Amer. llama-herds, 212
Atbara, river, 43
Athapascans, 201, 202
Athene, olive patroness, 102
Athens, rise of, 93; asylum for polit. exiles, 94
Attica, soil of, 91
auchenias, *see* llamas
Auracanians, llama-herds, 212
Aurangzib, Mughal emperor, 191
Avars, 171
axe-head, persistence of form, 237
ayllu, Andean tribe, 203
azobacters, 18
Aztecs, 281

305

INDEX

Babylon, 59
Bachue, Mother Goddess, 211, 222
Bakewell, R., 267
Baluchistan, Bronze Age culture, 66
barley, wild, habitat, 35
Baudhayana, *Sutra*, 183
Beas, river, 64
Bede, the Venerable, 250
Belgorod, as peasant outpost, 180
Bengal, 196
Bihar, 196
Bilharzia haematobius, in the Nile, 48
Bishop, Carl Whiting, 156
bison, of N. America, never domesticated, 34
Blith, Walter, 262
Blue Nile, source of, 43
Boeotia, 93; Boeotians, 284
'Boomers", 144
Bos primogenius, 30
Bramahputra, river, 64
breadcorn, Attica, production of, 103
brotherhood, basis of Indian society, 183, 184
bubonic plague, 254
buffalo, domestication of, 30
Bulgars, 171, 172

Caesar, Julius, 249, 253
Canaanites, 287
Cañari people, 211
Caribs, 214
Carmel, Mt., early farming site, 39
Carthage, 119, 128 *et seq.*
Casas, Las, 215
caschcrom, Scots digging stick, 276
Cato, agricultural monograph of, 136
Celts, agricultural economy, 241
Celtic plough, 247
Ceres, *see* Demeter (284)
Cetywayo, 86
Chanca, of Peru, 205

charqui, "jerked" meat, 216
Chazars, 171, 172
Chemistry Applied to Agriculture and Physiology, J. von Liebig, 270
Chenab, river, tribut. of the Indus, 64
Chenopodium album, 77
Ch'êng-Tzu-Yai, Black pottery culture, 159
Cherokees, 141, 146
chernozem, black earth, 166
Cheyenne tribe, 146
Chibcha, 211
chicha, maize beer, 211, Plate III
Chickasaws, 141
Chile, 226
China, 151 *et seq.*; Neolithic, 154, 159
Choctaws, 141
Cimmerian farmers, 169
Cleon, Athenian statesman, 111
Clipper ships, 106
Clive, Robert, 192
coca, 224
Coke, of Holkham, 265, 266
Colla, of Titicaca, 215, 222
Collao, 216, 226
Columbia, 211
Columella, Roman agronomist, 136
Copara people, legend of origin of irrigation, 225-6
Cornwallis, Lord, 197-8
Corinth, aesthetic precocity of, 98
Cossacks, lapsed farmers, 37, 178
Cothon, the, at Carthage, 129
cotton, change in Nile ecology, 48
Crescenzi, Pietro dei, 258
Creeks, tribe, 141
Crete, trade with Indus Valley, 66
Crimea, conquered by Lithuanians, 175
Cumans, 173-4
Curaça, 206

INDEX

Cuzco, 203, 208, 222, 223
Cybele, 281
Cypraea, cowries, 157

Damatrius, Boeotian month of sowing seed, 284
Danube Culture, 24, 234
Darwin, Charles, on earthworms, 22
Dasas, or Dasyu, prehistoric folk of Indus Valley, 33, 287
Decennial settlement, 196
deforestation, effect on climate of Sind, 70
Delphic Oracle, 286
Demeter, 279, 281, 283, Plates II, IV
Dharma Sutras, 183
Diala, river, tributary of Tigris, 59
diffusion, of techniques, theory of, 41
Dinder, river, 43, 44
Dingaan, Zulu king, 86
Diodorus Siculus, 282
dirra, Indian measure, 195
Dmitri, Grand Duke of Moscow, 176
Dorians, *see* Achaeans
dry farming, Roman, 244
Dutch agricultural advancement, 259

Earth Mother, in Europe, 235
earthworms, function in soil, 21; annual wt. of casts, 22
Economic History of Rome, Frank, Tenney, 135
Egypt, Upper, extent of, 47
Egypt, Lower, origin and extent, 48
Elder Conklin, Harris, F., 144
Eleusis, 283; mysteries of, 283, 284, 286
Emmer, wild habitat, 35
Equites, Roman parvenus, 126

Esquimaux culture, 201
Eurasia, 151
Euboia, wheat exports, 104
Euphrates, river, 56
Europe, N.W. soils, 233
exploitation, of soil, methods, 32 *et seq.*

Feluja, Mesopotamia, 59
Fertility Cults, possible origin, 38-9
Fitzherbert, *Boke of Husbandrie* etc., 260
Flaubert, G., 133; his *Salammbo*, 6
Fly Agaric, fungus, 19
Francis, Sir Philip, 197
Frank, Tenney, 121, 123, 126, 135
Frazer, Sir J., 280
fungi, method of subsistence, 19

Gamboa, Pedro Sarmiento de, 203
Ganges, river, 64
Geuljik, Lake, 56
Gilbert, J. H., 271
Golden Age, historical basis, 31
Golden Bough, The, Frazer, Sir J., 280
Golden Fleece, The, Graves, R., 6
Golden Horde or *Orda*, 174 *et seq.*
Golden Warrior, The, Munz, H., 6
Goldsmith, O., 131
Goths, 170
Gothic kingdom between Don and Danube, 170
Grapes of Wrath, The, Steinbeck, J., 147
Graves, Robert, 6, 290
Great City Shang, 156, 160 *et seq.*
Greece, prehistoric, soils of, 92
Grihya Sutras, 183
Grostête, 260
guano, 222
Guthrie, Oklahoma, 145

Halaf, Tell, 62
Hallstatt, 240
Hammar, Lake, 56
Hanan-chacan, 225
Hannibal, 133-4
Harappa, ancient Indus city, 66, 68, 71
Harrington, survey of land in Swarappur, 194-5
Harvest Festival, 279
Harris, Frank, 144
Hart, Liddell, 134
Hassuna, Tell, 61
Hastings, Warren, 192, 197
Hausa, *see* Kado
Helots, of Sparta, 108; massacre of, 109
Herodotus, on health of Egyptians, 47
Hesiod, 277, 284; on Boeotian agriculture, 97
Heyn, Victor, 102
Homo militaris, as a disease of soil, 58
Horse-houghing husbandry, Tull, J., 264
Horus, falcon god, poss. origin as totem, 51
Howard, Sir A., 272
huanaco, *see* llama (212)
Huayna Ccapac-Inca, 205, 213
Huitzilopochtli, Aztec War God, 141, 286
humus, defined, 18
Huns, 171
hunting, 34

ideograms, Chinese, 161
Imbros, wheat exports, 104
Inca, 202, 203, 205
Inca Empire, 201 *et seq.*
India Act 1784, 198
Indus valley, 33, 64 *et seq.*; river, 64; delta, 66

inheritance of land in India, 186
Ionia, scientific precocity, 98
Iroquois, 201
iron, introduction to Italy, 121; dates of appearance, 240
irrigation, origins in Mesopotamia, 60
Ishtar, 281
Isomachos (*see Oikonomikos*, Xenophon), 103
Italy, West, soils of, 119
Italic peoples, arrival in Italy, 120

Jackson, J. W., 159
Jhelum, river, trib. of the Indus, 64
Jhenghizkhan, 174
Juchi, heir to Jhenghizkhan, 174
Judaism, religion of the Chazars, 171

Kabul, river, trib. of the Indus, 64
Kado, tribes, 158
Kailas glaciers, source of the Indus, 64
Kalikovo, battle of, 176
Kanungo, Indian land-tax official, 193 *et seq.*
Kazak, kozak, *see* Cossack
Khabur, river, tributary of the Euphrates, 58
Kharkov, 167
Khartoum, 43
Kiev, origin, 172; soil of, 173
Kipchaks, *see* Cumans
Kish, origins in alluvium, 63
Kishinev, 167

Lactarius deliciosus, fungus, 19
Lakorian Pass, prehist. irrigation, 67
La Tene culture, 240
Latium, soil and climate, 120 *et seq.*
Lawes, J. B., 271
Lemnos, export of wheat from, 104

INDEX

Leon, Cieza de, historian of the Incas, 209
Liebig, Justus von, 227, 270
Licinian-Sextian law, 125
Lithuanian peasants, against the Tartar nomads, 175
Lin Yutang, *My Country and My People*, 152
Livy, on crop failures and famine, 123-5
llamas, 204, 212, 215
loess soils, nature of, 29-30
Louisiana Purchase, 140
Lycurgus, Spartan law-giver, 109-10

Magdalenian paintings, 12, 232
Mago, Carthaginian agricultural scientist, 128
Maglemosian people, 239
Maia, 281
maize, 202, 211, 214, 217
Malmay, khan of the Golden Horde, 176
Mangazeya, tundra soil, Siberia, 179
Manglesdorf and Reeves, on maize, 215
manioc, 211, 214-15
Mārathās, rise of, 191
Markham, Sir Clements, 203
Markham, Gervase, 261
Mary, 281, 287
Mascall, *The Government of Cattell*, 260
Mashkai Valley, prehistoric irrigation, 67
matrilinear inheritance, in Egypt, 52
Maule, river, 204
Maya, the, 216
men, as soil members, 31; as disease organism, 81
Menelaus, King of Sparta, 108
Menes, Pharaoh, 55

Menken, H. L., *Treatise on the Gods*, 11
Merimde, early tillage, 40
Mesolithic food gatherers, 233
Mesopotamia, soil of, 56
Messenia, conquered by Sparta, 108
Mexico, 203
Michec (Quitchua, *viceroy*), 206, 213
millet, in Chinese prehistory, 162
Mirsky, D. S., 166, 167, 179
mitimaes, Incarial colonies, 208
Mohenjo-daro, city of the Indus, prehist., 66, 68-9, 71
Mommsen, Theodore, 126
monsoon, SW., course and influence, 46
Morganism, in anthropology, 51
Mughals, 188
Munz, Hope, *The Golden Warrior*, 6
Muscovy, origins, 172; as peasant champion, 175
Myres, Sir J., 70

Naaman, 231
Nahuanatlaca, 202
Naimuéna, Earth God of the Untoto, 212
Nasca Valley, 226
Natufians, probable first cultivators, 39
Natural Laws of Husbandry, J. von Liebig, 270
Neolithic cultivators, first sites of, 35
Nile, source of, 43
nitrosomas bacteria, 20
Niz, territory of Moscow, 173
Novgorod, origins, 172
Nungui, Earth Goddess of the Jibaros, 212

oca, esculent tuber, 217
Oikonomikos, Xenophon, on cattle breeding, 103

Oklahoma, 138, 141, 144 *et seq.*
olive, *Olea europaea,* as sub-soil exploiter, 99, 102
Omdurman, 43
Ondegardo, Polo de, 203
open-field system, 253
oracle bones of Anyang, 161

Pachacuti Yupanqui, Apu-Ccapac-Inca, 205, 223
Pachamamma, Earth Mother among the Inca, 204, 222, 279
Painted Skeleton people, 169
parasitism, on soil, 28 *et seq.*
Paria-cacca, God of Copara, 225
pastoral communities, patriarchy, 37
Payne, D. L., 144
Payne, E. J., 214
Pelasgoi, 287
Pereyaslavl, peasant city, 173
Perioaeci, 108
Persephone, 283, Plate II
Phoenician navy, at Salamis, 106
photosynthesis, 23
Piany-bor, prehist. peasant Russian community, 172
Piggott, Stuart 67
plantation slavery, Carthaginian, 130
Plato, 14
Platt, Sir Hugh, 260
Plebeians, Roman political party, 124
Pleistocene, hunters and painters, 232
Pliny, 247
plough, origin of, 276; Saxon, 277; Celtic, 247
Pluto, 283
Poland-Lithuania, as peasant champion, 178
Poltava, 167
Proclus, 282
Prussia, compared with Sparta, 110
puquios, Andean irrigation canals, 227

Purcell, Oklahoma, 145

Qazaq, 181
Quetchua, *see* Quitchua
Quimbaya, 208
quinoa, hardy leguminous plant, of the Andes, 217
quipu, Andean recording and mnemonic device, 204
Quitchua, language, adopted by the Incas, 208
Quito, 226

Rahad, river, 43
raiyats, or *ryots,* definition, 188
Raja Todar Mal, Mughal fiscal reformer, 191
Rangpur, 196
Ravi, river, tributary of the Indus, 64
rice, in Chinese prehistory, 162
Rigveda, collection of Aryan hymns, 33
Rocca, Apu-Ccapac-Inca, 225
Roman Conquest of Europe, 240
Roman methods of agriculture, 244
Rothamsted, Research Station, 271
Royal Society, 290
Ryazan, Russian mercantile republic, 176
ryots, see raiyats

Sahara, 130
Salammbo, of Flaubert, G., 6, 133
Salaman, Redcliffe N., 214
Samarkand, Mongol capital, 177
Samsat, or Samosata, Mesopotamia, 56
Sarastov, on the Volga, 167
Sarmatians, 170
Sarmiento, historian of the Inca (*see also* Gamboa), 210, 223

INDEX

Satrae, Thracian tribe, vinecultivators, cult of Dionysos, 101
scientific agriculture, 128
Scipio Africanus, 134
Scythians, as wheat exporters, 104; as pastoralists, 169
Sebek, crocodile god, poss. origin as totem, 51
Semele, Mother of the (Scapegoat) God, 282
Seminoles, 141
shadouf, Nile irrigation device, 47, 59
Shang (see also Great City Shang), 156
Shat-al-Arab, 56
She King, The, 162
Shepherd of the Sun, 213
shifting cultivation, African, 85
Shore, John, 198
Sialk, Tepe, Persia, site of Neol. cultivat., 62
Sicily, Carthaginian, 126
silt, Nile, annual deposit, 46
Slavs, 170-1
smallholding, Roman, 125
Smith, Elliot, 158, 159
soil, definition of, 17
soil community, explanation of, 12, 14
Sparta, aesthetic precocity, 98, 108
State, origin in the tribe, 51
Stein, Sir Aurel, 67, 72
Stevens, C. E., 244, 245, 247, 258
subsoil, nature of, 98
subsistence farming, nature of, 128
sucres, see andenes
Sumer, ancient soil origins, 59
Sutlej, river, 64

taccla, 218, 276, Plate III
Tahua-ntin-suyu, The Four Provinces, Inca Empire, 205

Tamerlane, or Timur, 176
Tana, Lake, 43
Tartars, 174
Tchaka, Zulu king, 86
Tepe Gawra, early cultivated site, 40, 62
terracing, antiquity of, 164
Thallasocracy of Minos, 96
Themistocles, 107
Theophrastus, 120
Thrace, 281
three-course rotation, 254
Thessaly, early soil stability, 93
Thorpe, J., 152
Thoth, Ibis god, possible origin as totem, 51
Thucydides, 4, 92, 93
Tiahuanaco, 203, 214
Tigris, river, source and course, 56
Titicaca, Lake, 203, 208, 214
Toktamish, khan of the Golden Horde, 177
Torello, 258
Townsend, Charles, Viscount ("Turnip"), 265
Trajan, Roman emperor, 138
Treatise on the Gods, Menken, H. L., 11
Tribunate, establishment of, 125
Tripolye, agrarian culture, prehist., 168
tropical soils, rapid circulation of fertility, 84
truth, intellectual concept of, 14
Tull, Jethro, 263 *et seq.*
Tusser, Thomas, 260
Tussilago farfara, 238

Uigurs, 174
ulluca, esculent tuber, 217
Untoto people, 212
Ur, origins in alluvium, 63

Ural mountains, 166

Vaicya, Indian farming class, 185
Van, Lake, Armenia, 56
Varro, as agronomist, 121, 123, 136
Vega, Garcilasso de la, the Inca, 203
Verelst, Governor of the Council of the E. I. Company, 193
vicuna (*see also* llama), 212
vine, *Vitis vinifera* ssp. *silvestris* Gmel, ancient cult., 100; habitat, 100; route of diffusion, 101
Vinogradoff, Sir Paul 252, 255
Viracocha (Kontiki Viracocha), God of the Andeans, 204, 225, 226; Apu-Ccapac-Inca, 227
virgin soil, 25
Vishaigorod, 177
Vitowt, Duke of Lithuania, 175-6

Walter of Henly, 260
wheat, wild, habitat, 35; in China, 162

Wheeler, R. M., 67
women, as food gatherers, 35; dominant in early cultivation, 40
Works and Days, Hesiod, 277
Wortledge's seed-drill, 262

Xenophon, observations of Mesopotamia in *Anabasis*, 59

yam, 217
Yang Shao, pottery, imprints of rice grains, 162
Yellow Earth, of China, 153 *et seq.*
Young, Arthur, 266
Yunca, irrigation works, 226
Yutang, Lin, 152

Zab, Great and Little, rivers, tribut. of Tigris, 59
zamindār, zamindāri, Indian fiscal official and his territory, 192 *et seq.*
Zeus, 286